A History of
QST
Volume 2: Advertising
1915-2013

Joe Veras, K9OCO

ARRL
100 YEARS

Cover Design
Sue Fagan, KB1OKW

Production—Design and Layout
Michelle Bloom, WB1ENT

Please e-mail us at **pubsfdbk@arrl.org** (publications feed-
back) to give us your comments on this book and what you
would like to see in future editions. Please include your name,
call, e-mail address and the book title, edition and printing in
the body of your message. Also indicate whether or not you
are an ARRL member.

Table of Contents

Foreword

Each month, *QST* arrives in your mailbox, chock full of interesting and valuable information for the active amateur. In addition to reading the articles and columns, you also pore over the advertising pages. What's new? What radio or antenna or accessory would be a good addition to the shack? What dream station would you build if you won the lottery? We all like to look at, and talk about, and debate the merits of the latest gear.

Along with the articles and columns, the products advertised each month reflect Amateur Radio technology, activities and interests at the time the issue was published. Through the advertising pages, author Joe Veras, K9OCO, traces the history of receivers, transmitters, antennas and other station equipment. As you turn the pages, technology changes, bands are added and modes of operation come and go. Looking through the ads collected in this book, you're sure to see many familiar names — along with many that gradually faded into history and some that barely got off the ground.

As *QST* enters its second century, you're likely to be viewing the ads on your computer screen, mobile phone or tablet in addition to the venerable printed page. One thing that won't change is that you'll find the latest Amateur Radio gear advertised each month, and you'll find plenty of interesting items to consider adding to your station.

David Sumner, K1ZZ
Executive Vice President
Newington, Connecticut
November 2013

Preface

I was licensed just before my 13th birthday and remember my Dad's (K9NA/SK) *QSTs* being around the house for years before that. When I received my Novice ticket, he emphasized how important the American Radio Relay League was to Amateur Radio and that it was equally important to be a member. You know what? As with so many things parents tell their children, he turned out to be exactly right.

Doing the research for this book required poring over a century's worth of *QST* ads and reading through the technical, educational, news and editorial materials printed down through the years. The experience left me convinced that I wouldn't be sitting here typing something about the Amateur Service if the League had not taken a strong position of intervention and advocacy over and over again during that hundred years. Absent that, Amateur Radio as we know it simply would not exist today.

Our founders were brilliant men who labored tirelessly to preserve and improve something that is a hobby, a pastime — and so much more than that. I want readers to understand the effort and sacrifice involved and be inspired to pick up the torch and carry it into our second century.

What part has advertising played in that? The reality of the publishing world is that editorial pages (the term for everything in a magazine except advertising) cannot exist without ad pages to pay for them. Sure, *QST* is partly a membership-supported journal, but it would have neither the content nor the quality without the support of advertisers. The Amateur Radio business is not one blessed with large profit margins, and I am amazed at — and grateful for — the hundreds of different companies who have displayed thousands of products in the pages of *QST* over the years.

I chose ads from each decade of *QST's* first century. Some represent evolving technology and changes in equipment to comply with regulatory matters. Others were interesting to me graphically or just plain said something about Amateur Radio at the time. It made for a lot of tough choices; many favorites ended up on the "cutting room floor!" I also attempted to relate some history through the captions, introducing equipment and personalities along the way. The text part of each chapter is about what was going on in the world of Amateur Radio through the decades and is not necessarily restricted to advertisements or advertisers. It seeks to put in context the things represented in the ads, telling the story that flows from the remainder of the magazine's pages.

Readers of my vintage remember the big Sears, Roebuck & Co catalogs and those from other mail order companies. They often served as kind of an everyman's dream book. It was possible to while away hours paging through them, imagining what it would be like to place an order for whatever struck one's fancy, then anticipating its arrival at the front door a few days hence. *QST's* ad pages are the radio amateur's dream book. Let me introduce you to some of those ads and let your imagination re-create the dreams they might have once inspired. Page through the current issues and create dreams of your own.

Acknowledgements

Each of the following is owed a debt of gratitude for help in the preparation of this manuscript. Without their aid it would be missing facts, photographs, and key pieces of information about companies and products that appeared on the advertising pages of *QST* during its first century: Jon Weiner, K1VVC; Jim Long, W4ZRZ; Bill Frost, WD8DFP; Mike Brubaker, WA8NOP; Herman Cone III, N4CH; Todd Bigelow, KA1KAQ; Rod Blocksome, KØDAS; Jerry Vogt, WA2GCF; Antonio Vernucci, IØJX; Rick Jacinth, N6OK; and Jim Singleton, WA5BDR

The biggest *thank you* of all goes to my wife Gwen. Without her encouragement, love, and patience this book — and everything else in my life — would never happen. I love you, Dear!

Joe Veras, K9OCO
November 2013

About the ARRL

The seed for Amateur Radio was planted in the 1890s, when Guglielmo Marconi began his experiments in wireless telegraphy. Soon he was joined by dozens, then hundreds, of others who were enthusiastic about sending and receiving messages through the air—some with a commercial interest, but others solely out of a love for this new communications medium. The United States government began licensing Amateur Radio operators in 1912.

By 1914, there were thousands of Amateur Radio operators—hams—in the United States. Hiram Percy Maxim, a leading Hartford, Connecticut inventor and industrialist, saw the need for an organization to band together this fledgling group of radio experimenters. In May 1914 he founded the American Radio Relay League (ARRL) to meet that need.

Today ARRL, with approximately 155,000 members, is the largest organization of radio amateurs in the United States. The ARRL is a not-for-profit organization that:
- promotes interest in Amateur Radio communications and experimentation
- represents US radio amateurs in legislative matters, and
- maintains fraternalism and a high standard of conduct among Amateur Radio operators.

At ARRL headquarters in the Hartford suburb of Newington, the staff helps serve the needs of members. ARRL is also International Secretariat for the International Amateur Radio Union, which is made up of similar societies in 150 countries around the world.

ARRL publishes the monthly journal *QST* and an interactive digital version of *QST*, as well as newsletters and many publications covering all aspects of Amateur Radio. Its headquarters station, W1AW, transmits bulletins of interest to radio amateurs and Morse code practice sessions. The ARRL also coordinates an extensive field organization, which includes volunteers who provide technical information and other support services for radio amateurs as well as communications for public-service activities. In addition, ARRL represents US amateurs with the Federal Communications Commission and other government agencies in the US and abroad.

Membership in ARRL means much more than receiving *QST* each month. In addition to the services already described, ARRL offers membership services on a personal level, such as the Technical Information Service—where members can get answers by phone, email or the ARRL website, to all their technical and operating questions.

Full ARRL membership (available only to licensed radio amateurs) gives you a voice in how the affairs of the organization are governed. ARRL policy is set by a Board of Directors (one from each of 15 Divisions). Each year, one-third of the ARRL Board of Directors stands for election by the full members they represent. The day-to-day operation of ARRL HQ is managed by an Executive Vice President and his staff.

No matter what aspect of Amateur Radio attracts you, ARRL membership is relevant and important. There would be no Amateur Radio as we know it today were it not for the ARRL. We would be happy to welcome you as a member! (An Amateur Radio license is not required for Associate Membership.) For more information about ARRL and answers to any questions you may have about Amateur Radio, write or call:

ARRL—the national association for Amateur Radio®
225 Main Street
Newington CT 06111-1494
Voice: 860-594-0200
Fax: 860-594-0259
E-mail: **hq@arrl.org**
Internet: **www.arrl.org**

Prospective new amateurs call (toll-free):
800-32-NEW HAM (800-326-3942)
You can also contact us via e-mail at **newham@arrl.org**
or check out the ARRL website at **www.arrl.org**

Chapter 1

The Beginning

ARRL, *QST*, Regulation and War

Early Amateur Radio communication was limited in distance, often less than a hundred miles. Hartford, Connecticut, inventor and radio hobbyist Hiram Percy Maxim conceived a plan that would enable radio messages to be sent across a state or even across the continent using a series of relays from one station to another.

Hiram Percy Maxim explained his plan for an American Radio Relay League to the Hartford Radio Club in April 1914. The club voted to establish a relay organization, and a committee was appointed to do the work with Maxim and club secretary Clarence D. Tuska handling most of the task. They recruited stations for the League by writing letters to every amateur they were aware of. Enclosed with these letters were questionnaires eliciting detailed technical information about the amateurs' stations. An overwhelming response led to the founding of the ARRL in May 1914.[1] With members across the country, relay routes soon began functioning just as Maxim had envisioned.

Meanwhile, all was not well in the radio club crucible from which the League had been poured. The Hartford Radio Club desired more control over the League, while principals Maxim and Tuska wanted it to have less. As a consequence, the ARRL separated from the Hartford Radio Club and incorporated under Connecticut law in February 1915.

Issue number 1 of *QST* appeared in December 1915. An announcement on page 2 stated, "QST is published by and at the expense of Hiram Percy Maxim and Clarence D. Tuska." It went on to say the object of the magazine was "to help maintain the organization of the American Radio Relay League and to keep the Amateur Wireless Operators of the country in constant touch with each other."[2] It concluded with a reminder that every amateur would help himself and his fellow hobbyists by sending in 25 cents for a three month trial subscription.

A few pages further along, the "December Radio Relay Bulletin" column closed the appeal saying, "At the end of three months, the President and Secretary hope that *QST* will be able to pay for itself…and will have brought

in enough money to pay back the two officers mentioned."[3]

March 1916 *QST* carried a "General Notice" headlined in large, bold face type. The notice emphasized that more than hard work was necessary to ensure success for the League. Money was also needed. "This money can only be obtained through voluntary subscriptions…and the sale of Station Appointment Certificates, List of Stations Books, and *QST* magazine."[4]

A solution to the financial dilemma appeared as the lifeblood of print media started to flow through *QST's* veins. Advertisements from companies with products or services of interest to amateurs began to fill the pages of *QST*. That first December 1915 issue carried 6½ pages of paid ads, and the number grew to 24 pages a year later.

Meanwhile, editorial pages of the magazine detailed plans for trunk lines and traffic routing to better accomplish the League's initial purpose of passing messages from one end of the country to the other.[5] Well equipped amateur stations routinely covered distances of 300 to 400 miles, with 900 or 1000 miles

achieved on occasion. An established relay system could deliver a message from any point in the country to another in one or more hops.

At the same time, the battle with the government for control of the air waves went on. The Department of the Navy, whose main interest was communication between ship and shore stations, sought government purchase of all existing commercial stations and the closing down of noncommercial (amateur) installations. Testifying before Congress, D. W. Todd, director of naval communications, stated, "Strong government control becomes more necessary as ship and shore stations increase. Interference and consequent inefficient communication will continue until such control is obtained." [6]

The proposed legislation became moot on April 7, 1917, when US President Woodrow Wilson signed a declaration of war against Germany. The Navy took over the operation of 60 stations engaged in maritime communication. The presidential proclamation ordered all other stations, including amateurs, off the air for the duration of the war.[7]

In the earliest years of Amateur Radio the Loose Coupler, or receiving transformer, was placed in the receiver circuit ahead of the detector and provided a means of tuning the receiver. Loose Couplers varied in complexity and sold for between $4 and $35 back in the 'teens.

The Department of Commerce's Office of the Radio Inspector issued a directive that all amateur antennas be immediately lowered to the ground and that both transmitters and receivers be disconnected from antenna and ground circuits and rendered inoperative. Amateurs received a form on which they had to note their compliance with the order. A "rigid investigation" was promised to anyone failing to sign and return the form promptly.[8]

Wartime needs of the military also helped break the logjam of patent litigation regarding vacuum tubes.[9] At war's end, the US government's push for majority American ownership of communications companies resulted in the formation of the Radio Corporation of America by General Electric in 1919. When the armistice ending the war was declared on November 11, 1918, amateurs expecting a quick return to the air were disappointed. The government lifted the ban on amateur activity in two phases. The ban on receiving was the first to go in April 1919. Transmitting privileges were not restored until September of that year.

The ARRL felt a dramatic impact from the long period of inactivity. QST ceased publication with the September 1917 issue and did not resume until an eight page "Special Bulletin" was published in April 1919. The magazines published in the months following the declaration of war suffered a sharp decline of editorial pages and the ad pages necessary to support them.

From its inception until early 1917, Maxim and Tuska had effectively been the sole officers of the League. On the last day of February of that year, a group of prominent amateurs met in New York City to better organize the League's structure. A series of subsequent meetings resulted in a new constitution and the adoption of procedures for the election of officers and directors.[10] One of the new officers was Arthur A. Hebert, 2ZH (later W1ES), who was elected General Manager. From that time until March 1919, the League's administration was conducted from Hebert's New York City business office or his home in Nutley, New Jersey.

At a February 1919 meeting of the ARRL board, General Manager Hebert reported on the state of the League since its last meeting in April 1917. He noted that during the war years, all memberships had lapsed and the treasury had dwindled to $33. He recommended that a paid secretary be hired and that the League purchase QST.[11]

Although its signal was still broad, the rotary spark gap produced a note in the receiver rather than the raspy buzz of a fixed gap. Commercially-made rotary spark gaps cost $12 or $13 before WW I, rising to nearly $30 (about $400 today) in spark's last days as a legal mode. The unit pictured is a reproduction.

Publication of the first post-war QST was funded out of the pockets of board members. In order to purchase QST and carry on other League business, the board of directors came up with an innovative plan. Hoping to raise $7500, the board authorized a bond issue having a two-year maturity and an interest rate of 5% per annum.[12]

In March 1919, the ARRL board purchased QST from owner Clarence Tuska and began operating it as a part of the League. By the time the July 1919 issue was in the mail, QST's fortunes showed much improvement. Ad pages built to numbers far surpassing those of the pre-war years, plus there were all the wartime technological advances to fill the editorial pages.

"King Spark" remained the dominant transmitting technology, even as vacuum tubes started appearing in QST and amateurs' stations for receiving applications. Tube receivers with regenerative detectors worked well to receive spark signals. Some amateurs who had served as radio operators during the war already knew of the dramatic difference between the effectiveness of continuous wave (CW) signals in comparison with spark's damped waves. It was not uncommon to span the same distances using a

5 W tube transmitter as with a 500 W spark set. In 1919, the weak link in CW communication was the receiver. The variometers commonly used as tuners ahead of receiving detectors had a difficult time tuning in the much narrower CW signals. The problems and complexities of the task would wait until the early 1920s for John Reinartz, 1QP, to provide a solution.[13]

Notes

[1] C.B. Desoto, *200 Meters & Down* (West Hartford, Connecticut: 1936), pp 38-43.
[2] "Announcement," *QST*, Dec 1915, p 2.
[3] "December Radio Relay Bulletin," *QST*, Dec 1915, p 3.
[4] "General Notice," *QST*, Mar 1916, p 67.
[5] H. Maxim, "Practical Relaying," *QST*, Feb 1916, pp 19-22.
[6] "Government May Buy Every Radio Station," *QST*, Jan 1917 p 22.
[7] M. Bensman, *The Beginning of Broadcast Regulation in the Twentieth Century* (Jefferson, North Carolina:2000), pp 11-12.
[8] "War!," *QST*, May 1917, p 3.
[9] Bensman, p 11
[10] "ARRL, The Early Years," *QST*, Feb 1964, pp 66-70.
[11] Desoto, p 56.
[12] H. Maxim, "A.R.R.L. Bonds," *QST*, Apr 1919, p 4.
[13] J. Reinartz, "A Receiving Tuner for CW," *QST*, Jun 1921, pp 5-7.

Figure 1.1 — Manhattan Electrical Supply Company's ad occupied the back cover of the first issue of *QST*. It touted a rotary spark gap as well as a crystal detector holder, common hardware for a 1915 amateur station. The company was first located on Cortlandt Street, later the heart of Radio Row, before moving a few blocks north to Park Place. (Dec 1915)

Figure 1.2 — The loose coupler, or transformer, went between the aerial and detector. It tuned the radio and provided some selectivity without sacrificing sensitivity. Many amateurs wound their own but this "Navy Type" transformer represented the high end of the commercial market. (Jul 1916)

Figure 1.3 — Pacific Research Laboratories manufactured and sold the Moorhead tube. The diode device was said to work as a detector "in any circuit." Its lack of a grid helped Pacific Research avoid the tube patent wars raging at the time. (Sep 1916)

CRYSTALOI
DETECTOR

TYPE O

TYPE AA

═ ALWAYS READY ═

Almost any detector will give you good results if conditions are right.
But the kind you want is the one which can be depended upon at all times.
Not only is the Crystaloi made in such a manner that it is next to impossible
for it to get out of order but the fact that all the functional parts are enclosed in the dielectric cylinder renders them immune to moisture, oxidation and
other external influences so detrimental to the proper working of the
ordinary detector.

Write for Booklet.

PRICES

Type O. Crystaloi Detector $3.50
       By parcel post prepaid   3.60

Type A.A. Crystaloi Detector $6.00
       By parcel post prepaid   6.20

MANUFACTURED ONLY BY

CONNECTICUT TELEPHONE & ELECTRIC COMPANY
INCORPORATED
MERIDEN, CONNECTICUT

All rights and patents under which the Crystaloi is made were purchased from the inventor,
Eugene A. Turney

Figure 1.4 — Despite the great strides made in vacuum tube technology during the war, the crystal detector was still being refined and used as 1919 drew to a close. Price and general availability gave the crystal a temporary advantage over the tube. (Aug 1919)

Two New Bunnell Specialties

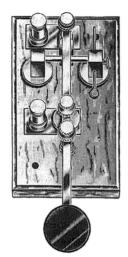

The Straight Line Renewable Contact Radio Key

By far the BEST and HANDSOMEST transmitter yet produced. Not only are the contacts renewable, but they are kept in a straight line with perfect surface contact until completely work out, and the lever remains in its original horizontal position.

Fading signals caused by varying resistance of contact points are entirely eliminated.

Its binding posts automatically clamp the wires, making loose connections impossible.

Net Price, $7.50

Send for descriptive circular.

The Jove Detector Holder

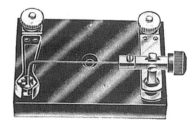

The most perfect of crystal holders.

Holds one or two different crystals of any form at once without the use of a clampscrew.

A sensitive point of either crystal quickly found, the correct pressure held constantly without moving a single screw or nut.

Beautifully finished and mounted on dark glazed porcelain.

Net Price, $1.00

_____

SEND FOR OUR NO. 36 WIRELESS CATALOG

_____

J. H. Bunnell & Co., Incorporated
32 Park Place—Broadway Block
New York

Figure 1.5 — The J.H. Bunnell Company had already been in business 37 years when this advertisement appeared in the first issue of *QST*. Better known for its telegraph instruments, the company's product line also included the crystal detector holder promoted here. (Dec 1915)

Figure 1.6 — J. F. Arnold's loose coupler tuned to 3500 meters (85 kHz) although federal regulations restricted amateur transmitters to wavelengths of 200 meters (1.5 MHz) and down. The Wireless Manufacturing Company ad illustrates the geographical expansion of amateur manufacturers and supply houses as the hobby grew. (Jan 1916)

Figure 1.7 — *QST's* ad pages provided parts manufacturers ready access to the amateur market. Home built gear did not always equate with inexpensive. The price of the Turney Company's variable condenser alone would be more than $158 in today's money. (Sep 1916)

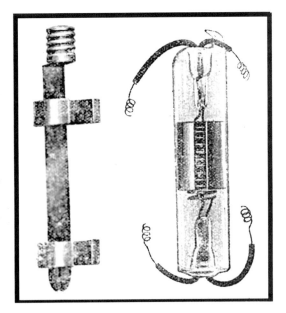
Figure 1.8 — Cos-Radio (later Watkins Mfg.) of Kansas City sold tubes and components as well as its own branded equipment. De Forest's Type-T tubular Audion featured a more robust design than the original bulb, also differing in that it did not have to be returned to the factory for replacement. (Apr 1916)

R16 LAMP DETECTOR

Simple

Compact

Efficient

Serviceable

Designed

by Experts

for the

Discriminating

Operator

The R 16 Lamp Detector is specially designed for long distance work on both arc and spark signals. It has the latest and most efficient circuit for reception of these signals. It is compact and yet the efficiency has not been sacrificed in the proper spacing of wire and parts. The detector is a result of over a year of experimental work on lamp detectors, and the circuit and spacing employed is the result. The R 16 in connection with an R 6 Paragon Amplifier has broken all records for amateur work. Signals from amateurs on the Atlantic Coast have been copied on the Pacific Coast.

This detector is sold without lamp, but a tested lamp of any make will be put on and adjusted at the nominal charge of Five ($5.) Dollars. All parts to this set sold separately. Write for price list.

The R 16 Lamp Detector (including "Everready" B batteries) $30.00

We are Pacific Coast Agents and Distributors for Adams-Morgan Co., and time may be saved by ordering from us.

SPECIAL THIS MONTH WHILE THEY LAST, TIGERMAN TUBES.......................$5.00

We are in a position to make apparatus to your specifications and will guarantee satisfaction or money refunded.

Pacific Wireless Specialty Company

1526 CRENSHAW BLVD. Los Angeles, California.

GALENA

Very Sensitive

One ounce ....15 cents

Two ounces ....25 cents

Post Prepaid

F. M. ANDREWS

2331 Orange Avenue,
Birmingham, Ala.

BRANDES RECEIVERS MURDOCK, DEFOREST AUDION, CLAPP-EASTHAM GOODS PACKARD TRANSFORMERS WIRELESS EXPERT IN CHARGE.

Southern California Electric Co.

LOS ANGELES, CAL.

625 S. Main   316 W. 7th St.

HERE THEY ARE AT LAST!
AN ELEGANTLY FINISHED HIGHLY POL-ISHED BLACK FIBRE KNOB!

Just the thing for that panel you are thinking of making. There is no one thing which leads more to the appearance of a cabinet set than a truly artistic knob. Descriptive circular and prices free for the asking. You will also be interested in our switch points, switch levers, cardboard tubing, etc.

WINGER ELECTRIC AND MANUFACTURING CO.
711 SO. DEARBORN ST., CHICAGO, ILL.

Figure 1.9 — Pacific Wireless Specialty touted its lamp (tube) detector as superior for long distance work. Amateur experimenters also pressed the early triodes into service as post-detection audio amplifiers. Partial page display ads, such as those shown here, gave smaller companies an opportunity to show off their wares. (Apr 1917)

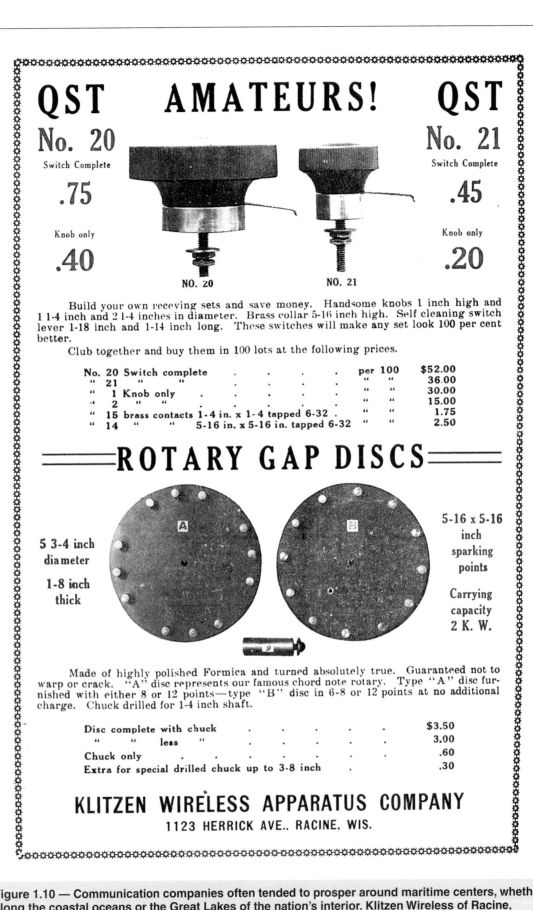
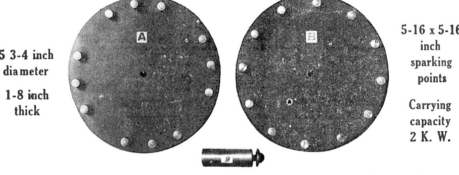
Figure 1.10 — Communication companies often tended to prosper around maritime centers, whether along the coastal oceans or the Great Lakes of the nation's interior. Klitzen Wireless of Racine, Wisconsin, exemplified the latter. (Mar 1917)

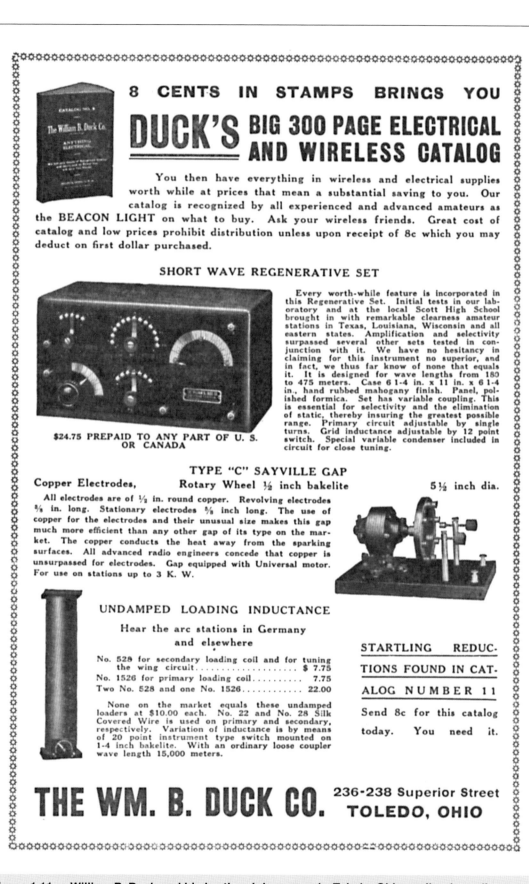

8 CENTS IN STAMPS BRINGS YOU

DUCK'S BIG 300 PAGE ELECTRICAL AND WIRELESS CATALOG

You then have everything in wireless and electrical supplies worth while at prices that mean a substantial saving to you. Our catalog is recognized by all experienced and advanced amateurs as the BEACON LIGHT on what to buy. Ask your wireless friends. Great cost of catalog and low prices prohibit distribution unless upon receipt of 8c which you may deduct on first dollar purchased.

SHORT WAVE REGENERATIVE SET

$24.75 PREPAID TO ANY PART OF U. S. OR CANADA

Every worth-while feature is incorporated in this Regenerative Set. Initial tests in our laboratory and at the local Scott High School brought in with remarkable clearness amateur stations in Texas, Louisiana, Wisconsin and all eastern states. Amplification and selectivity surpassed several other sets tested in conjunction with it. We have no hesitancy in claiming for this instrument no superior, and in fact, we thus far know of none that equals it. It is designed for wave lengths from 180 to 475 meters. Case 6 1-4 in. x 11 in. x 6 1-4 in., hand rubbed mahogany finish. Panel, polished formica. Set has variable coupling. This is essential for selectivity and the elimination of static, thereby insuring the greatest possible range. Primary circuit adjustable by single turns. Grid inductance adjustable by 12 point switch. Special variable condenser included in circuit for close tuning.

TYPE "C" SAYVILLE GAP

Copper Electrodes,   Rotary Wheel ½ inch bakelite   5½ inch dia.

All electrodes are of ½ in. round copper. Revolving electrodes ⅝ in. long. Stationary electrodes ⅝ inch long. The use of copper for the electrodes and their unusual size makes this gap much more efficient than any other gap of its type on the market. The copper conducts the heat away from the sparking surfaces. All advanced radio engineers concede that copper is unsurpassed for electrodes. Gap equipped with Universal motor. For use on stations up to 3 K. W.

UNDAMPED LOADING INDUCTANCE

Hear the arc stations in Germany and elsewhere

No. 528 for secondary loading coil and for tuning the wing circuit...................... $ 7.75
No. 1526 for primary loading coil.......... 7.75
Two No. 528 and one No. 1526............ 22.00

None on the market equals these undamped loaders at $10.00 each. No. 22 and No. 28 Silk Covered Wire is used on primary and secondary, respectively. Variation of inductance is by means of 20 point instrument type switch mounted on 1-4 inch bakelite. With an ordinary loose coupler wave length 15,000 meters.

STARTLING REDUCTIONS FOUND IN CATALOG NUMBER 11

Send 8c for this catalog today. You need it.

THE WM. B. DUCK CO. 236-238 Superior Street TOLEDO, OHIO

Figure 1.11 — William B. Duck and his brother John opened a Toledo, Ohio, mail order radio parts business in 1908. In addition to parts, the company sold house branded equipment to amateurs and other wireless enthusiasts. (Jun 1917)

Figure 1.12 — The Lenzite Wireless Detector received the endorsement of the ARRL — with a personal word from C. D. Tuska, no less. (Dec 1916)

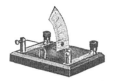
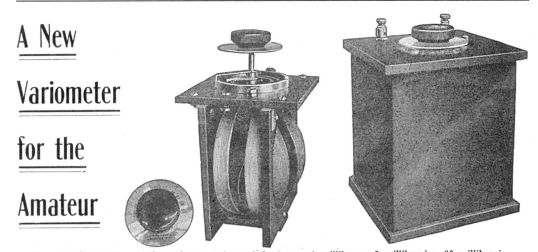
Figure 1.13 — Because the ARRL was a purely amateur organization, Clarence Tuska resigned as League secretary in March 1919 to open a radio manufacturing business. The C.D. Tuska Company's first *QST* ad ran in that year's July issue. The Clapp-Eastham Company began as a manufacturer of X-ray machine coils in 1906 and was soon also making radio parts. Melville Eastham, a company founder, later left to start the General Radio Company. (Jul 1919)

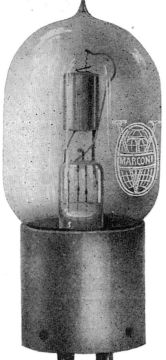

The Only Vacuum Tube

which

Amateurs Can Use

Agreements recently effected have made vacuum tubes available for experimental use. The Marconi V. T. is the only vacuum tube, or audion, which may be sold to amateurs, laboratories, schools of instruction and experimenters.

MARCONI V.T.

$7.⁰⁰ each

Standard base, $1.50 additional

Fleming Pat. No. 803684
DeForest Pat. Nos. 841387-879532

A highly developed, all-round tube for use as a detector and amplifier in wireless communication. It has practically the same electrical constants as the tube used by the Allied armies and navies throughout the war in continuous wave transmission and reception. The terminals of the elements of the tube are brought out to a 4-prong standardized base, fitting into the standard four-contact bayonet sockets.

Filament current 0.7 ampere. Filament potential, 4 to 6 volts.
Plate potential, 20 to 60 volts for reception.

For lighting filaments a **lead** storage battery is preferable because of its constancy of voltage. Ordinary dry cells or flashlight batteries may be used to provide plate voltage.

The approximate operating life of the MARCONI V. T. is 1,500 hours.

Delivered postpaid in special container insured against breakage to any address upon receipt of purchase price

COMMERCIAL DEPARTMENT

Marconi Wireless Telegraph Company of America

Sole Distributors for De Forest Radio Telephone & Telegraph Co.

WOOLWORTH BLDG. 233 Broadway NEW YORK

Figure 1.14 — With patent wars raging over the licensing and manufacturing of vacuum tubes, Marconi Wireless Telegraph Company (later the Radio Corporation of America) advised amateurs that their brand was the only tube amateurs could legally use. (Aug 1919)

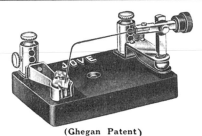
Figure 1.15 — Few amateurs today would consider repairing a defective tube, but the Vacuum Tube Repair Company of Oakland, California was established for just that purpose. (Dec 1919)

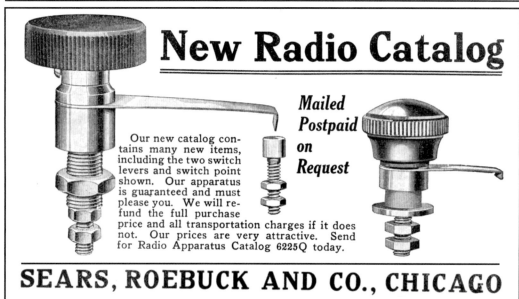
Figure 1.16 — Even other publications such as Everyday Engineering advertised in the pages of *QST*. Sears, Roebuck and Co. added radio apparatus to their catalog offerings and Tresco sold knocked down condensers at a discount. (Sep 1919)

Figure 1.17 — Chicago Radio Laboratory's underground antenna system was designed to reduce static in the receiver. Today it might be attractive to amateurs battling restrictive covenants. The Elliot Electric regenerative receiver offered quality materials and workmanship at a moderate price. (Aug 1919)

Figure 1.18 — Two years after the government shut down Amateur Radio with a ban on both transmitting and receiving, it lifted the restriction on receiving. Amateur transmitters remained off the air for another six months. (Jul 1919)

Figure 1.19 — Hams and manufacturers alike celebrated the return of activity to the amateur bands nearly a year after the signing of the armistice. (Nov 1919)

Figure 1.20 — The YMCA conducted radio schools at branches around the country to help meet the demand for operators from the Merchant Marine and others. (Jun 1919)

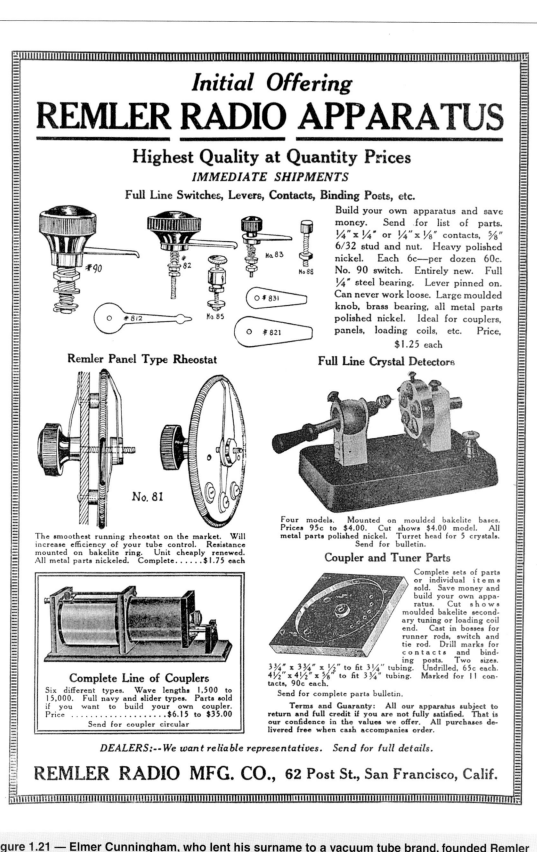
Figure 1.21 — Elmer Cunningham, who lent his surname to a vacuum tube brand, founded Remler Radio Manufacturing in San Francisco. The company sold radio components in addition to completed sets. Remler did all its own metal stamping, machining and Bakelite molding in house. (Nov 1919)

Figure 1.22 — North American Aerial Spar Manufacturing of Dubuque, Iowa, supplied everything needed to construct the gigantic, multiconductor antennas some amateurs used on 200 meters. Alfred H. Grebe of Richmond Hill, New York, was still a teenager when he first manufactured radio gear for sale to amateurs. The Barr device employed a small cup of mercury topped with a thin layer of oil to detect radio signals. (Nov 1919)

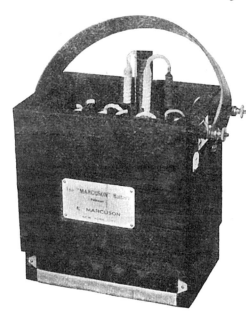
Figure 1.23 — The storage battery provided plate voltage for tubes before conventional power supplies became common. The batteries could be recharged using dc (Edison type) household circuits. (Nov 1919)

Figure 1.24 — Benwood Specialty's rotary spark gap was claimed to be quiet in operation, an asset at a time when even-quieter CW transmitters were replacing spark rigs. (Dec 1919)

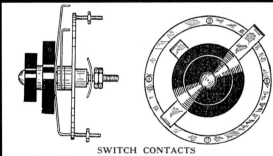
Figure 1.25 — Headphone sets frequently appeared in ads during *QST's* first decades. Both commercial and amateur users considered them an integral part of the radio experience. The other ads on the page illustrate the widespread geography of businesses serving the radio hobby. (Dec 1919)

Figure 1.26 — Adams-Morgan manufactured and sold completed sets and parts via mail order. A notable partner in the firm was Paul F. Godley, 2ZE, who traveled to Scotland on behalf of the ARRL to participate in the successful 1921 transatlantic tests. (Sep 1916)

Figure 1.27 — Ads for American Radio and Research Corporation's AMRAD brand appeared often in the front pages or on the back cover of *QST* shortly after World War I. (Oct 1919)

Chapter 2

The 1920s

Behind the Diamond, Regulatory Battles, Changed Operating Practices

A series of articles in *QST* ushered in the 1920s with a big push for CW. One such article stated, "Amateur continuous wave telegraphy has at length arrived."[1] ARRL Traffic Manager J.O. Smith, 2ZL, junked his spark set, saying it was, "Outgrown." He replaced it with an oscillator consisting of several small tubes in parallel. Signals from the small CW transmitter successfully reached from his station in Rockville Center, New York, to points as distant as Chicago and West Palm Beach at times when spark failed over the same circuits.

Accurately and easily tuning in CW signals with the station receiver remained a persistent problem, however, and some operators resorted to first establishing contact with spark then switching to CW on the same frequency to continue. Another way around the reception problem involved the use of modulated CW — imposing an audio tone on the RF signal — a technique developed by the National Bureau of Standards.[2]

It wasn't until 1921 that receiver development began to match the pace of CW transmitters. Two radio pioneers made significant contributions to the cause. John L. Reinartz, 1QP, labored diligently on his "Reinartz" tuner, documenting the device's evolution in the pages of *QST*.[3] Receiver designer and manufacturer McMurdo Silver's work appeared in the magazine as well. Silver emphasized that simplicity in design and operation were essential attributes for a good CW receiver, saying, "The Fewer the controls the greater the ease of finding an unknown station."[4]

In July 1920, the ARRL announced its adoption of the diamond emblem as its logo.[5] The League registered the design as a trademark and it has gone on to become an internationally recognized symbol for both the organization and Amateur Radio in general. In an unusual twist, the Canadian indie-rock band Arcade Fire adopted a similar emblem (with the League's permission) 90 years after the League first used the logo. It's okay, though — two of the band's members are grandsons of Alvino Rey,

W6UK (SK), ham operator and famous musician.

Before 1920 came to an end, Amateur Radio faced another legislative crisis.[6] A bill languishing in the Senate Committee on Naval Affairs, but not yet acted upon, threatened Amateur Radio and all civilian radio services. The Navy urged creation of a National Radio Commission which would be given authority to formulate regulations governing the operation of all classes of radio stations and to change the regulations any time it saw fit.

In addition to sending representatives to hearings in Washington, the League enlisted amateurs across the country to oppose the bill. The names of senators sitting on the Naval Affairs committee were published in *QST* and the membership was asked to contact these senators directly.

August 31, 1921, marked the opening of the first ever ARRL national convention at the Edgewater Beach hotel in Chicago. Attendees included members from all nine US call districts and a number of Canadian amateurs were present as well.[7]

On December 12, 1922, station 1BCG in Greenwich, Connecticut, sent a 12-word message and Paul F. Godley, 2ZE, listening in Ardrossan, Scotland copied it.[8] The DX age dawned with Amateur Radio's bridging of the Atlantic.

Paul Godley used an Armstrong super heterodyne on the Scottish end of the transatlantic tests and ads for superhet receivers appeared in *QST* during the following months. It represented a significant advance in receiver technology that, in one form or another, dominated decades into the future.

In the midst of reporting all the ocean-spanning communications excitement, *QST* reached a significant milestone. The print run for the May 1922 issue was 50,000 copies, making the magazine a powerful marketing tool for advertisers.

Seemingly always lurking just around the corner, new regulatory struggles confronted the Amateur Service in June 1923. The Department of Commerce issued a

The National Company first entered the shortwave receiver market with the SW-2. The two-tube set sold in basic panel and chassis form as pictured here. National constructed the receivers without the aid of production tooling. (1928)

The C.D. Tuska Company, owned by the co-founder of the League and *QST*'s first publisher, produced this one-tube regenerative receiver in 1922. It covered 150 to 650 meters. ($35)

General Letter spelling out changes in a new set of regulations. The letter created a tiered license structure consisting of General, Restricted, Special, and Amateur Extra First Grade licenses.[9] The new regulations and license classes specified emission types, transmitting power, wavelengths of operation, and made a provision for "quiet hours" to reduce interference to broadcast listeners.

Licenses issued under the new regulations would not, for the first time, specify a particular wavelength on which the station was permitted to transmit. Thus did the concept of *bands* — a range or band of frequencies — come into being. Then, as today, the ranges were referred to by wavelength. In general, the regulations gave amateurs the spectrum between 150 and 220 meters, which was subdivided according to license class and emission type (pure CW, unfiltered CW, modulated CW, phone and spark). The unfiltered CW designation applied to a transmitter operated directly from the ac mains without sufficient filtering in the plate supply to produce a pure CW tone.

The new band operation solved one problem — the interference caused by many stations operating on the same frequency — and introduced another. With the freedom to move about a band, it became necessary to set one's transmitter to the same frequency as the received station. In addition, amateurs of different license classes using various emission modes found it necessary to ensure the wavelength employed was commensurate with the station's privileges. State of the art at that time meant using a wave meter to calibrate the transmitter.

In order to assist amateurs in calibrating their wave meters or station receivers, the Bureau of Standards began transmitting standard frequency signals from its Washington, DC, radio station WWV during July through October of 1923. Early transmissions covered wavelengths of 200 to 705 meters, with WWV later moving to more amateur-specific wavelengths between 150 and 222 meters.[10]

Once amateurs moved below 200 meters, they didn't stop there. A year after the 1923 regulations, the Department of Commerce authorized use of new amateur bands at 80, 40, 20, and 5 meters. In a letter to Kenneth B. Warner, the League's secretary, Bureau of Navigation commissioner D. B. Carson said, "It is hoped that sufficient experimentation can be carried on on the short wave lengths by amateurs to accumulate some dependable data …," which would be used to determine frequency allocations at the next National Radio Conference. Commissioner Carson urged the ARRL to publicize the need for tests on the new bands both in *QST* and via messages transmitted from the League's official station.[11]

In only a few weeks' time, 40 and 80 meters bustled with activity as hundreds of stations tested the new bands, but it took a bit longer for things to get going on 20. The 5 meter allocation was another story altogether as experimenters explored the territory. Completely new designs, some termed "crude" by their own inventors, were made to function. The consensus was to make the circuits simple by eliminating everything not absolutely necessary for operation.

A set of new regulations issued by the Department of Commerce in January 1925 all but outlawed spark, saying, "Amateur spark transmitters produce considerable interference and consequently are responsible for many complaints…owners of such transmitters should abandon their use as early as possible…." Those continuing to use spark were restricted to the spectrum between 170 and 180 meters.[12] Phone stations were also allowed in this same range and soon acquired an additional allocation in the 80 meter band.

An article in January 1926 *QST* announced that the crystal control was "here to stay." It went on to say, "The crystal-controlled transmitter produces a signal the frequency of which is beautifully steady and whose note is splendid to copy."[13] The year that followed certainly belonged to crystal control as *QST* published one article after another on the technology. The League's timing was

The Regenaformer receiver resulted from research done by Glenn Browning and Frederick Drake at Harvard University. They sought to create a more efficient receiving transformer that would provide better sensitivity and selectivity than that of their mid-1920s competition. The National Company manufactured the central components of the sets. ($95, 1925)

fortuitous. After 15 years under the Radio Act of 1912, regulation of all things radio changed with the passing of the Radio Act of 1927 in February of that year. The new law created the Federal Radio Commission and its five member board.[14]

QST was not hesitant to express a dissenting opinion when it came to some of the new commission's proceedings. A March 1928 editorial said, "So many people who knew nothing about radio never before assembled in the same room to talk about it," referring to a shortwave hearing held that January.[15] With both commercial and military interests aligned against them in the battle for spectrum, amateurs needed the high profile advocacy the League provided.

The new Radio Law and regulations flowing from it mandated that amateurs either comply with the more stringent technical standards or else lose transmitting privileges altogether. The League took on the mentoring of its membership — and all amateurs — to achieve this compliance. A significant movement to this end was the association of Ross Hull with ARRL headquarters. Hull, an Australian amateur (oa3JU) and also honorary secretary of the Wireless Institute of Australia, was put in charge of the League's Information Service (a department created to answer technical questions). The announcement of his appointment was termed "somewhat extraordinary" by ARRL secretary Kenneth B. Warner.

Articles by Hull made a regular appearance in QST, including one he penned to kick off the League's campaign to prepare amateurs and their equipment for the regulatory changes coming in 1929. The magazine's editor called it "one of the most important articles ever published for the radio amateur."[16] It summarized the results of a program looking into the modification and improvement of amateur equipment put forth by the Board of Directors. Chief among the equipment needing modification, improvement, or elimination altogether, was the transmitter using a self-excited oscillator.

Not all changes revolved around technical or spectrum matters. In October 1928, US stations began preceding the district number in their call signs with the letter W. The call 1SZ became W1SZ, for example. Stations in US territories such as Puerto Rico or Hawaii employed a K prefix. Canadian amateurs had already begun using VE. Some, but not all, member countries of the International Amateur Radio Union followed suit with official prefixes of their own.[17]

The 1920s closed with Amateur Radio a much different hobby from the one of a decade earlier. Indeed, an editorial in QST called January 1, 1929, "The dividing line between the old and the new in Amateur Radio."[18] Ten years before, spark reigned as king with stations tightly grouped around the allocation at 200 meters. Amateur communication had not yet spanned the Atlantic.

The world of Amateur Radio across the 1929 dividing line consisted of new modes and bands, including wavelengths shorter than one meter. CW signals not only covered longer distances than spark but did so at a fraction of the power. This long distance communication helped the hobby become international in scope.

Notes

[1] "The Advent of Amateur C.W.," QST, Apr 1920, pp 13, 14, 16.

[2] "Auto-Modulated C.W. Telegraphy," QST, Feb 1920, pp 47-48.

[3] "A Receiving Tuner for C.W.," QST, Jun 1921, pp 5-7.

[4] M. Silver, "Some Experimental Regenerative Tuners," QST, Mar 1921, pp 19-20.

[5] "The A.R.R.L. Emblem," QST, Jul 1920, pp 23-24.

[6] "Dangerous Legislation Confronts Us," QST, Dec 1920, pp 5-6, 12.

[7] "Our First National Convention," QST, Oct 1921, pp 7-22.

[8] "The Story of the Transatlantics," QST, Feb 1922, pp 7-14.

[9] "The New Amateur Regulations," QST, Aug 1923, pp 13-15.

[10] "Hundreds of Wavemeters Being Calibrated," QST, Oct 1923, pp 14-15.

[11] "The New Short Waves," QST, Sep 1924, pp 7-8.

[12] "New Regulations for Transmitting Stations," QST, Mar 1925, p 29.

[13] "Practical Crystal-Controlled Transmitters," QST, Jan 1926, pp 21-25.

[14] "President Signs the Radio Control Bill; Will Name Board of Five to Regulate Air," The New York Times, Feb 24, 1920, p 1.

[15] "Editorials," QST, Mar 1928, pp 7-8.

[16] R. Hull, "Overhauling the Transmitter for 1929," QST, Aug 1928, pp 9-19.

[17] "Editorials," QST, Oct 1928, pp 7-8.

[18] "Editorials," QST, Jan 1929, pp 7-8.

Figure 2.1 — High-impedance headphones, common from Amateur Radio's earliest days until well past World War II, were often considered as important a part of the receiving system as the station receiver itself. They were, in fact, referred to as receivers and sometimes credited with making an otherwise difficult contact possible. C. Brandes and Wm. J. Murdock headphones had a particularly good reputation. (Oct 1920)

AUDIO TRON

The Original Tubular Vacuum Detector, Amplifier, Oscillator

NOW FREE FROM ALL RESTRICTIONS

Dealers and Amateurs !

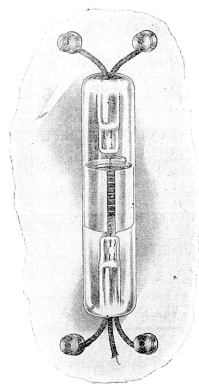

AUDIO TRONS, recognized as the most sensitive detectors ever produced are now licensed under Fleming Patent No. 803,684 for amateur and experimental uses only in radio communication. They are no longer limited to radio frequency and can now be used as detectors and oscillators as well as amplifiers.

All patent questions have been definitely settled. Vacuum tube patents are basic and have been sustained by the Federal Courts.

Be sure to get genuine AUDIO TRONS, they outclass any other form of detector and are absolutely free from all legal restrictions or difficulties. These new uses make it even more necessary to insist on the genuine. You can always tell a real AUDIO TRON by the name stamped plainly on the glass.

Insist on the name AUDIO TRON on every tube you purchase. Fully guaranteed by the AUDIO TRON Mfg. Co. **(Read the guaranty below).**

Your last chance for an AUDIO TRON double filament DETECTOR

Manufacturing reasons make it impossible to continue the present hand-made AUDIO TRON.

This type has a double filament of special thorium tungsten and the operating life is over 2,000 hours. No special socket is required. The electrical and mechanical dimensions result in a heavy plate current and corresponding signal strength. Plate voltage under 40.

The few thousand that will still be produced, however, will be of the same standard of excellence that has characterized every AUDIO TRON.

Already recognized as the most sensitive detector on the market, these few that will remain, with all re-

strictions on amateur use lifted, are undoubtely the greatest opportunity ever offered to amateur radio operators.

See your dealer at once or order direct. Be sure to benefit by this last opportunity to secure a hand-made super-sensitive, double filament AUDIO-TRON Detector, Amplifier, Oscillator.

$6.00 each
(No increase in price)

The AUDIOTRON Exclusive Guaranty: Each and every AUDIO TRON is guaranteed to arrive in good condition and to prove fully satisfactory. Replacement of unsatisfactory tubes will be made free of charge.

Dealers—

Get in touch with the AUDIOTRON Mfg. Co. at once. We will give you full information about settlement of all patent difficulties. **You will also be interested in our new proposition for wide awake dealers.** After the present supply is exhausted, new types of AUDIOTRON, manufactured entirely by machinery, will be offered for sale. Our extensive advertising during the Fall will establish definitely the superiority of the AUDIO TRON and will create new sales for you. Be sure to take advantage of our full co-operation at once. Prepare to cash in on the AUDIO TRON reputation, established since 1915. **Write us today for full details.**

AUDIO TRON MFG. COMPANY
(Successors to the AUDIO TRON Sales Co.)

Dept. Q,   Lick Bldg.,   San Francisco, California

Figure 2.2 — Elmer T. Cunningham was a combatant in the vacuum tube patent wars of the early 1920s. He changed the name of his company from AudioTron Sales to AudioTron Manufacturing and soldiered on with products supplied by RCA but bearing his own name on the tubes and the packaging. (Sep 1920)

Figure 2.3 — A. H. Corwin & Company of Newark, New Jersey, sold radio parts such as the handsome dial and knob combination shown here. The rectifier tube advertised by the Wireless Equipment Company helped supply dc plate power for tubes from the commercial ac mains. League co-founder and president Hiram P. Maxim was also a brilliant inventor with a wide-ranging field of interests that included airplanes and automobiles. One of his best known non-radio inventions was the Maxim firearms silencer. (Jun 1920)

Figure 2.4 — G.F. Johnson and The Wilcox Laboratories supplied hobbyists with radio parts from Springfield, Illinois, and Lansing, Michigan, respectively — using mail order to achieve a nationwide reach. (Dec 1920)

Figure 2.5 — Ralph Mathews, 9ZN, and Karl Hassel, 8AKG, founded Chicago Radio Laboratory in 1919. Mathews served on the ARRL Board of Directors and was also the League's Central Division manager. As this ad indicates, the company changed its name to Z-nith (Zenith) in early 1921, writing the first chapter in a long-running story that included both radio and television in the following decades. (Feb 1921)

Our Chicago Store

MONTGOMERY
High Grade
Order Direct From These Pages.

Navy Type Receiving Transformer

Improved Model

63S600—A very selective instrument for the more advanced stations. Primary inductance is controlled in steps by units and tens switches. Secondary has 12-point control. Has wave range up to 4,000 meters. Formica panels. Metal parts of brass. Single silk covered windings. Mahogany finished wood work. Base is 18 inches long, 6½ inches wide. Ship. wt. 25 lbs. Price...................**$17.95**

Arlington Type Receiving Transformer

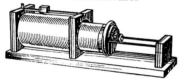

63S601 — An efficient high-grade, long wave tuner. Has same winding as our Navy type. Will receive all government time stations such as Arlington and Key West. Works up to 4,000 meters. Primary controlled by slider. Secondary inductance varied by a 12-point switch mounted on Formica. Silk covered wire windings, Brass metal parts polished and lacquered. Mahogany finished wood work. Base, 18 inches long; 6 inches wide. Shipping weight, 14 pounds. Price.......**$7.90**

Junior Loose Coupler

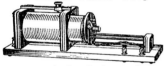

63S5103—A fine instrument for 200 to 600 meter work. Primary controlled with slider, secondary by 5 point switch. Metal parts brass, polished and lacquered. Woodwork mahogany finish. Base, 12 x 3½ inches. Ship. wt., 6 pounds. Price..**$5.70**

Two Slide Tuning Coil

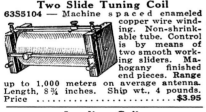

63S5104 — Machine spaced enameled copper wire winding. Non-shrinkable tube. Control is by means of two smooth working sliders. Mahogany finished end pieces. Range up to 1,000 meters on average antenna. Length, 8¾ inches. Ship wt., 4 pounds. Price **$3.95**

Loading Coil

63S5105—Essentially the same as two slider tuning coil, but has only one slider. Will add about 300 M range to any set. Ship. wt., 3 lbs. Price...........**$3.40**

SATISFACTION GUARANTEED OR YOUR MONEY BACK

Radio amateurs will no doubt welcome the opportunity that they now have to obtain high grade radio apparatus from this large mail order house. Montgomery, Ward & Company has a record of 50 years of fair dealing with their customers who now number over 5,000,000. This institution was the first to adopt the guarantee of **Satisfaction or Your Money Back**. This guarantee applies to all radio goods shown on this and the five following pages. Order any of the apparatus on these pages and give it a 5 day trial. If at the end of 5 days it is not what you expected it to be, return it to us in the same condition in which you received it and we will promptly return your money together with the transportation charges you have paid.

Universal Detector

63S5304 — A detector of correct construction. Permanent adjustment. Galena, silicon and other minerals can be used. Moulded base and adjustment knob. Metal parts of brass, polished nickel finish. Tested piece of silicon included. Base size, 2½x3½ in. Ship. wt., 1 lb. Price.................**$1.88**

Standard Galena Detector

63S5305 — A popular detector. Tested piece of galena is mounted in cup which can be rotated. Crystal contact of phosphor bronze wire coiled and pointed and set on flat spring. Very fine adjustment obtainable with screw. Moulded base and adjustment knob. Base, size, 3x3 inches. Ship. wt., 1¼ lbs. Price.........**$1.43**

Murdock Detector Stand

63S5302 — A good low priced detector stand. Will do very satisfactory work. Moulded black composition base. Adjustable cup and contact. Nickel plated binding posts. No crystals included. Size, 2⅝x1½x2 in. Ship. wt., 4 oz. Price.....................**70c**

Detector Crystals

GALENA

Genuine Arlington Tested Minerals. Absolutely the best crystals that can be purchased for any price. All are thoroughly tested and guaranteed. Extremely sensitive. Packed separately in sealed boxes. Ship. wt., about 3 oz.

63S5320—Supersensitive Galena. Per crystal....................**29c**
63S5322—Supersensitive Silicon. Per crystal **29c**
63S5324—"Radiocite". Per crystal...**25c**

Radiotron V.T. Detector

63S5194 — This is a "soft" tube especially suited for detector use and is also an excellent audio frequency amplifier. It produces excellent results in regenerative circuits. Has the familiar hissing point and low B battery potential requirements. Standard four-prong mounting. Ship. wt., 1 lb. Price...**$5.00**
63S5620—4000 ohm potentiometer graphite. Often used with soft vacuum tubes. Semi-circular, 2⅛ in. diam., ⅜ in. wide, ¼ in. thick copper plated ends. Price **$1.15**

Radiotron Amplifier Oscillator

63S5192—A high vacuum amplifier and detector. Requires no critical adjustment. Designed for amplification and undamped wave reception by the regenerative method. May be used singly for receiving continuous waves or in cascade as a two or more step amplifier. Ship. wt., 1 lb. Price.....**$6.50**

Socket for Vacuum Tube

63S5342—Socket is mounted on bakelite sheet. Four binding posts for connections. Screw holes for flat mounting, screws in side of base for panel mounting, permitting either upright or vertical position of tube. Ship. wt., 8 oz. Price................**$1.40**

Improved V.T. Socket

63S5343—Improved long flat spring contacts insure positive contact on any standard tube base prongs. Glossy black composition base. Nickeled tube. Marked screw connections. May be used and wired in any position. Ship. wt., 8 oz. Price..**$1.00**

Order direct from these pages. See instructions on second page following this one.

Montgomery Ward & Co.
Satisfaction Guaranteed or Your Money Back

CHICAGO, ILL.   KANSAS CITY, MO.
Send Your Order to House Nearest You.

Figure 2.6 — Montgomery Ward joined Sears, Roebuck and Co. in adding Amateur Radio gear to their mail order offerings. (Feb 1921)

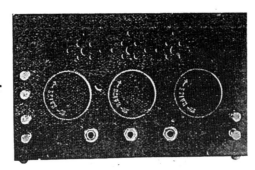

Figure 2.7 — NOLA Radio served the New Orleans amateur, commercial and maritime markets in the early 1920s. (Aug 1920)

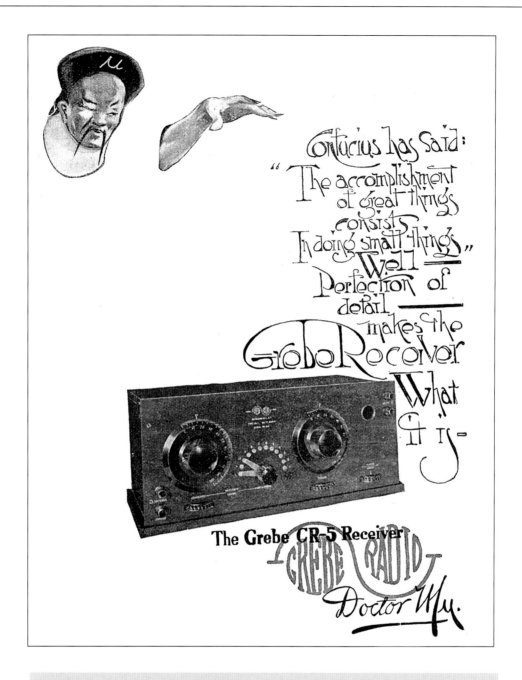

Figure 2.8 — Grebe's Dr. Mu used quotes from Chinese philosophers such as Confucius and Lao Tzu to market the company's receivers. (Jan 1922)

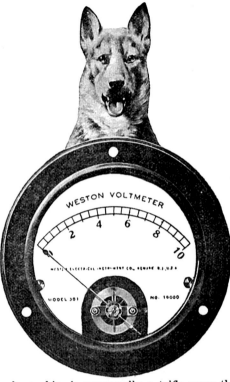

Figure 2.9 — The price of vacuum tubes in the 1920s made investing in instrumentation a wise choice for amateurs wishing to achieve maximum performance and long life from their tubes. (Jan 1922)

Build Your Own Radio Tower

THINK of the benefits and pride you would enjoy by having a real radio tower right on your own grounds. Think how much better you could hear and how much further you could send. Think how your reputation as a radio operator would travel through your community!

You can now build a tower yourself from standard materials which are all sold by your local dealers — build it from 40 to 100 feet high — economically and safely — from the easy-to-understand Hull blueprint plans that are as simple as A-B-C.

CORRECT PRINCIPLES

For years we have been building heavy transmission towers for big central stations all over the country. Now we have started a department to permit radio operators to have the benefit of our tower building experience. At great expense we have drafted simple, yet detailed architects' blueprint plans for radio towers of seven popular heights. Every problem is properly covered—foundations, weights, stresses, wind pressures, etc. You do not have to figure out any sizes or what to use. Everything is shown plainly, right down to where and what size to bore the holes.

YOU SAVE MONEY

Our plans call for everything that is best for strength, yet cheapest to use; you waste no money on useless parts. And, of course, because you build the tower yourself it costs you but a fraction of what you would pay for one ready-made.

SIMPLE TO ERECT

The erection of your tower is simplicity itself. No long, awkward, heavy pieces are used; everything is light, strong and easy to handle. After cutting the pieces to size and boring the holes, you start building up and up, merely bolting each piece into position. You number each piece as you make it, according to blueprint numbers—you can't go wrong. To the operator who likes to make things, building this tower will be real sport.

SPECIAL OFFER

As a special introductory offer, for a limited time we have reduced the prices of all Hull radio tower working blueprint and erection diagram outfits exactly 50%:

40-ft. and 50-ft. Hull Tower Plans,
regularly $ 4.00—special $2.00
60-ft. and 70-ft. Hull Tower Plans,
regularly $ 7.00—special $3.50
80-ft. and 90-ft. Hull Tower Plans,
regularly $10.00—special $5.00
100-ft. Hull Radio Tower Plans—
regularly $12.00—special $6.00

All orders filled promptly upon receipt of money-order or draft; send letter registered if it contains currency. Select the size tower you want to build and order the plans now; get everything ready to build your tower this Spring.

S. W. HULL & COMPANY
Steel Tower Specialists
General Offices
3720 Prospect Ave.   Cleveland, Ohio
Address Department Q

HULL
RADIO TOWERS

Figure 2.10 — As ever, amateur operators dreamed of higher towers and bigger antennas. S.W. Hull & Company supplied tower blueprints and detailed instructions for fabrication using materials purchased locally by the builder. (Mar 1922)

Reduce those QRN Atmospherics NOW with Burgess "B" Batteries

NOISELESS! That describes Burgess "B" Batteries. **Absolutely noiseless!** Weak and distant audio frequency signals can be received with multi-stage amplifiers and Burgess "B" Batteries because Burgess "B" Batteries **do not drown out signals.**

BURGESS "B" Batteries assure clear receiving. They will increase the efficiency of any receiving set. They are cheapest in hours of service. And they are sold by all reliable dealers in radio equipment. Look for the black and white stripes. If you can't get Burgess "B" from your dealer, just drop a line to us, care Dept. D.

BURGESS BATTERY COMPANY

General Sales Office

Harris Trust Bldg., Chicago

Offices and Distributing Warehouses

Chicago, Ill., 111 W. Monroe St.
Madison, Wis., Main & BeverlySts.
Kansas City, Mo., 2109 Grand Ave.
St. Paul, Minn., 2362 UniversityAv.
Boston, Mass. 136 Federal St.
New York, 50 Church St.
Winnipeg, Man., 701 Wellington Av.

As indicated in the illustration. Burgess Batteries are supplied with both flexible wire terminals and binding post terminals. The binding post terminals are complete with hexagon nuts and brass nuts, making it possible to attach wires directly to the cells without the use of solder or bolts.

Figure 2.11 — Battery companies, makers of both storage batteries and dry cells alike, competed fiercely in the amateur market. Besides the Burgess company shown here, others included Eveready (National Carbon Co.), McTighe, Westinghouse, Kimley Electric, Prest-O-Lite, Willard and Novo. (May 1922)

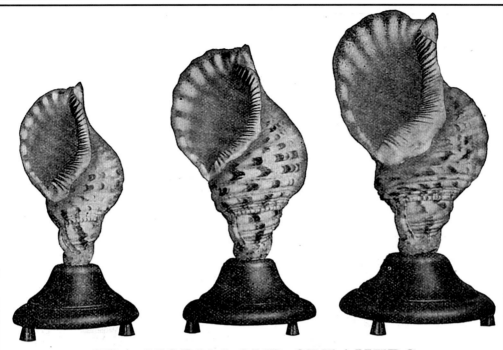

SEA HORN LOUD SPEAKERS
NATURE'S PERFECT AMPLIFIER
THE BEST AMPLIFYING HORN OFFERED
SPLENDID DEFINITION

Artistic and Ornamental Genuine Sea Shells mounted on rich mahogany finished bases complete with phone clamp. 12 to 13 inches high $8.00; 13½ to 14½ inches high $12.00; 15 to 16½ inches high $15.00.

☞ FOR IMMEDIATE DELIVERY AND MONEY BACK IF YOU ARE NOT SATISFIED. ORDERS FILLED IN ROTATION AS RECEIVED.

Precision Condensers
Without Dials

43 Plate	$4.00
23 Plate	3.50
11 Plate	3.25
3″ Dials	.85
Vacuum Tube Sockets Unbreakable	1.00

May be used for either panel or base mounting.
Phone clamps for Victor and Columbia phonographs enable you to use the horn on tone chamber of phonograph for a Loud Speaker $1.50.

The above articles are ready for immediate shipment with the understanding that money wil be refunded if goods are not satisfactory.

THE ORO-TONE CO.
Mfr's of Phonograph and Wireless Equipment
DEALERS SEND FOR SPECIAL FOLDER

1000 to 1010 George St.,   Chicago, Ills.

Figure 2.12 — Hold a sea shell to your ear and you're supposed to hear the sound of the ocean. These Sea Horn loudspeakers from Oro-Tone produced the sound of radio signals instead, and also provided a novel decorating touch for the radio shack. (Jun 1922)

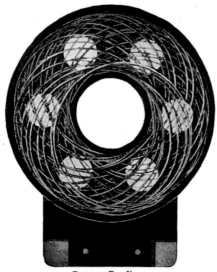

Figure 2.13 — The term Curtate Epitrochoid used in this coupler ad no doubt sent many prospective buyers scurrying to their dictionaries and math books. (Feb 1923)

Figure 2.14 — Paul F. Godley, 2ZE, used an Armstrong superheterodyne receiver at the Ardrossan, Scotland, station in the ARRL's successful November 1921 transatlantic tests. (Dec 1922)

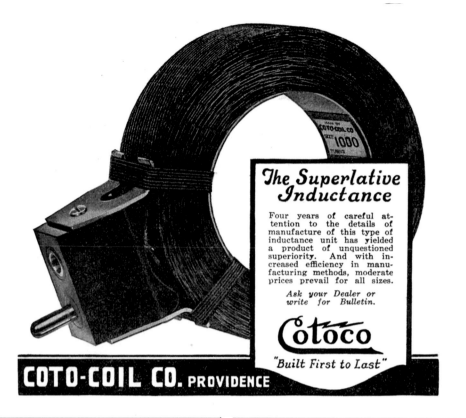

Figure 2.15 — A decade before introducing its first communication receiver, Hammarlund was known as a manufacturer of quality radio components, especially variable capacitors. Coto-Coil and the Rhamstine company were veterans in the radio component business and longtime *QST* advertisers as well. (Mar 1923)

Mu-Rad R-F

Amplifying Transformers

200-600
Meters
Air Core

Part of the Celebrated Mu–Rad Receivers

THE heart of the great sensitivity of Mu-Rad Sets, a marvel of a marvelous science, is the Mu-Rad Transformer. No loss by capacity effect. No eddy current or iron losses. A type for every stage. Ask your dealer.

Dealers Profit When Mu-Rad Apparatus Builds Confidence of Customers in Their Stores

Three Types

Type T-11 for the first stage 6.00

Type T-11A for the second stage $6.50

Type T-11B for the third stage $7.00

Write NOW for Proposition

Mu-Rad Laboratories, Inc.

804 Fifth Ave. Asbury Park, New Jersey

Figure 2.16 — Mu-Rad Laboratories marketed directly to radio parts supply houses, who then sold to amateurs and other hobbyists. The company also manufactured and sold receivers of its own design in the mid-1920s. Mu-Rad went out of business in 1928. Radio Specialty Company did business by mail order, selling radio parts and supplies at steeply discounted prices. (May 1923)

Figure 2.17 — Dr. H.P. Donle, chief engineer for Connecticut Telephone & Electric Company, developed the sodium-ion tube, along with several receiver circuits employing the device. The company sold the Sodion products through its radio division. (Dec 1923)

The Most Popular Radio Insulation

Week by week the amount of Formica used for radio insulation by amateur and commercial operators increases. It is the most popular material of its kind. This great demand for Formica is due to its high dielectric strength, and the low power and hysteresis losses with high frequency currents where it is employed.

It is due also to the handsome, good looking panels that Formica makes and to the fact that it machines easily. It is unaffected by weather conditions, oil, water, acids, alkalies. It retains its good looks and high efficiency indefinitely.

Formica is approved by the United States Navy and the Signal Corps!

Dealers: We co-operate to increase your Formica sales. You can buy Formica in 36" x 42" sheets and cut it yourself or we will cut it into any series of standard sizes that you want at a small extra cost. Write for our dealer helps. Let us send you electrotypes for your local newspaper advertising.

THE FORMICA INSULATION CO.

4620 Spring Grove Avenue,

Winton Place,   **Cincinnati, Ohio**

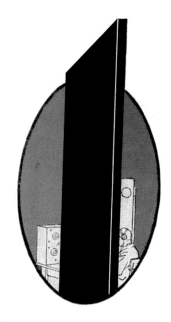

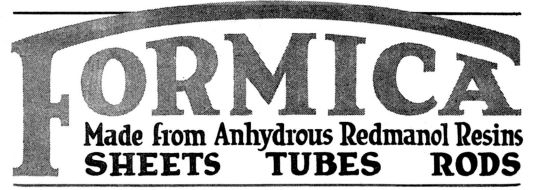

FORMICA

Made from Anhydrous Redmanol Resins
SHEETS   TUBES   RODS

Figure 2.18 — Long before becoming the ubiquitous laminate used on furniture and countertops, Formica was a popular insulating and panel material in the radio industry. (Mar 1922)

Figure 2.19 — The WC-5-SW receiver sold by Ott Radio of La Crosse, Wisconsin, was manufactured by Western Coil & Electric across the state in Racine. The tuned radio frequency set used four tubes. (Jan 1924)

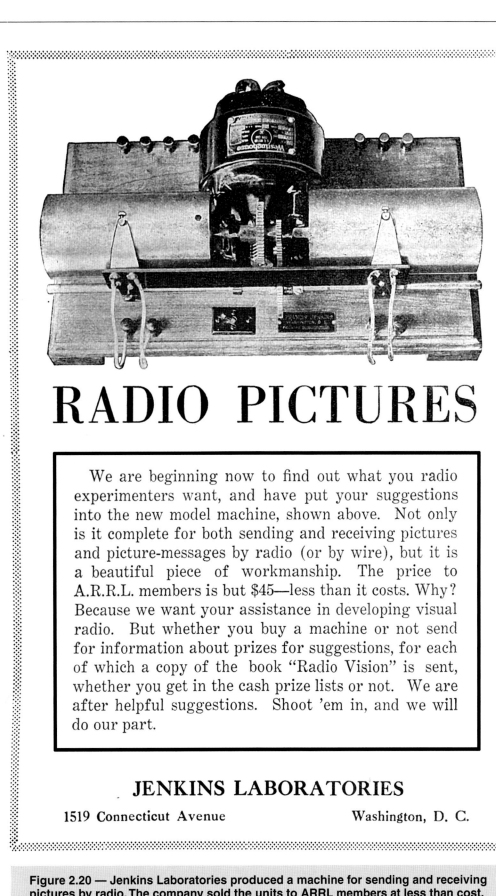

RADIO PICTURES

We are beginning now to find out what you radio experimenters want, and have put your suggestions into the new model machine, shown above. Not only is it complete for both sending and receiving pictures and picture-messages by radio (or by wire), but it is a beautiful piece of workmanship. The price to A.R.R.L. members is but $45—less than it costs. Why? Because we want your assistance in developing visual radio. But whether you buy a machine or not send for information about prizes for suggestions, for each of which a copy of the book "Radio Vision" is sent, whether you get in the cash prize lists or not. We are after helpful suggestions. Shoot 'em in, and we will do our part.

JENKINS LABORATORIES

1519 Connecticut Avenue   Washington, D. C.

Figure 2.20 — Jenkins Laboratories produced a machine for sending and receiving pictures by radio. The company sold the units to ARRL members at less than cost, looking to amateurs for assistance in developing "visual radio." (Jul 1925)

Figure 2.21 — The Vibroplex semi-automatic key is synonymous with the word "bug." First appearing in *QST*'s February 1925 issue, Vibroplex products remain in the magazine's ad pages 90 years later, even though the company has changed owners and locations several times along the way. (Dec 1925)

The New NATIONAL
Variable
Velvet Vernier Dial

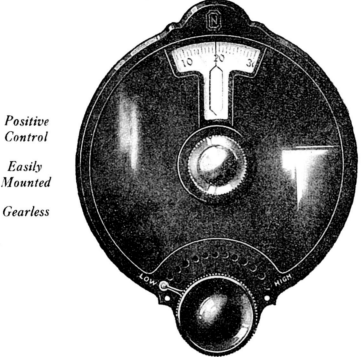

Positive Control

Easily Mounted

Gearless

Variable Ratio

Velvet Smoothness

Ornamental

TYPE B Patents Pending

THIS dial embodies a modified application of our "Velvet Vernier" mechanism designed to facilitate mounting on the ¼" shaft of any standard type of variable condenser, without the use of tools other than a screw-driver. It will replace plain dials on any receiver where sharper tuning is desired.

Of special importance is a new and novel device which enables the user to adjust at will the **reduction to any ratio from 6-1 to 20-1.** This feature aids greatly in the separation of stations operating on the lower wave lengths. This new dial is moulded from black bakelite in a highly ornamental design with perfectly uniform graduations.

Specifications	*Nickle Finish*	*Gold Finish*
Clockwise 0-200 (360°)	$2.50	$3.00
Counter-Clockwise (360°)	2.50	3.00

NATIONAL COMPANY, Inc.
W. A. READY, *President*

110 Brookline Street

Cambridge, Mass.

Figure 2.22 — National's "Velvet Vernier" tuning dial graced the front panel of several of the company's products and found favor with numerous radio builders for their own projects as well. The dial offered variable reduction ratios for finer tuning when needed. (Mar 1926)

Don't annoy your neighbor

How to avoid interfering with the broadcast listener

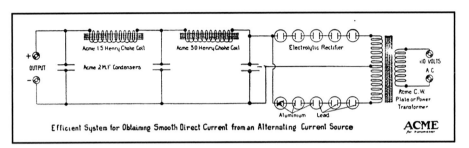

*Follow this diagram and you can make an
efficient filter for your set*

IN most cases where a complaint has been entered by a broadcast listener against an amateur using a straight C.W. transmitter, it has been found that the trouble has been due to an inefficient filter system. This interference is caused by a sixty cycle or motor-generator commutator frequency modulating the output.

The Acme Apparatus Company has always been interested in the amateur and offers this filter as a solution to the adverse criticism directed against him.

We do not say that the other filters will not work, but we have found the one shown above to be economically efficient.

The connection for an electrolytic rectifier is also shown. It is essential that the rectifier have sufficient jars, (1 per 75 volts) be properly formed, and be kept clean at all times. Use pure materials.

If tube rectifiers are used the same diagram may be used, substituting one rectifying tube for each series of jars. Acme Apparatus Co., Cambridge, Mass.

Specifications of Acme Choke Coils

Henries	Current	Type	Prices	Henries	Current	Type	Prices
1½	.150	Single	$4.00	6	.300	Single	$14.00
1½	.150	Double	6.00	6	.600	Single	18.00
1½	.500	Single	6.00	30	.150	Single	18.00
1½	.500	Double	8.00	30	.300	Single	25.00
6	.150	Single	10.00	30	.600	Single	33.00

 **ACME** *for transmission*

Figure 2.23 —The problem of interfering with non-ham neighbors' reception is apparently as old as commercial broadcasting itself. ACME's filter provided an early-days solution. (Apr 1924)

Figure 2.24 — The Allen D. Cardwell Manufacturing Company pioneered modern, low-loss variable capacitor construction methods. Cardwell made high-quality components for both transmitting and receiving. (May 1928)

SM "ROUND THE WORLD" FOUR

Just What the Name Implies!

The trimmest short wave set ever—that's the verdict everywhere on the new 730 S-M "Round-the-World" Four. It does everything you expect of a short-wave receiver —everything, even, that you expect of an S-M receiver. The Radio Broadcast Laboratory, in initial tests of the 730, received English 5SW daily on the speaker, during

New S-M 131 Plug-In Coils (used in the 730) wound on moulded bakelite, fit any 5-prong tube sockets. Wound, $1.25, or blank, $0.50 each.

afternoon hours. 9BBW, receiving on the "Round-the World" Four, worked in one evening stations in Germany, France, England and Italy. Low-power amateur code stations over the U. S. and Canada are received regularly on the 730. And for television work, it's ideal!

The "Round-the-World" Four is a complete four-tube regenerative, non-radiating short wave receiver kit with aluminum shielding cabinet. It has one screen grid r.f. stage, a regenerative, non-radiating detector, and two high-gain Clough audio stages. It tunes from 17.4 to 204 meters with four plug-in coils. The kit is $51.00, complete with cabinet, four coils, and full instructions—ready for immediate shipment.

The 731 "Round the World" Adapter is the two-tube, r.f. amplifier and detector, less the two stage a.f. amplifier of the above set. With an adapter plug, it converts any set to long-distance short wave reception. Price, complete with cabinet and four coils (17.4 to 204 meters) $36.00. The 732 "Round the World" Essential Kit contains the two tuning and tickler condensers, the four plug-in coils, coil socket, and three r.f. chokes, with full instructions for building a one, two, three or four tube short wave set. It costs but $16.50 complete.

And it beats anything for getting out into the short-wave "Thrill Band." Choose the kit you prefer—and "step out!"

---

720 Screen Grid Six
The Year's Biggest Value

This is the set that S-M gets squarely behind and tells you it's the biggest value in broadcast-band receivers to be found today. A man-sized recommendation!

Successor to the famous Shielded Grid Six that took the country by storm, the 720 is the kind of a set you can build in an evening, on its pierced metal chassis. When it's finished and you put it on the air—then the real surprise begins. Distant stations will come in, one after another, with local

volume, and positive 10 kc. selectivity. As to tone, the 720's superiority is insured by the new 255 and 256 audios, as described at the right.

Look at the 720's features as you see them in the picture, and remember that S-M backs it to the limit—assures you that you can't get more actual radio elsewhere at twice the cost. Then note the prices: Custom-built complete in a beautiful two-tone brown metal shielding cabinet, $102.00. Complete kit only $72.50, with the same cabinet $9.25 additional. Better order now—such values spell scarcity!

Are you receiving the "The Radiobuilder" regularly? Every month it gives you all the earliest S-M news, operating hints and kinks. To S-M Authorized Service Stations, it comes free of charge, with all new constructional Data Sheets. If you build professionally, write us about the Service Station franchises.

SILVER-MARSHALL, Inc., 858 W. JACKSON BLVD. CHICAGO, - - U.S.A.

Audio Transformers
Just Two Years in Advance

Radically new in principle, these transformers are the first to give freedom from the hysteretic distortion found in all other types. They combine decided advances in both tone and volume, as will be seen below. E is the two-stage curve for the large size transformers (S-M 225, 1st stage, and 226, 2d stage, $9.00 each); D is that of the smaller ones (S-M 255 and 256, $6.00 each). Note the marked advantage over A, B, and C—all standard eight and ten dollar transformers under equal conditions.

And you can have this finer performance in any set at less than average transformer costs!

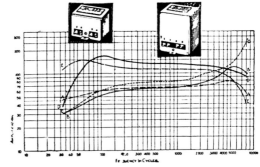

The S-M catalog describes all these products, as well as A and B Power Supplies, Power Amplifiers, Modulation Transformers, etc.

Silver-Marshall, Inc.
858 W. Jackson Blvd., Chicago, U. S. A.

....Send your complete catalog, with sample copy of the Radiobuilder.

....For enclosed 10c, send five sample S-M Data Sheets.

Name...

Address......................................

Figure 2.25 — Silver Marshall, yet another of the McMurdo Silver companies, offered its "Round The World Four" receiver in kit form. The four tube regenerative set used a screen grid tube for RF amplification. (Sep 1928)

Bradley Leak, absolutely noiseless and stepless, **2.95**

2000 to 30,000 ohm resistance. List $5, special $2.95.

$4. Bradleystat No. E-210 Special 1.60

Signal Buzzer Set International Code on Baseboard $2.45
Belden braid ¼ inch wide, ft. .06

$7. Acme B-6—"B" eliminator transformer, 235 v. each side of centre tap. 2.45

Acme 500 w. plate transformer, 1000-1500-2000 each side of centre tap, 24.00.
Acme B.H.-1 transformer, 255-510 each side of centre tap; also 2 fil. windings of 4 v. each side of centre tap, $10.25.
Acme C.W. 30 Henry choke. $18 list—150 M. A. single $14.40; also other sizes at special prices.

ACME POTENTIOMETER RHEOSTAT

A combined Pot. and filament Rheo.

6 ohm rheo-100 ohm pot.
30 ohm rheo-100 ohm pot.
30 ohm rheo-300 ohm pot.
TWIN RHEO for low voltage tubes. List $3.00. Special each 65c

ACME TRANSFORMER

Listed at $5.00. The universal transformer for Super Het. 30 K.C. Limited quantity at $1.10

ACME CHOKE COIL

A high quality choke 1/10 Henry at 100 mils. List $5.00. Special $1.25

GENERAL RADIO
Type 285 AUDIO TRANSFORMER

Ideal for high and even amplification.

Type 285-H—6 to 1
Type 285-D—3.7 to 1
Type 285-L—2 to 1
List $6.00 Now only $3.25

LEEDS
The Home of RADIO
45 VESEY STREET
NEW YORK

New York's Headquarters for Transmitting Apparatus
When in Town Visit Our Store

Full Line of Acme -- Thordarson -- Jewell -- Flechtheim -- General Radio -- Signal -- Bradley

SPECIALS

Dubilier Mica Condenser .002 cap. 6,000 working volt 1.95
General Radio 247D .001 cond. plain or with vernier 1.75
Dubilier cond. 1.f mfd. 1,000v D.C. test; 650v. working voltage 1.39
Dubilier cond. .5 mfd. 1,000v D.C. working voltage .85
R.C.A.—U.V. 1716 Super Het. transformer 1.45
Ward Leonard Resistances; fits standard base receptacles; sizes 300—600—900—1200 and 2000 ohms .95
$15. Imported German head sets; very sensitive 3.45
Honeycomb Coils unmounted, all sizes in stock at ½ price.
$8 Signal Corp adjustable arm micro-transmitter for panel mounting 2.45
$9. Dubilier condenser, 4mfd; 600 v. D. C. working type 903; limited quantity 2.25
R.E.L. Transmitting Inductances, per set, 8.80
Bristol 50 Henry choke 2.75
6.50 Acme .0005 enclosed condenser .95

Pyrex Low-loss V.T. sockets, each 39c.

Flechtheim Condensers, all types 35% off list.

ACME VARIABLE RATIO AUDIO FREQUENCY TRANSFORMER

Get any ratio you want.

SPECIFICATIONS

Type V A-2

	Primary Secondary			Primary Secondary	
RATIO	Binding Posts	Binding Posts	RATIO	Binding Posts	Binding Posts
2.5:1	1-4	5-6	4.25:1	1-3	5-8
3:1	1-3	5-6	4.75:1	1-2	5-7
3.25:1	1-4	5-7	5.25:1	1-2	5-8
3.5:1	1-4	5-8	7.5:1	2-4	5-6
3.75:1	1-2	5-6	9.5:1	2-4	5-7
4:1	1-3	5-7	11.5:1	2-4	5-8

On the primary side the binding post in use having the higher number should be connected to the B+ and likewise, the secondary post having the higher number should be connected to the grid.

By using binding posts 3-4, still higher ratios may be obtained if desired, but the above selection will usually fill all requirements.

Other specifications similar to type A-2. Price $7.00 each. Special $2.75

GENERAL RADIO
POWER AMPLIFIER
and "B" ELIMINATOR KIT

All necessary parts; operates from 105 to 125 volts A. C.— gives "A" "B" and "C" for amplification and "B" for set. Type 390 uses type 280 tube. Type 395 uses "B. H." Raytheon tube. List $50. Special $19.50

MAIL ORDERS FILLED SAME DAY
10% Must Accompany All Orders

Cardwell condensers, double spaced for transmitting, .00025 cap. **3.45**

No. 12 Enameled copper wire, any length, ft. ....$.01
No. 10 Enameled copper wire, any length, ft. .... .01½
Genuine Bakelite Panel 10x14x¼ 1.50
Baldwin phones type C, pair 5.95
Myers $5 4½ volt Det. or Amp tube, complete with mounting clips .... .85

Ward Leonard Resistance
$4.75 list-6½ inch long—800-1000 -1200 -3000 -6000 -8000-11000 ohms; can be used for 2-50 watt tubes or less. **$1.45**

Television disks as specified in QST special $1.95.
General Radio No. 358 Short Wave Meter, 14 to 225 meters, list $22, special $14.50.

NEON GLOW LAMPS

Made by General Electric Co., type G. 10, standard base. 101 uses, as illustrated in QST May issue page 17 Price only 65c

RADIO FOUNDATION TRANSFORMER

Mfg. for McCullough A. C. tubes. Will carry 6 tubes or its equivalent—2½-3-3½ v. List $6.00 Special $2.25

VARIABLE FILAMENT TRANSFORMER

125 watt—110 volt—60c. tapped at-4-7-10-13-17-20-24-30 volts. Limited quantity. List $19.
Special $4.45

We carry the largest stock of **GENERAL RADIO PARTS** in the country

Figure 2.27 — Allied Radio Corporation, founded in 1928, established a home base in Chicago which served as a mecca for those seeking Amateur Radio and consumer electronics gear. Allied's expanded its reach with a thriving catalog business. Allied created an Allied Electronics subsidiary in 1962 and relocated to Fort Worth, Texas in 1970. (Dec 1928)

CRYSTAL CONTROL TONE
for C. W. Transmission

REL Cat. No. 215 Basic CW Telegraph Unit is the typical modern multi stage transmitter for the amateur who desires to use the best. Frequency flexibility throughout each amateur band with crystal controlled note at all times. Shift quickly and easily anywhere in the bands.

CAT. 215 TELEGRAPH UNIT

The REL Cat. No. 215 transmitter kit is furnished with all necessary parts including metal case, drilled and engraved aluminum front panel and a very concise instruction booklet giving information on the assembly and operation. Extremely simple to operate. Consumes minimum amount of power. Employs standard broadcast receiver tubes. May be operated from B batteries, ordinary B eliminators or other similar sources delivering 300 volts D.C. A complete low power transmitter ready for immediate operation. Employs UY-227 master oscillator tube, UY-224 screen grid buffer tube and UX-245 power amplifier tube. Will deliver 10 watts to the antenna as a CW telegraph transmitter.

The Cat. No. 215 CW transmitter kit has been specially priced to meet the demands of every amateur. The price including one set of plug-in coils for any of the three popular bands is **$56.00.** (When ordering specify for which band you desire the coils.) Additional coils to cover other bands may be purchased at *$7.00* per set of three.

100% MODULATION
for Phone Work

REL No. 225 modulator and speech amplifier unit designed to operate in conjunction with Cat. No. 215 CW telegraph transmitter functions as 100% system modulator. When used with Cat. No. 215 unit will deliver 30 watts on modulation peaks into the antenna.

The REL Cat. No. 225 modulator and speech amplifier kit comprises all apparatus necessary and also includes metal cabinet and drilled and engraved aluminum front panel. The cabinet has the same height and depth dimensions as the transmitter. The modulator may be placed directly alongside of the Cat. No. 215 thereby giving a very neat appearance.

The same type of power supply may be used except that the plate voltage necessary will be 550 to 600 volts. The UX-250 tube is employed as modulator and the UY-227 tube is employed as speech amplifier. The No. 225 modulator kit sells for **$42.00.**

CAT. 225 MODULATOR UNIT

> The amateur who desires a modern station should install both of these units. He will then have a perfect CW transmitter and a clear 100% modulated phone set. REL will be glad to forward you literature describing these two units

RADIO ENGINEERING LABORATORIES
100 WILBUR AVENUE, LONG ISLAND CITY, N. Y.

Figure 2.28 — Charles Srebroff began Radio Electronics Laboratories in 1921, making coils and capacitors on his mother's kitchen table. A variety of kit receivers and transmitters, along with more elaborate production facilities followed. The company served the amateur, government and commercial markets up into the early 1970s. (Dec 1929)

Chapter 3

The 1930s

Ham Industry Grows, Technology Evolves, Spectrum Explored

The Amateur Radio industry as we know it developed during the 1930s. Familiar names began appearing in the ad pages. International communication became commonplace. Prior to November 6, 1929, that communication had been done with telegraphy. On that date the Federal Radio Commission authorized radiotelephone operation on 20 meters, the best DX band.[1] Technical developments made receivers powered by ac household current practical, although inadequately filtered transmitter power supplies continued to be a problem.[2]

Amateurs weren't the only ones who found 20 meters great for intercontinental communication. When shortwave broadcasters cast covetous glances at that amateur band, the League strongly advocated increased amateur activity on 20.[3]

The decade kicked off with another battle against proposed legislation that sent Hiram Percy Maxim to Washington, DC. In January 1930 Maxim testified at length before the Senate Committee on Interstate Commerce in opposition to a senate bill sponsored by Michigan's Senator James Couzens. Senate bill S6 proposed the creation of a national commission to control all forms of wired or wireless communication. The League's Board of Directors entrusted Maxim with seeing that Amateur Radio would have a seat at any table around which such a commission was gathered. In the end, the legislation failed to pass and few who heard Maxim's impassioned advocacy on behalf of Amateur Radio forgot it.[4]

QST Technical Editor James J. Lamb, W1CEI, wrote frequently on improving the station receiver and kept pace with innovations from commercial manufacturers.[5,6,7,8] The *Single Signal Superheterodyne* ranks as one of Lamb's most important developments. In an August 1932 article, Lamb described the functions and construction details of a receiver circuit designed to overcome the weaknesses of current ham receivers. His designs dealt effectively with the increasing interference on densely

Frank Jones, W6AJF, designed Lafayette's 5 meter receiver. It overcame many shortcomings of the typical super-regenerative sets used in the 1930s. The six-tube receiver was more selective, less noisy, and smoother operating than most contemporary gear. (1935)

occupied bands.[9] Three months later, Philadelphia's M & H Sporting Goods advertised "Everything You Need to Make the Single-Signal Superhet." The ad contained a complete list of parts and their prices.[10] The following month the company offered the receiver in partial kit form; the unit had all its parts assembled but was not yet wired.[11] The M & H version was based on an article by Don L. Lusk, W3ZF.[12]

Lamb's mentoring also extended to transmitters. He introduced the Tri-Tet oscillator to QST's readers in a June 1933 article.[13,14,15] Indeed, his detailed writings covered a wide range of subjects including the 5 meter and higher bands, more efficient phone transmission, automatic gain control and noise

limiters for receivers, and (with frequent collaborator J. L. A. McLaughlin) dual-diversity reception.

George Grammer, W1DF, QST's assistant technical editor, contributed an article on building a low cost CW transmitter in November 1930.[16] The following month, Leeds Radio Company ran an ad announcing it had all the parts for building Grammer's transmitter design. The ad also introduced Jerome Gross, W2AAE, as the company's "shortwave specialist."[17] By 1931, Gross had opened his own store — Gross Radio, informally known as "Jerry's Place" — only a few blocks away.[18] Gross developed a line of transmitters during the 1930s and among the store's offerings were free code classes and

National's ads emphasized that the NC-44 receiver was "inexpensive" rather than "cheap," promising performance better than that of competing receivers in the same price range. ($49.50, 1934)

personal advice from Jerry himself on radio equipment problems.

A ham store fronted by a strong personality willing to give individual attention to customers became a trend in the industry, even when the business was one with nationwide reach. Uncle Dave's Radio Shack — run by Dave Marks, W2APF — exemplified this business model. Marks was in the ham business for more than half a century (in later years as Fort Orange Radio and Distributing Company).[19] Uncle Dave remained a presence in QST's pages into the mid-1960s. Each ad contained a caricature of W2APF, a big cigar clamped in his jaw, calling CQ.

New York City had its "Radio Row" district with radio stores and parts supply houses filling lofts and store fronts. Many small towns boasted a ham store, even if the ham shack was a spare room in the back of a radio repair shop. Big city or small town, the consistent ingredient was an extension of the fraternity felt on the air or at radio club meetings. A large coffee pot was frequently present as well.

Out in Cedar Rapids, Iowa, a young man designed and constructed transmitters in his basement. His name and that of the company he

built would go on to rank among the most well-known and prestigious in communications electronics. January 1932 QST carried a small "Crystal Transmitters" ad placed by Arthur A. Collins Radio Laboratories.[20,21] The company name would change to Collins Radio Transmitters and then Collins Radio Company by the end of that year. It became a division of Rockwell International in 1973 and withdrew from the ham radio business a decade later. Under all of the company names, though, Collins advertised regularly in QST, appearing hundreds of times in a 50 year span.

National introduced its SW-3 receiver in 1931. By eliminating the push-pull audio output stage of the company's more elaborate and expensive SW-5, National was able to sell the SW-3 at a price more manageable on Great Depression era budgets. The three tube regenerative set remained in the company's catalog for another 15 years.

In 1932, National announced the AGS receiver, a nine tube superhet developed for the US Department of Commerce's Airways Division. The AGS designation stood for *Air Ground Station*. It was a step above the competition and, even

though marketed to hams, was priced beyond the means of all but government, commercial and affluent amateur users.[22]

The AGS was quickly followed in the National lineup by the FB-7, a seven tube superhet designed expressly for the amateur and selling for a more modest price.[23] National added crystal filters and other performance upgrades to both the AGS and FB-7 during their life spans.

National's real receiver masterpiece was its model HRO. The curtain went up on it in 1934 after being teased for several months in the ads penned by James Millen.[24] Although the receiver continued to evolve well into the 1960s, the DNA of its basic concept and appearance was rooted in that first HRO.

Hammarlund Manufacturing Company entered the radio business as a manufacturer of radio components and also broadcast receivers. In 1932, it added a communications receiver — the Comet Pro — to its product line.[25] Unlike the National receivers, the Comet Pro used separate dials for main tuning and band spread. Hammarlund would continue to employ this convention — nearly a trademark — for most of the receivers to follow in the company's long history. Successive versions followed the original Comet Pro, adding features such as better audio output, a crystal filter, automatic volume control, and front panel BFO tuning.

Lloyd Hammarlund, son of company founder Oscar Hammarlund, personally introduced the Super Pro in a March 1936 *QST* ad. More than four years of engineering, testing, and revising had gone into the project Hammarlund considered the ultimate in receivers. The company refined the design again and again as the Super Pro nameplate stretched its lifespan out to nearly 40 years.

William Halligan christened his radio company The Hallicrafters when he formed it in 1932.[26] The Hallicrafters was connected to a number of other Chicago area radio names including McMurdo Silver, Echophone, Silver Marshall Manufacturing and Howard Radio, being involved with all of them in some way during in the 1930s.

Halligan produced his first receiver, the S-1, in 1933 and nick-named it the "Skyrider." When the S-4 showed up in the pages of *QST* in early 1935, it was "The Super Sky Rider."[27] In one form or another, "Skyrider" was attached to many more Hallicrafters models in the decade that followed.

These companies shared something in addition to producing radio equipment. They spent their formative years struggling through the Great Depression and none had an easy time of it. If a company could find the capital to finance the means of production, potential customers often lacked the resources to buy their goods.[28] Advertising represented a good way of reaching customers who did have the money but meant spending precious dollars needed elsewhere for marketing.

The ARRL weathered the rough economy and published *QST* each month through the perilous times. On February 17, 1936, however, fate struck a blow that might have taken a weaker organization down for good. Hiram Percy Maxim passed away at age 66.[29] It is a testament to Maxim's original concept, his organizational skills, and his tireless struggle against anything which threatened Amateur Radio that the League persisted after his passing.

War clouds foreshadowing the complete overcast soon to come for Amateur Radio gathered on the horizon in the late 1930s. One after another, European countries shut down Amateur Radio as the continent moved toward war in 1939. As the US attempted to remain neutral, the country's hams were cautioned against expressing any opinions about the conflict on the air.[30]

Notes

[1] "'Twenty-Meter' 'Phone Authorized," *QST*, Jan 1930, p 26.

[2] B. Dudley, "The A.C. High-Frequency Receiver," *QST*, Jan 1930, pp 9-14, 78, 80.

[3] "Editorial," *QST*, Apr 1930, pp 7-8.

[4] C.B. Desoto, *200 Meters & Down* (West Hartford, Connecticut: 1936), p 122.

[5] J. Lamb, W1CEI, "What's Wrong With Our C.W. Receivers?," *QST*, Jun 1932, pp 9-16.

[6] J. Lamb, W1CEI, "Developments in Crystal Filters for S.S. Superhets," *QST*, Nov 1933, pp 21-24.

[7] J. Lamb, W1CEI "Automatic Gain Control for the Superhet," *QST*, Nov 1933, p 32.

[8] Radio Manufacturing Engineers ad, *QST*, Jun 1938, p 79.

[9] J. Lamb, W1CEI, "Short-Wave Receiver Selectivity to Match Present Conditions," *QST*, Aug 1932, pp 9-20, 90.

[10] M & H Sporting Goods Co. ad, *QST*, Nov 1932, p 96.

[11] M & H Sporting Goods Co. ad, *QST*, Dec 1932, p 81.

[12] D. Lusk, W3ZF, "The Single-Signal Super in Another Dress," *QST*, Nov 1932, pp 31-32, 90.

[13] J. Lamb, W1CEI, "Advanced Transmitter Design," *QST*, Jun 1930, pp 21-28, 80, 82.

[14] J. Lamb, W1CEI, "A More Stable Crystal Oscillator of High Harmonic Output," *QST*, Jun 1933, pp 30-32.

[15] J. Lamb, W1CEI, "Tritet Multi-Band Crystal Control," *QST*, Oct 1933, pp 9-15.

[16] G. Grammer, W1DF, "A Complete Push-Pull C.W. Transmitter at Low Cost," *QST*, Nov 1930, pp 8-14.

[17] Leeds Radio Company ad, *QST*, Dec 1930, pp 6-7.

[18] Gross Radio ad, *QST*, Oct 1931, p 79.

[19] Obituary, *QST*, Apr 1992, p 64.

[20] K. Braband, *The First 50 Years ... A History of Collins Radio Company* (Cedar Rapids, Iowa: 1983)

[21] Arthur A. Collins Radio Laboratories ad, *QST*, Jan 1932, p 77.

[22] National AGS ad, *QST*, Feb 1933, p 95.

[23] National FB7 ad, *QST*, Mar 1933, p 76.

[24] National HRO ad, Oct 1934, Cover III.

[25] Hammarlund Comet Pro ad, *QST*, Apr 1932, p 96.

[26] C. Dachis, WD5EOG, *Radios by Hallicrafters* (Atglen, Pennsylvania: 1996), p 8.

[27] Hallicrafters ad, *QST*, Jan 1935, p 73.

[28] D. Muzzey & A. Link, *Our American Republic* (Boston, Massachusetts: 1963), pp 557-558.

[29] "Hiram Percy Maxim, Silent Key," *QST*, Apr 1936, pp 7-15.

[30] "War," *QST*, Nov 1939, p 60.

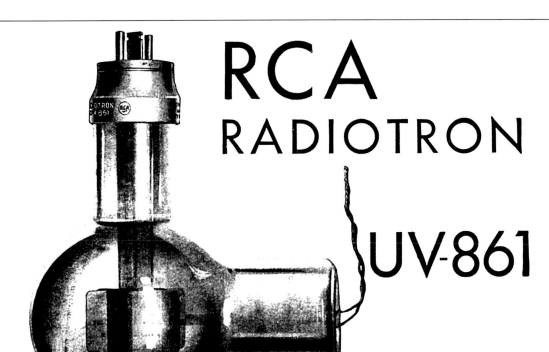

RCA
RADIOTRON

UV-861

A 500 watt screen-grid R. F. Power Amplifier

ONE of the newest transmitting tubes suitable for amateur use is Radiotron UV-861 —the largest member of the screen-grid Radiotron family.

It is ruggedly built and especially designed for high-frequency service. Its fourth electrode— *the screen*—shields the grid from the plate and thereby effectively reduces feed-back and self-oscillation within the tube itself.

As a result, remarkable operational stability and large R.F. power output may be obtained from Radiotron UV-861 even at the higher frequencies.

The excellence of its characteristics and the gratifying smoothness of its performance will enable amateurs to accomplish amazing results in the field of high-frequency transmission.

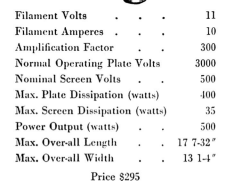

Filament Volts . . .	11
Filament Amperes . . .	10
Amplification Factor . .	300
Normal Operating Plate Volts	3000
Nominal Screen Volts . .	500
Max. Plate Dissipation (watts)	400
Max. Screen Dissipation (watts)	35
Power Output (watts) . .	500
Max. Over-all Length . .	17 7-32″
Max. Over-all Width . .	13 1-4″

Price $295

Write nearest RCA District Office for further information

Figure 3.1 — RCA's UV-861 looked as if it were an art piece from a glassblower's studio. The 500 watt tetrode, introduced in 1929, later used the designation VT-19 when employed in WW II military transmitters. (Jan 1930)

Figure 3.2 — Cartooning played a frequent role in Amateur Radio advertising. Thordarson's ad also contains a subtle hint for hams to adopt the 1930 standards that the ARRL encouraged and the government required. (Feb 1930)

World-Wide Reception

with the NEW

Norden-Hauck   -   Short Wave

SUPER DX-5

Size: 9 x 19 x 10 inches.   Weight 30 pounds

Ideal for Amateur Reception

Entirely New Advanced Design   New Pentode Tube

Sensational Distance   Range 20-200 Meters   Reliable Performance

Adaptable for Long Waves and down to about 10 meters for
Experimental Reception

A-C and D-C Models

NORDEN-HAUCK, Inc.   Engineers

5-7 South Street   Philadelphia, Pa., U. S. A.

Write, telephone or cable TODAY for Complete Information

Figure 3.3 — C.R. Leutz Company (formerly of Long Island City, New York) manufactured the six tube DX-5 receiver in Altoona, Pennsylvania. Sued by RCA for patent infringement, Leutz sold the design to Norden-Hauck. (Jul 1930)

What Transmitter for 1931?

REL presents a super unit for C.W. transmission. 1931 Standards are tighter than ever. A clear signal will be your ticket to transmit, without it — you'll be left in the cold. This kit measures up to every specification. It is a triumph of REL's engineering and research. Look over these features and tell us if any more need be said.

1. Kit is furnished with all necessary parts including metal case, drilled engraved aluminum front panel and instruction book.

2. Extremely simple to operate.

3. Consumes minimum amount of power.

4. Employs standard broadcast receiver tubes.

5. May operate from B batteries, B eliminators or similar 300 volt DC source.

6. It is a complete low power transmitter ready to operate.

7. Employs UY-227 master oscillator tube, UY-224 screen grid buffer tube and UX-245 power amplifier tube.

8. Will deliver 10 watts to the antenna as a CW telegraph transmitter.

9. Ideal as a basic master oscillator buffer and intermediate amplifier to excite a 50, 75 or 250 watt power amplifier stage.

10. Kit includes one set of plug-in coils for any of the three popular bands. When ordering specify for which band. Additional coils to cover other bands may be purchased for $7.00 per set of three.

Now do you agree with us when we say that you can't find a more ideal piece of apparatus of this type anywhere. The price? — it's in keeping with tough times, only $56.

> Write for our large loose leaf handbook full of information, kept up to date by regular bulletins. Price only 50c.

> Our booklet 50 describes this Modern Short Wave Transmitter together with a "bang up" Receiver.
> *Write for it, It's FREE!*

RADIO ENGINEERING LABORATORIES, Inc.

100 WILBUR AVENUE ، ، ، **LONG ISLAND CITY, N. Y.**

Export Department: 116 Broad Street, New York City

Figure 3.4 — Radio Engineering Laboratories presented this transmitter as being modern enough to meet 1931 standards. The addition of a Heising modulator option put the 10 W CW rig on AM phone. REL supplied the transmitter and modulator in kit form. (Jan 1931)

There IS *Something New Under the Sun*

IT'S THE
PIEZO-ASTATIC
Crystal Microphone

TYPE D-104

SUSPENSION OR STAND MOUNTING

LIST PRICE **$17⁵⁰**

See Your Dealer or Order Direct

A highly developed general purpose microphone ruggedly constructed having excellent frequency response. Cannot be overloaded acoustically. No adjustments required. No carbon rush or internal noise. No blasting or freezing; no button or field current; no polarizing voltage. Connects direct to grid or may be used with matching transformer. Chrome plated, 3″ diameter, 1″ thick, with 6 ft. shielded cord.

THE MOST PRACTICAL MICROPHONE EVER OFFERED

LICENSED UNDER BRUSH DEVELOPMENT CO. PATENTS

A S T A T I C   M I C R O P H O N E   L A B O R A T O R Y ,   I N C .
YOUNGSTOWN, OHIO

GULF RADIO SCHOOL

Radiotelegraphy   Radiotelephony

Radio Servicing

SECOND PORT U. S. A. } 1007 Carondelet Street NEW ORLEANS, LA.

G O - D E V I L
THE MECHANICAL FIST

The New Design Twin-Pivot Automatic Transmitting Key

A FEW FEATURES FOUND ONLY IN THE GO-DEVIL

The Only Key Obtainable with Practical Up-To-Date Improvements.

Single or double ratio lever action doubles the intensity of the dots and makes operating a pleasure.

Eleven adjustments instead of half as many to eliminate difficult setting.

All contacts close squarely, regardless of throw between them, thereby prolonging their life, adding to the quality of your signals.

Ten to fifty words per minute with one single weight. Suitable for beginners or experienced operators.

Husky contacts, no higher priced model necessary for high voltage.

Simple stop is noiseless while operating.

Rugged fool-proof construction. 3 pound non-skid base.

Black crystallized base, all other parts brass, fibre handle.

$6.00   VERY BEAUTIFUL APPEARANCE   **$6.00**

Absolutely guaranteed to be more than satisfactory

A. H. EMERY, 263 Mill St., Poughkeepsie, N. Y.

OCTOCOILS WITH BYRD
IN THE ANTARCTIC

29 to 58 Meters

Commander Byrd will use Octocoils at the South Pole because of their dependability. You should use Octocoils, too.

Actual size of these coils is 3⅝ inches high and 1⅞ inches in diameter.

Octocoils are moulded in genuine bakelite in four distinctive colors, green, brown, blue and red, and are wound with Nos. 12, 14, 16 and 25 enameled wire. They plug into the ordinary tube socket and have a rugged rim to grasp coils so they will not break.

Wave length range, 16 to 225 meters.

These coils will also cover the 10 to 80 meter amateur band if used with .00005 mfd. Midget Condenser.

Price, per set of 4, $2.25

Broadcast coil also furnished, price, $.75

Short Wave and Television Corporation

70 Brookline Avenue   **Boston, Mass.**

Division of General Electronics Corporation

Figure 3.5 — Astatic's D-104 microphone debuted in this 1933 ad and remains popular with amateurs well into the 21st Century. A. H. Emery manufactured the Go-Devil semiautomatic key in Poughkeepsie, New York, and touted it as "Absolutely guaranteed to be more than satisfactory!" The Short Wave and Television Corporation felt that if its Octocoils were good enough for Admiral Richard Byrd at the South Pole, they should please the average ham as well. (Nov 1933)

We are seriously interested in our customers' problems and the results that they are able to obtain from our products. It is our plan every month to use this page as a means of bringing to their attention various ideas and suggestions that we may feel will prove helpful to them.

Just for instance, my own phone station is operated mainly in the 3.5 mc band. Recently we shifted to the 14 mc band and for a short time were rather disappointed in the apparent poor performance of our particular FB7A. Of course, the trouble was quickly cleared up — but the incident left us wondering whether or not some other amateurs under similar circumstances might have failed to recall the necessity of readjusting the antenna trimmer to their particular antenna and consequently are not obtaining from their receiver on *all* bands the high degree of performance that the receiver is really capable of delivering.

All of the FB receiver coils are carefully tested and pretuned at our laboratory before shipment. These adjustments are quite critical and should the receiver be used at any time with an antenna differing appreciably from our laboratory standard, it is quite likely that the antenna trimmer condenser will require readjustment. This midget variable air dielectric condenser is located inside of each DET band spread coil and adjusted through the screw-driver hole in the handle. Checking of this adjustment is urged in the instructions that are furnished with each receiver and undoubtedly this is done when the receiver is first put into service. Frequently additional coils are added at a later date to the original equipment. We wonder if this important little adjustment is always remembered on such occasions?

Incidentally, if you are in doubt as to just how to make this adjustment properly, why not write for a copy of our booklet giving full alignment details for both the FB7A and FBXA receivers?

JAMES MILLEN

Figure 3.6 — Starting with the March 1934 issue, the National Company devoted one page each month for a short letter to the magazine's readers. The unique form of advertising not only shared product news, but also educated potential customers on the engineering and technology that went into the company's equipment. Millen continued to pen the monthly missive until he left National to start his own company in 1939. (Mar 1934)

THE HRO

TWO STAGES PRESELECTION

TWO AIR-TUNED I.F. STAGES

CALIBRATED BAND-SPREAD

AUTOMATIC VOLUME CONTROL

FOUR-GANG CONDENSER

MICROMETER DIAL

SINGLE-SIGNAL FILTER

ET CETERA

"Et Cetera" is a big phrase, and includes many obvious essentials such as single-control tuning and C. W. beat frequency oscillator, as well as luxuries such as a Vacuum Tube Voltmeter for indicating carrier intensities and an additional model with built-in power supply (for the *very* few amateurs who prefer it). The National General Catalogue, bound into this magazine, describes the HRO in detail.

NATIONAL COMPANY, INC.

Figure 3.7 — After several years' development work, National introduced the HRO in 1934. Produced in a series of versions, the tube-type HRO remained in the company's product line for 30 years. Its PW micrometer dial and plug-in coils set it apart from the rest of the crowd, as did its performance. (Oct 1934)

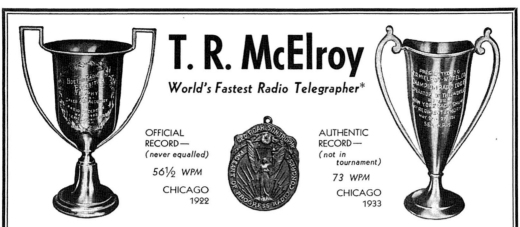

T. R. McElroy
World's Fastest Radio Telegrapher*

OFFICIAL
RECORD—
(never equalled)

56½ WPM

CHICAGO
1922

AUTHENTIC
RECORD—
(not in
tournament)

73 WPM

CHICAGO
1933

Announces the MAC-KEY the perfect Semi-Automatic and Straight Key

"I'll not write a lot of bunk about my key. I'll tell you these truths: Each **Mac-Key** is adjusted by myself and shows perfect speeds 8 wpm to 45 wpm; each is an exact duplicate of the key with which I've established records in sending Morse & Continental code these past 15 years. Each is sold with my guarantee that you can send better with a **Mac-Key** than with any other instrument made—or your money refunded after 5 days trial."

★ **No. 1**—Correctly designed vibration dampener.

★ **No. 2**—Straight key changeover lever.

★ **No. 3**—Absolutely accurate speed adjustment.

★ **No. 4**—Extremely costly and sensitive platinum contact points, adjustable without changing faces.

★ **No. 5**—Main spring selected after costly metallurgical research and personal painstaking experimental work.

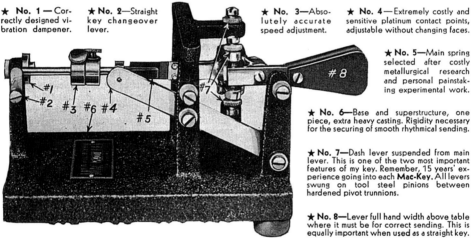

★ **No. 6**—Base and superstructure, one piece, extra heavy casting. Rigidity necessary for the securing of smooth rhythmical sending.

★ **No. 7**—Dash lever suspended from main lever. This is one of the two most important features of my key. Remember, 15 years' experience going into each **Mac-Key**. All levers swung on tool steel pinions between hardened pivot trunnions.

★ **No. 8**—Lever full hand width above table where it must be for correct sending. This is equally important when used as a straight key.

I EMPHATICALLY assert that my key is the only one made with which it is possible to send perfect Continental code with its multiple dash figures and letters.

Price $17.50 f.o.b. Boston. Temporarily subject to 40% discount.

Whether I can continue this customary discount depends upon volume. Take another peek at my guarantee. Then see your local dealer or write me direct enclosing money order for **$10.50.** If you think you've been enjoying ham radio heretofore, wait'll you try a **Mac-Key** and hear code you never dreamed yourself capable of turning out. But do it now, please. I've put my whole life into my key. Honestly, it is marvelous.

Won't you please justify my faith in ham operators and order NOW if you can dig up the ten fifty. 73'S EVERYBODY, AND I REALLY MEAN IT.

T. R. McELROY, 23 Bayside Street, Upham's Corner P. O., Boston, Mass.
Official champion of the world, 1922 to 1933.

Distributed in metropolitan Boston by the RADIO SHACK, 46 Brattle St., Boston

  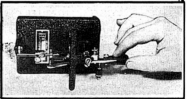

Figure 3.8 — Theodore McElroy, world's champion radio telegrapher, showman and master of self-promotion, manufactured a line of "Mac-Key" semi-automatic keys, straight keys and other telegraphy-related merchandise. (Dec 1934)

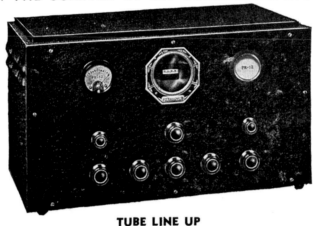
Figure 3.9 — About the time the PR-12 appeared in this Delaware Radio ad, Patterson pulled the model from production. In June 1935 the company announced, "Out of months of painstaking research and engineering, the completely revised PR-12 has finally been evolved." The receiver returned to Patterson's product line that month. (Dec 1934)

BARR
• D B 3 •
Class B Modulated Transceiver

AN OUTSTANDING VALUE

less tubes and batteries **$27⁰⁰—** List Price   *40% discount to amateurs*

The DB 3 utilizes a Class B Audio amplifier and modulator giving an output
of 2.1 watts, which is many times greater than that of ordinary transceivers.

SPECIFICATIONS

CASE: Size 11" long x 9½" high x 6½" wide, black wrinkle finish metal, heavy leather handle. All batteries are self-contained in case. Removable side panel for easy access to the batteries and tubes.

PANEL: Beautifully finished in black enamel with silver scales and lettering.

CONTROLS, ETC.: Two ceramic insulators are supplied for antenna, special large easy tuning knob, volume control on and off switch which acts as such in the receive position, and

as a gain control in the transmit position, transmit and receive switch, microphone and headphone jacks.

FREQUENCY: Will cover 56mc to 60mc (amateur 5 meter band).

BATTERY REQUIREMENTS: Three 45-Volt B Batteries like Burgess 5308, two No. 6 dry cells, and one 7½ Volt C battery.

TUBES USED: One type 30 — one type 19 — one type 49.

SHIPPING WEIGHT: 12 pounds.

Order from your nearest distributor — if not yet stocked we will temporarily fill orders direct
BULLETIN ON REQUEST

BARR LABORATORIES
1476 BROADWAY   +   +   +   +   +   NEW YORK

Figure 3.10 — Local communication on the 5 meter band grew in popularity during the 1930s and with it, the use of low power transceivers. The Barr DB-3, a typical unit, used three tubes and was powered by self-contained batteries. (May 1935)

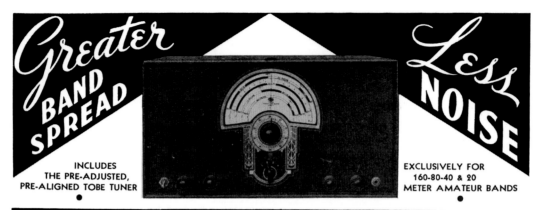

Greater BAND SPREAD

INCLUDES
THE PRE-ADJUSTED,
PRE-ALIGNED TOBE TUNER

Less NOISE

EXCLUSIVELY FOR
160-80-40 & 20
METER AMATEUR BANDS

TOBE AMATEUR *Communication* RECEIVER

AMATEURS! Here's the receiver you've dreamed of owning — at a price that makes ownership possible! Its band spread is a sensation and a revelation. Its superior signal-to-noise ratio is an accomplishment of greatly advanced circuit design. Its many practical operating features contributed by many amateurs will thrill all "Hamdom."

Its low cost is due solely to the fact that the amateur is required to build part of this job himself — a simple task, for the TOBE TUNER comes completely wired and pre-aligned. Enthusiastic testimonials from critical amateurs concur in the opinion that here is a *real* communication job giving the finest tuning control obtainable — regardless of price — plus sensitivity, selectivity and low noise level!

TUNING RATE AND SPREAD

The table below gives an accurate analysis of the band spread of the TOBE Amateur Communication Receiver. To appreciate these extremely important features read May 1935 QST, pages 20–28.

Band	Tuning Rate	Calibration Spread
160	26.5Kc	2 Kc
80	30 Kc	3.4Kc
40	18 Kc	2.0Kc
20	17 Kc	3 Kc

THE DISTINCTIVE AMATEUR BAND DIAL

Lays out each of the four bands over a wide area and clearly shows C.W. and phone sections. The limits and sections of each band are indicated in Kc. The operator can tell at a glance the band he is listening on, type of reception, and whether he is going up or down in frequency. Polar index lines permit logging of stations for reference.

12 FEATURES OF THIS NEW REMARKABLE RECEIVER!

- 1. SUPERIOR signal-to-noise ratio . . . permits DX reception even on the loud speaker.
- 2. ABSOLUTE single tuning control.
- 3. TOBE SUPER TUNER comes already wired and adjusted.
- 4. NO PLUG-IN coils.
- 5. EFFICIENT PRE-AMPLIFICATION on all bands.
- 6. FULL VISION DIAL calibrated for all bands.
- 7. SENSITIVITY on all bands 1 microvolt or better.
- 8. TRIPLE TUNED double band pass, I.F. filter (6 tuned circuits) assures high selectivity.
- 9. AUTOMATIC and manual volume control.
- 10. MANUAL I.F. gain control.
- 11. SMOOTH BEAT FREQUENCY oscillator for CW reception.
- 12. MECHANICAL AND ELECTRICAL design of TUNER and arrangement of parts permits maximum R.F. gain with stability and low noise level.

See your jobber or dealer at once. Listen to this marvelous receiver . . . or write us direct for complete parts list, specifications, diagrams, prices, etc.!

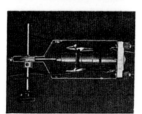

NEW TOBE ACCESSORIES FOR THE AMATEUR!

Realizing the need of amateurs for the highest quality parts for set building at a price they can afford to pay, TOBE has focused its sixteen years of radio experience on this field with the result that a complete line of accessories similar to those illustrated is being developed.

A complete line including variable and fixed coupling air and mica tuned I.F. transformers: high, medium and standard "Q" LITZ wound coils; beat frequency oscillators with air trimmers with

adjustable beat note; new type air trimmers and padders for complete range of capacities.

(1) TOBE air trimmers and padders, finest mechanical construction, Isolantite mountings.

(2) TOBE variable coupling I.F. transformer, panel controlled, arranged for ganging, air tuned.

Call at once at your jobber or dealer to see these highest quality parts, or write us direct for complete details to Dept. Q-95.

TOBE DEUTSCHMANN CORP.
Canton, Massachusetts
Export Dept: 105 Hudson St., New York, N.Y.

Figure 3.11 — The Tobe Deutschmann Company manufactured condensers, noise filters and test instruments. Its Model H ham band receiver, introduced in 1935, was sold in kit form with a factory-assembled tuner section. (Sep 1935)

Announcing the ALL-STAR BUILD-IT-YOURSELF TRANSMITTER

AT LAST! A transmitter you can build yourself! All you need is the foundation unit consisting of drilled and finished panels and bases and the necessary STANDARD parts. A screw driver, pliers and soldering iron — a few hours' time — and the job's done! With clear instructions as a step-by-step guide, the unit is easy to assemble. When completed, it looks and operates like a professional, ready-built job. Designed for standard rack and panel mounting.

From 40 to 500 Watts Nothing Discarded

Efficient performance is assured if you use the STANDARD parts recommended by the seven prominent manufacturers listed. These parts have been built into a completed unit that has withstood repeated tests for proved performance. You start with the smallest unit of 40 watts, either C.W. or phone, and expand to a 500-watt C.W. transmitter or a 400-watt plate modulated phone. *No units are discarded in increasing power or going to phone operation.*

Various Combinations

For C.W. operation, start with a 40-watt unit and low-voltage power supply. The addition of speech amplifier and power supply makes a 40-watt phone station with simultaneous screen and plate modulation, giving a peak power of 160 watts. To increase power, add high-power R.F. amplifier and high-voltage power supply. This gives the 500-watt C.W. transmitter. The same high-powered R.F. amplifier and high-voltage power

supply, with the addition of the 200-watt modulator, gives a 400-watt plate modulated phone, with peak power of 1600 watts.

40-Watt Transmitter

Input, 40 watts to final stage. No neutralization required. Operates on 20, 40, 80 and 160-meter bands. Same 40-watt unit also acts as exciter for amplifier having input of 500 watts. Tubes for 40-watt unit — 47 crystal oscillator, 802 buffer-doubler, push-pull 802's in amplifier. Two crystals will give operation on all four bands. Switching arrangement connects meter in plate circuit of any of three stages.

Seven Leading Manufacturers Make Standard Parts for ALL-STAR TRANSMITTERS

THORDARSON ELEC. MFG. CO., 500 W. Huron St., Chicago, Ill.
HAMMARLUND MFG. CO., 424 W. 33d St., New York.
CORNELL-DUBILIER CORP., 4377 Bronx Blvd., New York.
TRIPLETT ELECTRICAL INSTRUMENT CO., Bluffton, Ohio.
OHMITE MFG. CO., 636 N. Albany St., Chicago, Ill.
E. F. JOHNSON CO., Waseca, Minn.
CROWE NAME PLATE MFG. CO., 1749 Grace St., Chicago, Ill.

See Your Jobber

for STANDARD parts for ALL-STAR Transmitters, *or write*

any of the sponsor-manufacturers listed, or write direct to ALL-STAR HEADQUARTERS, 222 W. Adams St., Chicago.

★ BUILD YOUR OWN ★
ALL-STAR
TRANSMITTER

Unit at top and inset, 40-watt All-Star Transmitter. Panel, 400-watt phone transmitter complete.

• • •

Figure 3.12 — A consortium of seven radio parts manufacturers used the All-Star brand name for a line of build-it-yourself transmitters and receivers. The transmitters could be built in progressive steps, starting with a basic unit then working up in power and features without wasting any part of the project already constructed. (Feb 1936)

Figure 3.13 — The 150T was the first vacuum tube produced by Bill Eitel, W6UF, and Jack McCullough, W6CHE, under the EIMAC brand name. The company name remains synonymous with high power transmitting tubes. (Oct 1936)

WARDS ANNOUNCE

HALLICRAFTERS

HAMMARLUND

RCA

CARDWELL

TAYLOR

BRUSH

ELECTRO-VOICE

AIRLINE

TOBE

KEN-RAD

YAXLEY

APPOINTMENT OF *"Dixie Dave" Elam* - W9FPP AS DIRECTOR OF WARDS AMATEUR RADIO ACTIVITIES

MR. ELAM is shown here at the controls of the new Super Sky Rider. Long a Ham himself, he will be able to give you expert help.

● In order to better serve its thousands of amateur radio customers, Ward's have appointed Mr. David Elam (W9FPP) as director of its amateur radio activities. Prominent as a Ninth District amateur, his work as Business Manager of last September's "Ham Fest" in Chicago (biggest amateur affair ever held) will long be remembered. At present he is chairman of the Chicago Area Radio Club Council; is generally recognized as an outstanding authority on 5-meter work and writes extensively on short wave matters.

Mr. Elam is now at *your* service; he will give you the expert service and advice that you would expect from an unbiased brother Ham. Don't hesitate to write him of your problems. *In addition*—Wards have issued the finest radio catalog they ever printed. Experts — manufacturers, writers, editors of radio magazines agree on this. It has the sensational new developments in ham transmitters, receivers, parts, P. A. equipment and servicemen's supplies. *Everything can be bought on monthly payments;* terms as low as $3 Down, $4 a Month. If you haven't yet received your copy, send coupon for it TODAY!

MONTGOMERY WARD
9 Great Mail Order Houses • More than 500 Stores
CHICAGO • BALTIMORE • ALBANY • KANSAS CITY
ST. PAUL • DENVER • PORTLAND • OAKLAND • FT. WORTH

Have You Your Copy Yet?

Every active licensed amateur in the U. S. was sent a copy of this book. If for any reason, however, you didn't get yours, send coupon AT ONCE ... they're going fast.

MontgomeryWard, Dept. RA 1

Name _____

Street _____

Postoffice _____

State _____

Figure 3.14 — Montgomery Ward joined Sears, Roebuck and Co. in adding Amateur Radio parts and equipment to their catalog mail order offerings. (Feb 1937)

The RADIO SHACK
46 Brattle St Boston

TWO (2) STAR (★ ★) HAMGEAR SPECIALS

WE believe in specials when value-per-dollar quality accompanies a substantial saving to you. It pays to patronize the oldest New England Amateur supply house — for prompt and courteous service.

★ ★
$3.45

200 new KENCO KEYS — now a big saving for slim pocketbooks — your money back if you don't like it in one week — urs fer............ **$3.45**

★ ★
99 ¢

**40M
7200 —
7500
XTALS**

Regular 40 meter "X" cut xtals made by Nationally known mfgr — 7200 to 7500 kc — IDEAL fer new 28.5 30 MC fone — Fm Stock............................. **$.99**

The Dunco CDB X 1 is used by many for break in operation. 110V AC or or 6V DC control. CDB X 1 (DPSB)...... **$6.60**

Keying and control. Relay — single CKT.
ASB X 1........ **$3.85**

Time delay for 20 seconds — 110 AC TD 96.. **$8.80**

Heinemann overload circuit breakers — for quick action.
5 to 35 amps...... **$5.00**

◇

If it's relays — we have 'em in stock

UTC Plate Transformers and Chokes

20462A—1000-750-0-750-1000 AC at 300 MA. DC.... **$5.20**

20462B—1500-1250-1000-0-1000-1250-1500 AC at 300 MA. DC. **6.75**

20462C—2500-2000-1500-0-1500-2000-2500 AC at 300 MA. DC. **10.95**

20462D—1500-1250-1000-0-1000-1250-1500 AC at 500 MA. DC. **10.95**

20462E—575-525-0-525-575 AC at 500 MA. DC. _____**5.20**

20462F—Smoothing Choke - 20 Hy.-200 MA. 115 ohms DC Resistance. 2500 Volts Insulation _____ **$1.45**
20462FS — Swinging Choke — 5-25 Hy.-200MA. 115 ohms DC Resistance. 2500 Volts Insulation _____ **1.45**
20462G—Smoothing Choke — 20 Hy.-300 MA. 95 ohms DC Resistance. 3500 Volts Insulation _____ **2.85**
20462GS — Swinging Choke — 5-25 Hy.-300 MA. 95 ohms DC Resistance. 3500 Volts Insulation _____ **2.85**
20462H—Smoothing Choke — 20 Hy.-400 MA. 85 ohms DC Resistance. 5000 Volts Insulation _____ **3.45**
20462HS—Swinging Choke — 5-25 Hy.-400 MA. 85 ohms DC Resistance. 5000 Volts Insulation _____ **3.45**
20462I—Smoothing Choke—20 Hy.-550 MA. 55 ohms DC Resistance. 6000 Volts Insulation _____ **4.95**
20462IS — Swinging Choke — 5-25 Hy.-550 MA. 55 ohms DC Resistance. 6000 Volts Insulation _____ **4.95**

Brush crystal phone and lorgnette handle. For hard-of-hearing amplifiers etc. — Excellent as amateur crystal microphone. **$3.90**

Brush B2S sound cell — small size. Excellent quality for PA and radio work........... **$19.50**

◇

Also Astatic crystal devices carried in stock

Hallicrafters Hot Ham Hear 'em dx
1938 SX16, Best xtal ckt, Rollerskate Band Spread
IMMEDIATE DELIVERY — TIME PAYMENTS

★★ Also Taylor T-125's fer **$13.50** — and other "More Watts Per Dollar" Taylor tubes in stock — Raytheon RK47 es RK 48 beam tubes — Bassett concentric cable — Bliley mounted xtals — standard relay racks, **$13.50** — standard panels 1¾" to 14" black crackled sheet steel — standard plated chassis and a wide selection of cabinets — Cardwell receiving es hi-power xmtng condensers — socket hole punches — meter hole cutters — Weston es Triplett meters es test gear — Aladdin IF transformers — Dials, grommetts, soldering lugs, mounting strips, brackets, feed thru insulators, insulated washers, air dry black crackle at **50c** per can and all that necessary hardware for getting things in shape for Fall DX. Listened in on "ten" lately?

Figure 3.15 — The very first Radio Shack store, located in downtown Boston, supplied parts and equipment to shipboard radio officers as well as amateurs. (Oct 1937)

Presenting the RCA-807

The RCA-807, a new transmitting tube incorporating the up-to-date beam-power features of the receiving type RCA-6L6, is designed particularly for r-f transmitting applications. To meet the strenuous requirements of r-f power service, the RCA-807 has been provided with: ceramic base, top cap connection for high insulation and low interelectrode capacitances, and improved shielding to minimize the need for neutralization.

THE TRANSMITTING BEAM POWER TUBE YOU HAVE BEEN WAITING FOR—

$3.90 NET

HEATER RATINGS

Voltage . . . . 6.3 volts
Current . . . . 0.9 amps.

CLASS C TELEGRAPH RATINGS

Plate Voltage . . 400 volts max.
Plate Current . . 100 ma. max.
Plate Dissipation . 21 watts max.

Use the RCA-807 to obtain the best possible performance in r-f applications suggested for the 6L6. It is available at your RCA Transmitting Tube Distributor. For further data see him or write us.

Figure 3.16 — RCA developed the 6L6 tube with its beam power construction to circumvent patents used in other power tetrode designs. The company then brought out the 807 to overcome problems with the 6L6 when it was used as an RF amplifier. (Nov 1936)

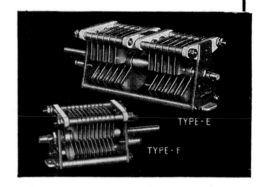

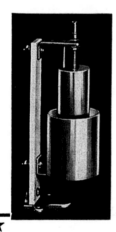

Figure 3.17 — Edgar F. Johnson started the company bearing his name in Waseca, Minnesota. E.F. Johnson initially supplied radio parts to both amateurs and commercial broadcasters. (Sep 1937)

TAYLOR CHAMPS

T-40   TZ-40

A pair of WONDER TUBES—setting an entirely new standard of value. Experienced Radio Distributors, Tube Builders and Engineers, marvel at Taylor's aggressiveness and ability to continually produce better transmitting tubes at "More Watts Per Dollar" values. You, the amateurs of the world will wonder at the more efficient results of these truly amazing WONDER TUBES. Read the characteristics and remember that the rugged carbon anodes used in these and other Taylor tubes operate at red heat without injury to filament emission. The T-40 and TZ-40 operate efficiently in all transmission services on all amateur frequencies. These new WONDER TUBES are destined to be the outstanding sales champs of 1938. See them before you buy —comparison sells Taylor Tubes.

T-40

A general purpose Triode with characteristics that make possible super-efficient performance in all Class C services on all Amateur Frequencies. Extremely easy to drive—the ratings given here are maximum requirements for high level modulated amplifiers. For CW or buffer operation the drive required is 50% less. Ask your distributor or write us for complete technical bulletins.

T-40

GENERAL CHARACTERISTICS

Filament	7.5 volts
Filament current	2.5 amps.
Amp. factor	25
Plate to Grid cap.	4.5 MMF

CLASS C OPERATION
(1.7 MC. to 60 MC.)

Plate volts	1000
Plate current	115 MA
Grid volts	–80
Grid current, Max.	35 MA
Driving power, Max.	10 watts

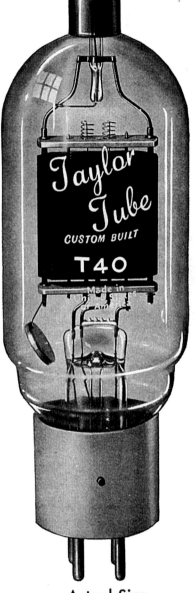

Actual Size

Recommended by Leading Parts Distributors

"*More Watts Per Dollar*"
TAYLOR TUBES, INC., 2341 WABANSIA AVE., CHICAGO, ILLINOIS

Figure 3.18 — Taylor Tubes, initially known as Taylor Vacuum products, manufactured tube designs licensed to them by RCA and General Electric. (Mar 1938)

PRIDE OF POSSESSION

The satisfaction that comes from the ownership and operation of an RME-69 Receiver can only be measured by its actual performance. Thousands of users can vouch for this fact.

You will see these receivers at the Chicago Trade Show in June—208 Marconi Boulevard

RADIO MFG. ENGINEERS, INC., PEORIA, ILLINOIS

Figure 3.19 — Radio Manufacturing Engineers created its first product in Eric Shalkhauser's, W9CSZ (later W9CI), Peoria, Illinois, basement. Shalkhauser, an electrical engineering professor at Bradley University, partnered with his former pupil Russ Planck, W9DGH, in the RME venture. (Jun 1938)

The "Rubber Crystal"
that REALLY WORKS!

Meissner SIGNAL SHIFTER

AT LAST! A remote frequency control that gets you out from under the QRM! Unbelievable frequency stability — superior to that of many crystals — obtained by use of special Hi C electron coupled oscillator circuit and dual buffer arrangement to isolate load. Rigid, fool-proof construction insures against changes due to ordinary handling and usage. Maximum variation of calibration observed during 21-day actual operation at W9WWI under varying conditions of temperature and humidity was .008% or 300 cycles at the operating frequency of 4,000,000 cycles (75 meters). Frequency shift with load variation, tested during this period, was less than 500 cycles from full-load to no-load.

Your SIGNAL SHIFTER will be handmade in the famous Meissner Laboratories by Meissner engineers. ASK YOUR PARTS JOBBER or write the factory!

- Accurate and Stable Calibration! (Dial calibrated 0-100 with vernier pointer)

- 5 Sets of Plug-in Coils Cover 10, 20, 40, 80 and 160 Meter Bands!

- Output Constant Over Entire Range of Each Band.

- Power Output More Than Sufficient to Eliminate the Use of One or Two Doubler Stages.

- Tubes Remain at Constant Operating Temperature Whether Signal Shifter is in Use or "Standing-by."

 **"A FAMOUS NAME FOR TWO DECADES"**

MT. CARMEL, ILLINOIS

Figure 3.20 — Meissner's original Signal Shifter gave flexible frequency coverage over the entire 1938 amateur HF spectrum. (Jun 1938)

Figure 3.21 — Howard advertised itself as "America's Oldest Radio Manufacturer." The company not only produced communications and broadcast band receivers under its own name but also assembled them for other manufacturers such as Hallicrafters and McMurdo Silver. (Jul 1938)

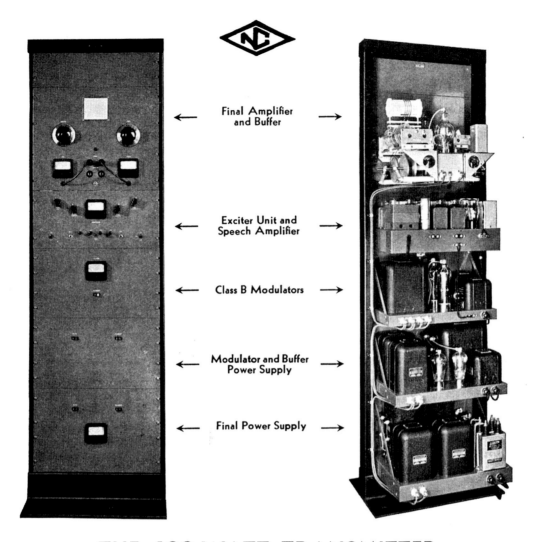

Final Amplifier
and Buffer

Exciter Unit and
Speech Amplifier

Class B Modulators

Modulator and Buffer
Power Supply

Final Power Supply

THE 600-WATT TRANSMITTER

The National 600-watt Transmitter is so thoroughly engineered that the newcomer can proceed with confidence, yet the units are so flexible that they allow the constructor almost complete freedom in building to suit his own particular requirements. The basis of the 600-watt Transmitter is the set of Foundation Units, panels and chassis completely finished and ready for assembly, supplied with the necessary special parts and hardware. The power supply and modulator chassis are punched to receive standard Thordarson CHT Units, combining convenience and reliability at low cost. More complete information on this efficient and economical transmitter will be found in the National "600-watt Transmitter" Booklet, newly revised, and in the National Catalogue, both available from your dealer.

NATIONAL CO., INC.   MALDEN, MASS.

Figure 3.22 — Economy-minded hams wanting a National 600 watt transmitter could construct one by adding their own components to the foundation units sold by National. Factory made from National, the transmitter sold for $1727.50 — more than $27,000 in today's money. Very few units, either kit form or complete, ever reached the amateur market. (Dec 1938)

Figure 3.23 — Stores such as Terminal Radio in New York City employed a sales staff of licensed amateurs. As the ad says, it made the shopping experience "Just like going to a hamfest." Many stores contained a working ham shack to offer customers a hands-on experience. (Apr 1939)

JAMES MILLEN

Announces

that on May first 1939, he completely withdrew from the National Company, Inc., in order to establish a new company to be devoted primarily to the design and manufacture of new radio communication products including component parts, receivers, and transmitters. The new company is known as the James Millen Manufacturing Company, Inc., 6 Pleasant Street, Malden, Massachusetts.

Figure 3.24 — With a simple, one page ad in the June 1939 *QST*, James Millen announced his resignation from National and the establishment of his own company. (Jun 1939)

AMATEUR *Guthman* GEAR

U-36 SIX BAND PHONE-CW TRANSMITTER
6- and 110 Volts

2 tube transmitter. Switch choice of three xtal frequencies. Selects between standby or either of two ant. matching coils. Modulator and power supply, 105-125 volt, 50-60 cy. A.C. Output up to 10 watts. Controls: Key-jack, 3 pos. xtal switch, 6-110 volt selector, oscillator tuning, on-off, meter-selector, amp. tuning, output coupling, standby, mike jack. Panel cut for 2" meter. 6 volt socket on chassis rear. Uses 7A4, 7C7, 83V, two 7C5s. Ship. weight, 16 lbs. Size 12¼"x7"x7½".

	List	Net
U-36K KIT, less meter, crystals and tubes; with 5-10 meter coils	$49.95	$29.97
U-36W WIRED, tested	62.45	37.47
U-36 TUBE KIT	8.25	4.95
U-37 CABINET	4.00	2.40
4399-440 Coils for 20-40 meters	3.00	1.80
4401-02 Coils for 80-160 meters	3.00	1.80

U-10A FREQUENCY METER-MONITOR

Temperature stabilized. Fundamental range 840-1030 kc. strong harmonics covering 5 thru 160 meters. 7¾" dial may be set with extreme accuracy on WWV or 19 broadcast stations. Voltage regulated. Added frequency standard thru built-in 100 kc. oscillator. Detector tube provides audio monitoring and zero beating; cathode ray tube connected to monitoring detector gives visual deviation. For 105-125 volts, 25-60 cycle, A.C.-D.C. Uses one each 43, 25A7, 6J5, 6E5, VR-105, 55-A.

Size: 10½"x9½"x7¼".
Shipping weight: 15 lbs.

	List	Net
U-10A WIRED, less tubes	$48.75	$29.25
U-11 TUBE KIT	8.75	5.25

U-42 HIGH GAIN PRE-SELECTOR

Complete, independent power. Connect between ant. and any receiver to improve gain, selectivity, signal-to-noise ratio. Five bands, low C regenerative R.F. amplifier tuning 490 to 46,000 kc. Dial 5½", calibrated over 324 degrees, 5:1 vernier knob. Amplification controlled by regenerative knob. High selectivity. Controls: regeneration, on-off, band switch, in-out switch, ant.-gnd. doublet and output terminals at rear. Phone jack allows monitoring phone-c.w. When oscillating, serves as heterodyne frequency meter.

Size: 12¼"x7"x7½".

	List	Net
U-42K KIT	$27.50	$16.50
U-42W WIRED, less tubes, cabinet	33.00	19.80
U-37 CABINET	4.00	2.40
U-42T TUBE KIT, one 7A7, 80	2.30	1.38

U-31 "SEND-'CEIVER"

Three tube regenerative receiver, six bands, 10-700 meters. Basic xmitter one tube. 3 band xtal controlled oscillator, band switching. Output nearly ten watts. Three position crystal, operation on 3 bands in xmitter circuit, and 6 bands when 7C5 amplifier tube added. 3 position lever selects coils which cover 5-10, 20-40 or 80-160 meters. Space on panel and chassis for adding power amplifier, or 1 or 2 tube modulator. Key, mike, jacks on panel. A.C. power supply and 0-150 plate m.a. included. Size 17"x7"x7½".

	List	Net
U-31K KIT	$49.95	$29.97
U-31W WIRED	62.45	37.47
U-32 CABINET	4.95	2.97
U-33 AMPLIFIER KIT: 3 coils, tuning condenser, knob, socket, condenser, resistors, to add power amplifier	6.50	3.90
U-34 MODULATOR KIT: mike transformer, socket, resistors, condensers, for adding a 7C5 modulator tube for phone	6.00	3.60
U-31T TUBE KIT: 1—7C7, 80 and 2—7C5	5.30	3.18

U-50 "SUPER"

11 Tubes

Uses controlled regeneration. Excellent image rejectivity, selectivity and signal-to-noise ratio. Three gang condenser. Eleven tubes, extra socket to add 100 kc. oscillator. Spread-band tuning in 6 bands. Illuminated gun-sight dial indicator magnifies figures 2½ times. Uses 7A7, 6J5, 6SF5, 6K8, VR-105, 6B8, 80, two 6SK7, two 7C5. Controls: S-meter, silencer, tone and on-off, phone jack, send-receive, ant. trimmer, dial, vernier tuning, AVC on-off, a.f.gain, b.o. switch, selectivity, beat-pitch. $79.88 net, WIRED with cabinet, speaker, tubes. $72.38 net KIT, with cabinet, speaker, tubes. Size: 17⅞"x9½"x10½".

	List	Net
U-50K "SUPER" assembled, ready-to-wire, less cabinet, tubes, speaker	$83.25	$49.95
U-50W "SUPER" WIRED, less cabinet, tubes, speaker	95.75	57.45
U-51 Hinged Top CABINET	5.84	3.50
U-52 SPEAKER, 8" case	16.50	9.90
U-53 TUBE KIT	15.05	9.03

U-39
5-10 METER CONVERTER

Mobile or home use. Has steering-post clamps. Connect between antenna and any set, output transformer of converter tunable any frequency between 1500-1600 kc. Tuning condenser rigid, two gang 20 mfd. capacity, excellent band spread through 7:1 tuning knob. Drain 3/10 amperes filament, and 12 ma. B current from home or auto set. Size: 6"x4"x4½".

	List	Net
U-39 KIT	$22.00	$13.20
U-39W WIRED	27.00	16.20
1 — 68K Tube	1.75	1.05

U-35 KEYTONER

Learn code rapidly with this unit. Plug-in key, connect to A.C. or D.C., and every dot-dash reproduced through built-in speaker. Knob selects one of five pitches between 300 and 3000 cycles. Ideal both for code mastery and class-room sending. Learn with Keytoner, and master hardest part of becoming an amateur. Size 7"x5"x4".

SIMPLIFIES CODE-LEARNING

	List	Net
U-35K KIT	$11.50	$6.90
U-35W WIRED, less tube	16.50	9.90
1—70L7GT Tube	2.35	1.35

U-44 FREQUENCY METER

Temp. stabilized. 100 kc. standard oscillator. Calibration against WWV. 5½" dial, 5 thru 160 meters. Voltage reg. socket provided. Controls: dial, on-off, standard freq. on-off switch, calibration zero-setter, freq. standard zero-setter, 105-125 volts, 25-60 cycles, A.C.-D.C. Size 12¼"x7"x7½". 70L7GT, 35A5, VR-105.

	List	Net
U-44K KIT	$25.00	$15.00
U-44W WIRED	33.00	19.80
U-44 TUBE KIT	5.00	3.00

See These Guthman Products at Your Leading Nearby Jobber or order direct, giving jobber's name if out of stock.

400 So. Peoria, Chicago, Ill. **EDWIN I. GUTHMAN CO., Inc.** Cable Address "GUTHCO"

Figure 3.25 — McMurdo Silver lent his engineering expertise to the Edwin I. Guthman company in the late 1930s. His work produced a pair of receivers, a transmitter and a line of accessories and test gear. (Oct 1939)

On Our Toes to Give You Fellows the Latest in Ham Radio!

SPECIAL

Low Priced Beam Tubing
75-Watt Modulator
Tuning Inductor for Vacuum Condenser
Parts Deal on Low Payment Plan

Figure 3.26 — Leo Meyerson, W9GFQ, founded Wholesale Radio Laboratories in Council Bluffs, Iowa, in 1935. His company prospered as World Radio Labs after World War II and Leo became W0GFQ when the FCC added the tenth call district. (Sep 1939)

Figure 3.27 — Nestled among other small display ads, Arthur A. Collins' announcement for his crystal transmitters kicked off the business that would become Collins Radio. (Jan 1932)

Chapter 4

The 1940s

War Again, Privileges Restored, Surplus Gear, New Modes and Technologies

The 1940s brought turbulence and disruption to Amateur Radio and to the world at large. Long-simmering international crises rooted in the 1930s came to a boil. American amateurs, some 56,000 strong, enjoyed nearly two years of operation in the new decade before war shut them down altogether.[1]

A new opportunity for experimentation opened up for amateurs in the early 1940s in the form of wide band frequency modulation.[2] A *QST* article by George Grammer, W1DF, and Byron Goodman, W1JPE, drew upon the work of Major Edwin Armstrong and gave amateurs sufficient guidance to begin using FM.[3] Frequency deviation for the audio bandwidths used by amateurs in those days was 24-25 kHz, much too wide for the already crowded HF phone bands. FM enthusiasts flocked to the wide open spaces of the UHF bands (1940s era hams considered anything above 56 MHz to be UHF) and put their rigs on the air.

In order to encourage the use of the UHF bands, as well as FM, the ARRL conducted The UHF Marathon for 1940.[4] During the year, stations would report their number of UHF contacts each month, scoring points for each contact based on the distance achieved. Point values ranged from 1 for distances of less than 25 miles to 50 for contacts covering more than 1500 miles. A multiplier for the band used increased the score as well — the higher the frequency, the more valuable the contact.

In January 1940 *QST*, R. B. Jeffrey, W8GDC, revisited an earlier article by Arthur Collins, W9CXX, and presented the pi-network in a way that retained the antenna coupling network's harmonic suppression while making it less dependent on specific feed line lengths.[5,6] Radiation on harmonics of the operating frequency had long been a problem for amateurs, one destined to grow increasingly severe when the television era dawned at the decade's end.

Collins designed the ART-13 for US Navy aircraft, and the transmitter went on to fly with other service branches during and after WW II. Collins produced about 26,000 ART-13s; more than twice that number were manufactured by other companies.

The BC-348-J, N and Q used single-ended tubes and were manufactured by Wells-Gardner. They were also eight-tube sets, having deleted the 991 VR tube from the lineup used in earlier models.

Another forward-looking article appeared in June 1941 *QST*. In it, J.L.A. McLaughlin described a receiving adapter that allowed selecting either of an AM phone signal's two sidebands, eliminating the heterodynes that plagued HF phone operators.[7] Although the circuit was designed with conventional double sideband AM signals in mind, some of the same principles would apply when single sideband suppressed carrier operation arrived at the end of the decade. The James Millen Company manufactured a commercial version of McLaughlin's adapter.

A winter storm struck a devastating blow to the Midwest, pushing as far south as Texas, on Armistice Day in 1940. Amateur Radio rose to the occasion, assisting in emergency and public service communication. With power systems and lines of communication down over a wide region, the weather

disaster offered amateurs an opportunity to shine — and they did. The Western Union Telegraph Company took out a full page in February 1941 *QST* expressing the company's "Admiration for and appreciation of Radio Amateurs during and after the devastating sleet storms …."[8] Western Union went on to single out by call sign and name 53 amateurs who had been especially instrumental in helping the company maintain prompt and efficient delivery of messages which would otherwise not have gotten through.

Even though the coming war did not yet involve the United States, the country's amateurs felt the first stirrings of disruption on June 5, 1941. FCC Order 72 prohibited communication with amateurs in any foreign country.[9] The order exempted contact with stations in US territories and US military bases on foreign soil, otherwise DXing was shut down. An FCC bulletin issued on July

22, 1941, temporarily restricted amateur operation between 3650 and 3950 kHz in the 80 meter band. The Commission's notice gave the frequencies over to the military for pilot training radio communications.[10] The other shoe dropped with the December 7, 1941, attack on Pearl Harbor. The FCC issued Order 87 suspending amateur operation in the continental US as well as all its territories and possessions on December 8.[11] Hams were once again off the air but, unlike the World War I suspension, the order did not prohibit the use of receivers or the installation of receiving antennas.

The League's response was immediate and patriotic. Before the war declaration, an executive order by US President Franklin D. Roosevelt established the Office of Civilian Defense (OCD).[12] The League urged members to equip themselves for work on the UHF bands, as it was thought likely any wartime amateur communication allowed would be limited to that part of the radio spectrum. ARRL President G.W. Bailey and Secretary K.B. Warner were both members of OCD's Defense Communication Board (DCB), as were several other prominent amateurs who were also serving military officers.[13]

Only a few months into the war more than 15,000 amateurs were in uniform. Thousands more with civilian status worked in government agencies, in research labs, and for equipment manufacturers. The ARRL maintained both a Personnel Bureau and an Apparatus Bureau, which fielded requests from government agencies or the military seeking assistance in locating trained radio experts or specific types of parts and equipment.[14]

Six months after the declaration of war the FCC created the War Emergency Radio Service. The WERS was initially intended to provide supplementary communications for national defense and security, but the mission later expanded to include things such as weather emergencies. Initially, the FCC authorized WERS operation in the former amateur bands at 112, 224 and 400 MHz. The 112 MHz band carried the bulk of the service's work during the course of the war.

Publishing a magazine for a hobby whose main activity had suddenly ceased proved an interesting proposition for the ARRL. Paper rationing limited the number of pages, traditional editorial content changed, and advertisers paid increased rates for less space, but not a single monthly issue of *QST* failed to be published in the war years.[15,16]

Known collectively as Command Sets, WW II military surplus ARC-5 and SCR-274N equipment reached the civilian market in 1947, remaining a plentiful source of inexpensive gear for more than 30 years. The BC-458 transmitter, when converted, was popular as a VFO for the 9 MHz exciters common during the early days of single-sideband operation.

The magazine got off to a shaky start during the first two years under the War Production Board's rationing but then continued to grow in both size and circulation.[17] Much of this can be attributed to *QST's* traditional advertisers sticking with it, some even paying for ad pages without running an ad. Many old friends showed themselves to be good friends. At the same time, these companies demonstrated how much they valued amateurs, their contribution to the war effort, and their help in advancing the state of the art.

In the opening months of the war, editorials in *QST* encouraged involvement in WERS. Technical articles explained the construction of equipment and antennas for use in the emergency service. Existing 5 meter band amateur equipment was useful, especially that which could easily be converted for mobile and portable operation. The League published a special Defense Edition of *The Radio Amateur's Handbook*. It functioned as a textbook for amateurs seeking knowledge needed to work effectively in Civilian Defense and did not replace the traditional *Handbook*.[18]

Well before anyone ever thought about Broadband Over Power Line (BPL) internet technology and its negative effects on amateur operations, power line communication by amateurs themselves became a hot topic during WW II. If not exactly a perfect substitute for traditional on the air activities, it at least provided a legal means to communicate while the ham bands were closed. Byron Goodman, W1JPE, introduced the technology to *QST's* readers in 1942 and others followed with additional articles as systems were implemented.[19,20]

Wartime *QSTs* also carried a variety of not-so-traditional material. The expected tutorials on radio fundamentals appeared as did periodic updates on regulatory matters. Civilian Defense and the training of operators for WERS duty figured prominently as topics. Articles addressed code instruction techniques and the construction of instruction equipment. Outside the mainstream, *QST* published features on cryptanalysis, audio and recording technology, and even a treatise on a cyclotron atom smasher.

National, Hammarlund, and Hallicrafters — names still familiar to many amateurs today — continued to advertise in *QST* throughout the war, often showing up on multiple pages each month. Many companies advertising in *QST* displayed the Army/Navy E Flag. The pennants were presented for distinguished and meritorious war production work.

Sadly, *QST* added new columns to the lineup. In addition to traditional Silent Key listings, wartime issues included rosters of Gold Star (killed in action) amateurs, as well as those missing in action or being held as prisoners of war.

May 8, 1945, brought a close to the war in Europe and the nation turned its resolve to wrapping things up in the Pacific Theater. On September 2, Japan signed terms of surrender and World War II ended.[21]

Even before the surrender documents were signed the ARRL jumped into action to reactivate Amateur Radio as quickly as possible. On August

The BC-610 was the military version of the Hallicrafters HT-4 transmitter. The '610 was manufactured from 1940 until 1954. Suffix letters A–F indicate production during the war years; G through I from '46 to '54. The unit here is shown with the BC-939-B antenna tuner. AM operation required the use of the BC-614 speech amp.

The six-tube BC-453 (R-23) receiver tuned from 190 to 550 kHz and had an 85 kHz IF. It was popular among post-war amateurs for use as an outboard IF to improve a communication receiver's selectivity. In this application, the BC-453 was known as the "Q5-er."

to the hobby. Tons of decommissioned surplus radio gear piled up in military depots and warehouses just waiting for the right person to see the golden opportunity glittering there. One such entrepreneur was Howard Anthony, a young engineer who owned the Heath Company.[26] Anthony began selling his acquired parts and equipment outright, but in 1947 produced Heath's first kit, an oscilloscope. Amateur gear followed and building a Heathkit became almost a rite of passage in the hobby.

Other companies, such as New York City's Terminal Radio, the Radio Service Company in Philadelphia, and Radio Specialties out on the west coast in Los Angeles sold not only ex-military transmitters and receivers but also every imaginable part and accessory. The surplus stockpiles took more than a decade to deplete. Parts and odd bits of gear kept ham projects going beyond that.

The late 1940s found Amateur Radio midstream in technological change. February 1946 QST carried a Sylvania ad for its 1N34 Germanium diode, a simple but revolutionary device fathered by radar research during the war.[27] Within months, construction articles for gear employing the diode appeared in QST.[28, 29] Amateur Radio's solid state era had begun.

Vacuum tubes still dominated in most applications, however. This older technology evolved as miniature tubes began showing up in post-war transmitters and receivers. Manufacturers took advantage of the miniatures' compact, space-saving features as well as their better performance at VHF.

A Collins Radio engineer, Ted Hunter, WØNTI, developed the permeability tuned oscillator (PTO) for use in military gear such as the AN/ART-13 transmitter.[30] The PTO went on to become a key component in premium ham gear lines from several manufacturers.

Significant changes occurred in amateur voice modes during the late 1940s, particularly on the HF bands. In the immediate post-war years, QST, FCC regulations, and several manufacturers gravitated toward the use of narrow band frequency modulation (NBFM) on HF. Jack Babkes, W2GDG, Chief Engineer for Sonar Radio, wrote an article pointing out the advantages of NBFM.[31] Military experiments during the war indicated an edge over conventional AM in readability, particularly at low signal levels. Babkes also pointed out that to get on NBFM phone one needed only a CW transmitter and a means of frequency modulating its oscillator. All audio stages were low-

14, President Harry S. Truman announced Japanese acceptance of the surrender terms. The following day the League petitioned the Bureau of War Communications (BWC) and the FCC for a prompt reopening of the amateur bands. On August 16, the BWC informed the FCC that it had no objection to temporarily restoring amateur communication on the 112 MHz band. Five days later the FCC did just that.[22] The start was a small one, but just the possibility of operating again after nearly four years off the air brought a thrill to eager amateurs across the country.

Budgetary and manpower constraints at the FCC slowed the process, but by November 15 action by the commission restored amateur frequencies above 28 MHz. Order 130 also granted pre-war licenses, which had been valid up to September 15, 1942, a temporary six month extension.[23]

The spectrum landscape changed in appearance from the way it had looked before the war. The new regulations shifted the 112-118 MHz band to 144-148 MHz, creating a 2 meter allocation. A move of the 5 meter band to a new 6

meter home at 50-54 MHz soon followed. As the military phased out use of 80 meters, it returned a part of the band to amateur use. Similarly, both 40 and 20 meters returned to the amateur fold in half-size pieces.[24]

Effective April 1, 1946, the old familiar call sign terrain changed somewhat as well. Because of an anticipated need for new 1×3 call signs, the new regulations created a tenth call district. The new calls would have a zero after the prefix letter. The FCC carved this district out of the existing 9th call area and some states were realigned within already existing call areas.[25]

With the war behind it, it was time for the League and Amateur Radio to begin rebuilding. Even subtracting the years off the air, the 1940s would turn out to be an exciting decade for the hobby. Marvels of technology created during wartime filtered down to amateurs with the coming of peace. Thousands of returning servicemen and women who had no contact with Amateur Radio before the war, but who had been trained as military communicators during the conflict, formed a pool of potential newcomers level, similar to those found in receivers, and no high-power plate modulator or associated hardware was needed. His article detailed the circuit and operation of such a transmitter. A few months later Sonar advertised a commercial version of the circuit and eventually produced a complete line of NBFM gear.

In the second half of 1948, Hallicrafters joined the NBFM movement with a pair of transmitters. The first to debut, the HT-18, was intended to be used as a VFO and CW/NBFM exciter for a higher-powered transmitter. The HT-19 followed and offered the amateur a complete 125 W, 80-10 meter transmitter with a built-in VFO.

Although NBFM could be slope-detected on a conventional AM receiver, a dedicated FM detector allowed the user to take full advantage of the mode's attributes. Manufacturers such as National and RME sold plug-in adapters to convert several of their receiver models for FM use.

The FCC took a graduated approach to NBFM on the HF bands. On August 1, 1947, it authorized the mode on narrow segments of the 80, 20 and 10 meter bands as well as a portion of the 6 meter VHF band.[32] The Commission granted annual extensions the next two years.

NBFM on the HF bands failed to capture the imagination of most amateurs and gained few adherents, although the mode saw limited use into the mid-1950s. Single sideband suppressed carrier (s.s.s.c. — sideband or SSB hereafter) was another story. In his January 1948 editorial Kenneth B. Warner called SSB, "The most significant development that has ever occurred in

Amateur Radiotelephony."[33] Warner's crystal ball proved accurate. In the coming decades, SSB took over the territory once occupied by AM phone on the HF bands and FM became the dominant voice mode at VHF/UHF.

As if to put an exclamation point on the 1940s as a decade of change and challenge for Amateur Radio, commercial television broadcasters took to the air, bringing with them the specter of television interference (TVI). Ironically, in the October 1949 QST, two major amateur equipment manufacturers (National and Hallicrafters) ran large ads for their brands of television receivers.

Notes

[1]"Growth Statistics," QST, Nov 1940, p 25.

[2]G. Grammer, W1DF, and B. Goodman, W1JPE, "Wide-Band Frequency Modulation in Amateur Communication," QST, Jan 1940, pp 11-19, 92, 94.

[3]E. Armstrong, "A Method of Reducing Disturbances in Radio Signal by Using a System of Frequency Modulation," Proc. IRE, May 1936.

[4]F. Handy, W1BDI, "A.R.R.L. Announces U.H.F Marathon for 1940," QST, Jan 1940, pp 26-27.

[5]R. Jeffrey, W8GDC, "Improved Pi-Section Antenna Coupler," QST, Jan 1940, pp 40-41.

[6]A. Collins, W9CXX, "A Universal Antenna Coupling System for Modern Transmitters," QST, Feb 1934, pp 15-17.

[7]J. McLaughlin, "The Selectable Single Side-Band Receiving System," QST, Jun 1941, pp 16-17, 74.

[8]Western Union Telegraph Company ad, QST, Feb 1941, p 91.

[9]Federal Communications Commission Order 72, QST, Jul 1940, p 12.

[10]Federal Communications Commission Public Notice, QST, Sep 1941, p 9.

[11]"War Comes!" QST, Jan 1942, supplement p A1.

[12]M. Harris, DCPA, Significant Events in United States Civil Defense History (Washington, D.C.: 1975)

[13]"Defense Communications Board," QST, Aug 1941, p 29, 88.

[14]"It Seems To Us," QST, Jun 1940, pp 7-8.

[15]"It Seems To Us — Paper and QST – A Report," QST, Dec 1943, pp 9-10.

[16]"Index to Advertisers," QST, Dec 1943, p 114.

[17]"It Seems To Us — Greetings!," QST, Jan 1943, pp 15-16.

[18]Special Defense Handbook ad, QST, Mar 1942, p 95.

[19]B. Goodman, "Wired Wireless," QST, Mar 1942, pp 12-15, 58, 60, 62.

[20]P. Wightman and H. Lyon, "Wired Wireless in Civilian Defense," QST, Aug 1943, pp 14-17.

[21]D. Muzzey, A. Link, Our American Republic (Boston, Massachusetts: 1963) p 616.

[22]"It Seems To Us — Reopening," QST, Oct 1945, pp 11-13.

[23]"Happenings of the Month," QST, Dec 1945, p 31.

[24]"Happenings of the Month," QST, Aug 1946, p 36.

[25]"Rules Governing Amateur Radio Service," QST, May 1946, pp 25-30.

[26]C. Penson, WA7ZZE, Heathkit: A Guide to the Amateur Radio Products (Hicksville, New York: 2003).

[27]Sylvania ad, QST, Feb 1946, p 105.

[28]R. Dellar, W4ICC, "A Combination Test Meter," QST, Sep 1946, pp 61-62, 152.

[29]M. Jones, W1PNX, and C. Sontheimer, "The 'Micromatch'," QST, Apr 1947, pp 15-20.

[30]T. Hunter, WØNTI, "Permeability-Tuned Oscillators," QST, Aug 1946, pp 42-46.

[31]J. Babkes, W2GDG, "A New Phase-Modulation Circuit for Narrow-Band F.M. Transmission," QST, Jan 1947, pp 11-15.

[32]"N.B.F.M. Authorized," QST, Sep 1947, p 48.

[33]"It Seems To Us — Single-Sideband," QST, Jan 1948, pp 11-12.

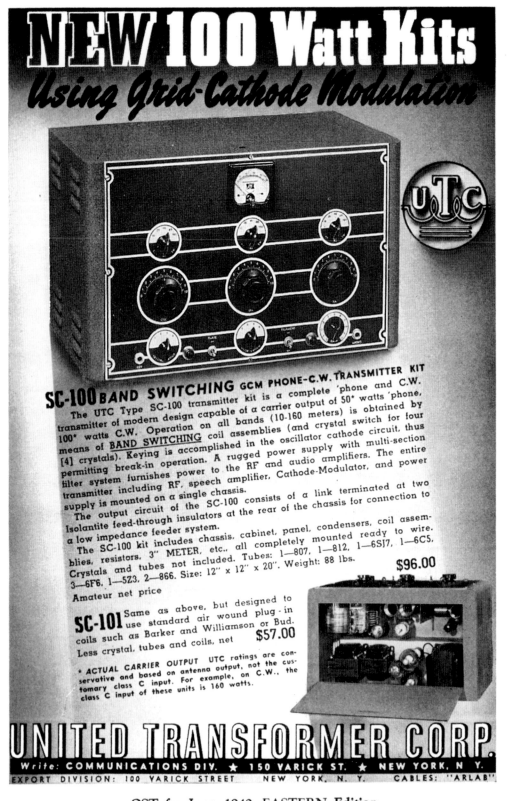

QST for June, 1940, EASTERN Edition

PRINTED IN U. S. A.
RUMFORD PRESS
CONCORD, N. H.

Figure 4.1 — United Transformer Company, a manufacturer of transformers and chokes, sold its transmitters in basic kit form. The 160-10 meter SC-100 changed bands with the turn of a switch; the Model 101 employed plug-in coils. (Jun 1940)

DESIGNED TO GOVERNMENT SPECIFICATIONS

A few fundamentals of the new SUPER SKYRIDER are 6 bands covering 540kc to 43mc—2 stages of preselection—high fidelity, push pull audio—band pass audio filter—a new and highly efficient crystal filter circuit—an additional and completely effective noise limiter—cadmium plated steel chassis—standard relay rack panel ⅛ inch thick —machine tool, gray wrinkle, well ventilated steel cabinet. Hallicrafters-Jensen *Bass Reflex* speakers available. Sells, complete with crystal and 14 tubes, less only speaker, for $159.50 net.

THE NEW 1941
S U P E R

Skyrider

the **hallicrafters** inc.
CHICAGO. U. S. A.

USED BY   33 GOVERNMENTS • SOLD TO 89 COUNTRIES

Figure 4.2 — The SX-28 appeared near the end of Hallicrafters' Super Skyrider line. They manufactured the receiver for government and military customers into the WW II years. (Aug 1940)

Something Radically New in ECOs
The RICE-VARIARM

There are many approaches to the ECO design, most of them having been described in the past; such as expensive, ruggedly-built h.f. oscillators with their external regulated power supplies, low-frequency dual heterodyne oscillators, etc. All have their merits, but are necessarily expensive to manufacture and must ultimately end up by selling in the 50 to 60 dollar price bracket.

A new approach to this problem has been evolved by Henry Rice, Jr., and was described in detail in January *QST*. Probably the outstanding feature of the Rice development is its high-performance-per-dollar which makes possible a factory built commercial ECO with modern performance, complete with tubes, ready to use, for less than 30 dollars!

MILLEN Model No. 90700 is now available at your dealer's at $29.50 net, complete with General Electric tubes

Figure 4.3 — January 1941 *QST* displayed Henry Rice's, W9YZH, "Variarm 150" VFO on the cover and featured an article by Rice detailing the circuit. The VFO appeared as the centerpiece of a James Millen Company ad the following month when Millen began manufacturing it. (Feb 1941)

"SUPER PRO" receivers occupy important positions in our national defense program. Engineers in both military and naval services have found that the "Super Pro" is able to do the most difficult jobs. That's because the "Super Pro" is not an experiment. It has been tried, proved and improved over a number of years, making it outstanding in every detail.

Complete technical information on the "Super Pro" is available for the asking. Write Dept. Q-10 for 16 page booklet containing diagrams, curves and other interesting technical information.

THE HAMMARLUND MFG. COMPANY, INC.
424–438 West 33rd St., New York

Figure 4.4 — As war approached, hams entering military service encountered brand names familiar from their civilian ham shacks. Hammarlund signed off this ad with a "V for Victory" in Morse. (Oct 1941)

Figure 4.5 — With normal ham activity suspended for the duration, the ARRL published a special *Defense Edition* of *The Radio Amateur's Handbook*. (Mar 1942)

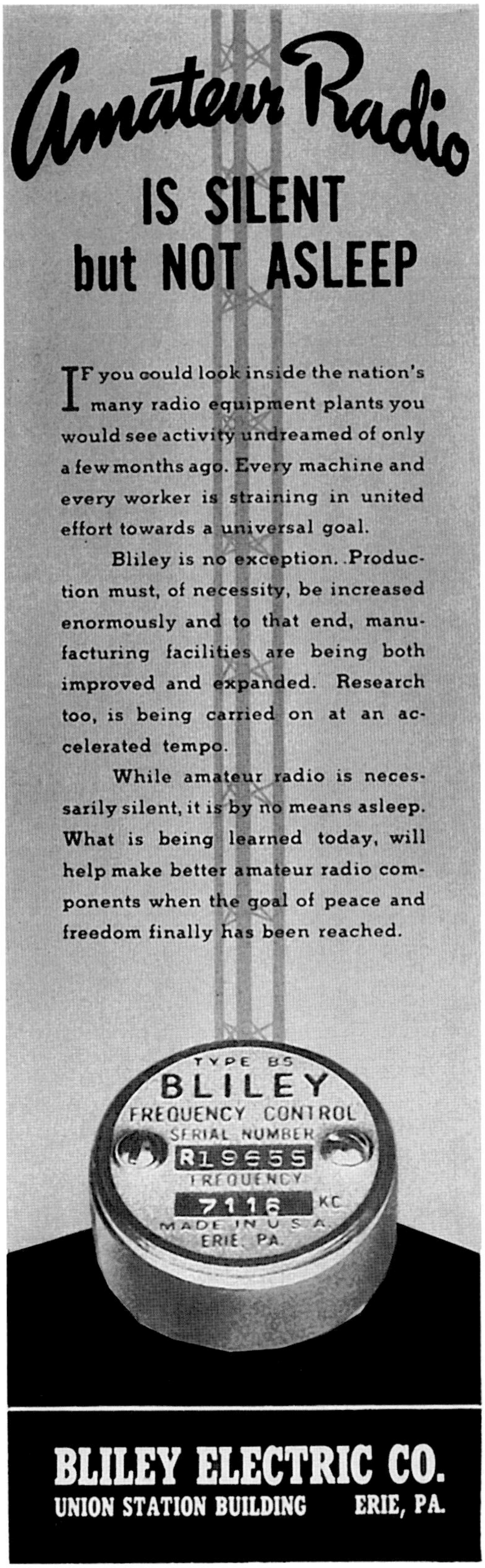

Figure 4.6 — Bliley Electric Company's ad from the early war years foreshadowed the advances in technology seen by Amateur Radio at the end of the conflict. (Apr 1942)

THE VIKING FAMILY FIGHTS FOR FREEDOM

Famed **Viking** products are on the war fronts of the world! We of the E. F. JOHNSON COMPANY take great pride in the knowledge that everywhere dependable JOHNSON components are a part of the mailed might that surges at the enemies throat. Day and night, through fair weather and storm the **Viking Head** trade mark is with our fighting men . . . with begoggled fighter and bomber pilots in lead filled skies . . . with the field artillery . . . the infantry . . . in the tanks and armored cars . . . on the battleships, carriers, cruisers, destroyers, and other vessels of our navy. JOHNSON products play a vital part in the protection of our civilian lives as well.

We could ask no greater reward for our efforts than the immense trust that is daily being placed in our products. The reliability of the equipment of war placed in the hands of our fighting men will be measured in life and death itself. Never will we be more proud of the fact that in the design and manufacture of our parts the utmost in scientific skill and dependability has ALWAYS been the primary consideration.

Figure 4.7 — E. F. Johnson, from America's heartland in Waseca, Minnesota, contributed to the war effort with the ferocity of the Norse warriors for which its product line was named. (Sep 1942)

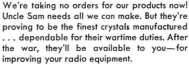

Figure 4.8 — During World War II, Leo Meyerson, W9GFQ, partnered in a company that manufactured crystals used in military gear. As Wholesale Radio Laboratories before the war, and World Radio Labs (and associated companies) afterward, Meyerson served the radio hobby for more than 40 years. (Mar 1943)

Figure 4.9 — Companies such as Hammarlund quickly shifted gears from war time production to the post-war market. The HQ-129-X shown here strongly resembles the pre-war HQ-120 and not the final HQ-129-X production model. (Oct 1945)

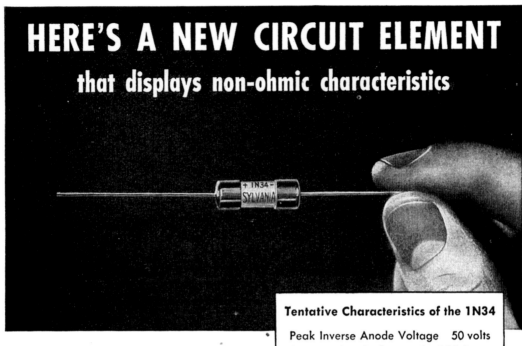

HERE'S A NEW CIRCUIT ELEMENT
that displays non-ohmic characteristics

Tentative Characteristics of the 1N34

Peak Inverse Anode Voltage   50 volts
Average Anode Current '   0-22.5 ma.
Peak Anode Current   60 ma. max.
Surge Current   200 ma. max.
Back Conduction at 50 volts 2 ma. max.

(Surge current refers to transient values; peak current refers to the maximum value of an applied AC signal.)

IMAGINE a circuit element that *violates* Ohm's Law. One that exhibits *polarized* non-linear current-voltage characteristics.

Such an element has now been made commercially available for the first time . . . Sylvania Electric's 1N34 G_x metal Crystal Diode. This tiny unit (shown full size in illustration) opens up many interesting potentialities in circuit design. Withstanding relatively high voltages, it is extremely useful as a circuit element.

Light in weight and equipped with pigtail leads, it is conveniently soldered into place . . . no sockets required. No heater supplies are needed—eliminating hum and noise, permitting both terminals to be connected far above ground potential.

The 1N34 Diode gives superior performance at high frequencies and with low values of load resistance.

Where Can You Use an Element Like This?

Among the expected applications of the 1N34 Diode are: DC restorors in television receivers; frequency discriminators in FM sets; peak limiters; video detectors; meter rectifiers; bias rectifiers; modulators and demodulators.

Perhaps *you* can see many other ways in which you can put this revolutionary circuit element to work. We'll be glad to send you further technical information to assist you in planning applications, and to discuss specific uses with you.

SYLVANIA ⚡S⚡ ELECTRIC

Electronics . . . 500 Fifth Avenue, New York 18, N. Y.

MAKERS OF ELECTRONIC DEVICES; RADIO TUBES; CATHODE RAY TUBES; FLUORESCENT LAMPS, FIXTURES, WIRING DEVICES; ELECTRIC LIGHT BULBS

Figure 4.10 — The solid state era begins. In 1946, Sylvania introduced the first commercial germanium diode. (Feb 1946)

Figure 4.11 — The design of the Astatic's Conneaut microphone looks backward to the Flash Gordon films of the 1930s and forward to the 1950s Detroit automotive styling. (Jul 1946)

Figure 4.12 — Harrison Radio Corporation, among many other ham stores, did a good business selling the glut of military surplus gear on the market after the war. (Mar 1946)

2C43
16 Watts Input at 1250 Mc.
Amateur Net......$9.50

8025-A
33 Watts Input at 420 Mc.
Amateur Net.....$11.00

826
75 Watts Input at 224 Mc.
Amateur Net.....$12.00

3 RCA Transmitting Triodes for Amateur UHF Bands

Designed for operation at 224, 420, and 1250 Mc., or lower bands at maximum ratings.

THE RCA-2C43, 8025-A, and 826 Transmitting Triodes offer the amateur unusual opportunities for experimental work in the comparatively unexplored frequency bands above 144 Mc.—or for general service at lower frequencies.

The RCA-2C43 "Lighthouse" Triode may be operated at maximum ratings as high as 3000 Mc.—either as a keyed or modulated oscillator in conjunction with concentric-line circuits. An outstanding feature of the RCA-2C43 is its low-frequency drift with variations in heater and plate voltage.

The RCA-8025-A may be operated at maximum ratings as high as 500 Mc. It makes an excellent oscillator, r-f power amplifier, or frequency multiplier. The RCA-8025-A has a double-helical, center-tapped filament to minimize the effect of filament-lead inductance. Its double grid and plate connections can be paralleled to reduce lead inductance.

The RCA-826 may be used as an oscillator, r-f power amplifier or frequency multiplier at maximum ratings up to 250 Mc. It also has a double-helical, center-tapped filament, and double plate and grid connections to reduce internal lead inductance.

For further details on these triodes, see your local RCA Tube Distributor or write RCA, Commercial Engineering Department, Section A-21D, Harrison, N. J.

COMPARATIVE TECHNICAL DATA

Tube Type No.	Fil. Volts	Plate Input Watts	Max. Rating Freq Mc	Drive Power at Tube	Plate Volts
2C43*	6.3	CCS 16	3000	—	450
8025-A†	6.3	ICAS 33	500	1.4w	800
826†	7.5	CCS 75	250	6.2w	800

*As self-excited c-w oscillator
†As plate-modulated class C amplifier

The Fountainhead of Modern Tube Development is RCA

TUBE DIVISION

RADIO CORPORATION of AMERICA

HARRISON, N. J.

Figure 4.13 — Miniature vacuum tubes, developed at the end of the 1930s and manufactured in huge quantities for wartime military use, began showing up in amateur gear in the mid-1940s. (Apr 1946)

RME Announces CAL-O-MATIC
TWO SPEED TUNING
AND
CALIBRATED BANDSPREAD

CONSTANTLY IMPROVED —
BUT NO YEARLY MODELS

In the RME 45 you will now find:

1 *Two Speed Tuning.* A dual drive mechanism is now provided, in line with the calibrated bandspread scale, which gives rapid tuning to cover the band, slow tuning to locate that station. Smooth, effortless, single dial control, calibration on five amateur bands, plenty of spread and real efficiency.

2 *Voltage Regulation.* Incorporated as an added feature, the RME 45 is now equipped with a VR-150 regulator tube to further reduce any drift to an absolute minimum and to stabilize the overall performance of an already fine instrument. You will like this addition.

3 *Improved Noise Limiter.* To make operation in a noisy location more enjoyable, a series noise limiter with an ON-OFF switch is being built into the RME 45. It works exceptionally well on all types of interference and goes after the spark-plug type with a vengeance.

Now more than ever, you MUST hear the RME 45 perform!

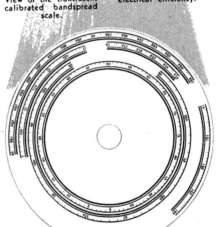

The two speed dial and calibrated bandspread scale provide the maximum in mechanical and electrical efficiency!

View of the translucent calibrated bandspread scale.

Figure 4.14 — The RME-45 included new features such as a concentric, two-speed tuning dial, but also paid homage to the company's pre-war designs. (Jun 1946)

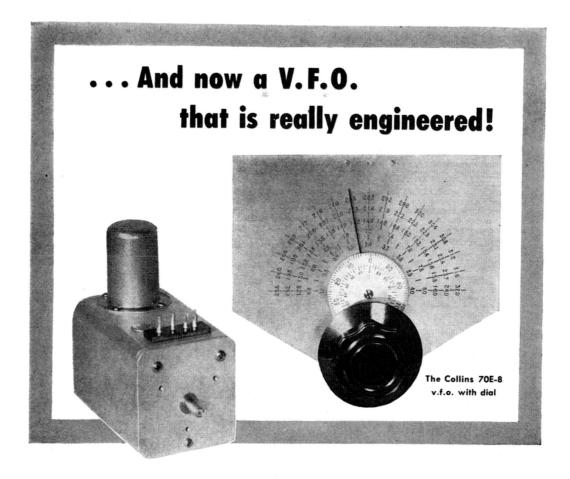

...And now a V.F.O. that is really engineered!

The Collins 70E-8
v.f.o. with dial

The high stability and accurate calibration of the Collins 70E-8 variable frequency oscillator are part of the Collins program to provide amateurs with equipment that is thoroughly engineered from all angles. This unit reflects the years of successful experience at Collins in oscillator research, design, and manufacturing for commercial and military applications.

A frequency range of 1600-2000 kc is covered by the 70E-8. Each dial division represents 500 cycles on the 80 meter band. Frequency deviation and reset accuracy are within 1 dial division under all conditions. Drift due to temperature change and normal voltage fluctuation is practically negligible. Keying is clean and crisp, without a trace of chirp.

The 70E-8 will make an ideal front end for your exciter—will give it professional performance and appearance. Its components are of the same select quality that was specified for wartime use. You can depend on it to give you long service free from trouble—and you always know your frequency.

Get one today. See your dealer, or write to Collins Radio Company, Cedar Rapids, Iowa; 11 West 42nd Street, New York 18, New York; 458 So. Spring Street, Los Angeles 13, California.

FOR RESULTS IN AMATEUR RADIO, IT'S ...

Figure 4.15 — The permeability tuned oscillator, developed by Ted Hunter and manufactured by Collins Radio Company during the war, exhibited accuracy and stability unheard of in previous VFO designs. (Jul 1946)

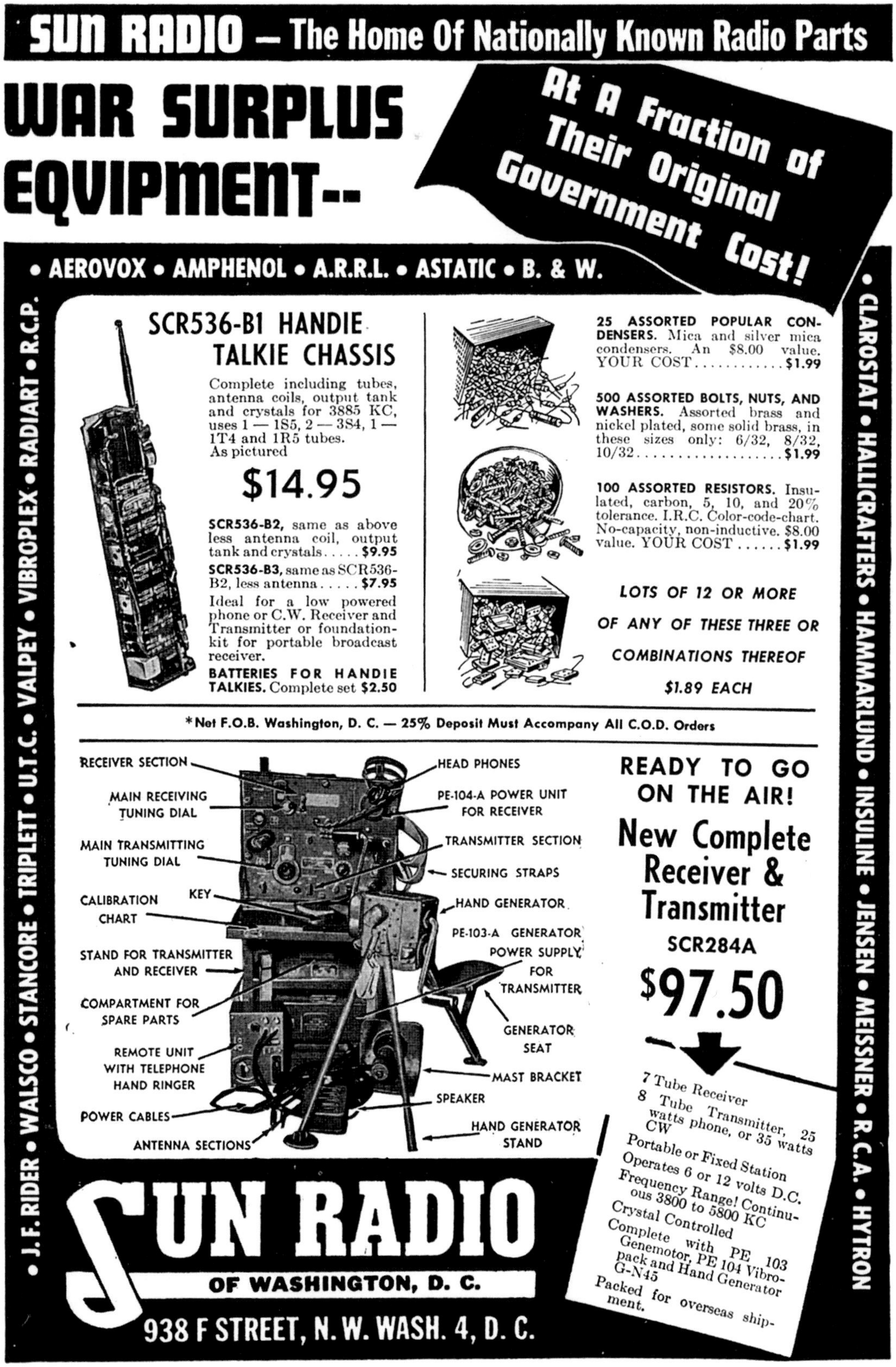

Figure 4.16 — Military surplus gear developed for operation in the field proved attractive to amateurs in the late 1940s and early '50s. Sun Radio's prices demonstrated the economic efficiency of purchasing by the carload. (Jul 1946)

A Triumph in

COMMUNICATIONS ENGINEERING

New Automatic Noise Silencer
Two Pre-Selector Stages
Turret Band Change
Four Gang Tuning and Band Spread Condensers
Series Parallel Crystal Filter
Calibrated Band Spread
Built-In Crystal Calibrator
Single Signal At All Times
Variable Hi and Lo Pass Audio Filters
550 Kilocycles to 40 Megacycles

The New Improved

KP - 81

Receiver

DESIGNED by Karl E. Pierson, creator of the famous PR series of receivers, the new KP-81 is now in production. We promise you this receiver will establish new standards of excellence in the field of radio communications. KP-81 incorporates many of the advanced features born of wartime research, and is years ahead in design, engineering and performance.

We are making every effort to meet the heavy demand for the new KP-81 receivers. However Pierson Electronic Corporation will adhere to their policy of precision construction, and suggest that you place your order well in advance.

PIERSON ELECTRONIC CORP.

533 EAST FIFTH STREET • LOS ANGELES 13, CALIF.

Manufacturers of Communication and Commercial Radio Equipment

Export Department: FRAZER & HANSEN, 301 Clay St., San Francisco 11, Calif., U. S. A

Figure 4.17 — Karl Pierson's KP-81 was a heavyweight in every sense of the word. Its separate speaker cabinet also housed the receiver's power supply and audio output stage. (Aug 1946)

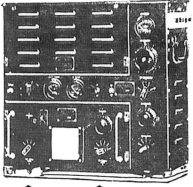

Figure 4.18 — For just over $100, the 1946 amateur could equip his station with a WW II airborne transmitter and receiver, about $1200 in today's money. (Sep 1946)

FIRST AGAIN!
THE NEW 10-11 METER
GON-SET CONVERTER
For Fixed — Mobile Use. Built In Pre-Selection

Actual size is slightly larger—3½″ x 5½″ x 5½″.

The new Gon-set 10–11 meter converter, complete with built-in pre-selection is designed for use with either broadcast, auto, or communication receivers. Attaching the converter to your present radio provides unexcelled mobile or fixed reception.

Gon-set converters have been manufactured since 1938 and are used world wide. Long experience, together with precision design and construction assures a superior product. Ideal for surplus receivers.

★ Tubes: 6AK5 R.F.—6AK5 Mixer— 6C4 OSC. OB2 Voltage Regulator
★ Complete Bandspread 27–30 MC.
★ Output: 1500–2000 KC.

★ 8–1 Vernier
★ Illuminated Dial
★ Connecting cables included
★ Weight: 2 lbs.
★ Single Dial Control
★ On-off Switch Provided
★ Completely wired and tested, not a kit

• IMMEDIATE DELIVERY •

Price Complete............................**$39.95**
Special Noise Silencer......................... **8.25**
High Frequency Antenna Lead Cable............ **.08 foot**
OPA Approved   W6VR

WATERPROOF ELECTRIC COMPANY
70 East Verdugo Avenue   **Burbank, California**

Figure 4.19 — The Gonset name, synonymous with amateur mobile operation in the late 1950s, was a shortened form of Faust Gonsett's, W6VR, surname. Faust's father Robert founded Waterproof Electric to manufacture electrical connectors for the US Navy. The company did business under the Waterproof name until changing to Gon-set in late 1947, dropping the hyphen a few months later. (Sep 1946)

Crystals in amateur service take a beating! To get high output, crystal currents run high ... voltages on the basic exciter stage are pushed to the limit. To have real stability with high output you want a rugged rock, one that will take the highest allowable heating without undue drift. That's where PRs come in. Even on the higher frequencies PRs stand firm ... with less than 2 cycles drift per MC per degree Centigrade. With PRs you get everything ... stability ... long life ... high activity ... moisture and contamination-proof. **EXACT FREQUENCY (INTEGRAL KILOCYCLE) AT NO EXTRA COST.**

Get PRs at your jobber's. Accept no substitute! They're unconditionally guaranteed. — Petersen Radio Company, Inc., 2800 West Broadway, Council Bluffs, Ia. (Telephone 2760)

SINCE 1934

PR Precision CRYSTALS

10 METERS PR Type Z-5.	Temp. coefficient less than 2 cycles per MC per degree centigrade. High activity. Heavy drive without crystal damage..$5.00
20 METERS PR Type Z-3.	Temp. coefficient less than 2 cycles per MC per degree centigrade. High power output. High activity $3.50
40 & 80 METERS PR Type Z-2.	Rugged. Low Drift (less than 2 cycles per MC per degree centigrade). High keying activity. High power output. Accurate calibration $2.65

Figure 4.20 — Peterson Radio's PR Crystal brand was a familiar name — seemingly one of dozens — when crystal control ruled the HF amateur airwaves. The long-lived company was founded by Bill Peterson in Council Bluffs, Iowa. (Feb 1947)

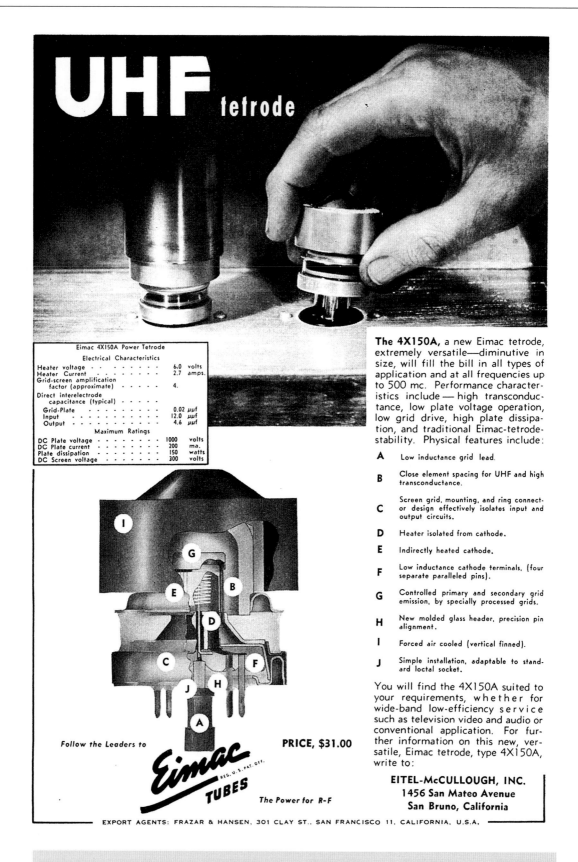

UHF tetrode

Eimac 4X150A Power Tetrode

Electrical Characteristics

Heater voltage	6.0	volts
Heater Current	2.7	amps.
Grid-screen amplification factor (approximate)	4.	
Direct interelectrode capacitance (typical)		
Grid-Plate	0.02	$\mu\mu f$
Input	12.0	$\mu\mu f$
Output	4.6	$\mu\mu f$

Maximum Ratings

DC Plate voltage	1000	volts
DC Plate current	200	ma.
Plate dissipation	150	watts
DC Screen voltage	300	volts

The 4X150A, a new Eimac tetrode, extremely versatile—diminutive in size, will fill the bill in all types of application and at all frequencies up to 500 mc. Performance characteristics include — high transconductance, low plate voltage operation, low grid drive, high plate dissipation, and traditional Eimac-tetrode-stability. Physical features include:

A   Low inductance grid lead.

B   Close element spacing for UHF and high transconductance.

C   Screen grid, mounting, and ring connector design effectively isolates input and output circuits.

D   Heater isolated from cathode.

E   Indirectly heated cathode.

F   Low inductance cathode terminals. (four separate paralleled pins).

G   Controlled primary and secondary grid emission, by specially processed grids.

H   New molded glass header, precision pin alignment.

I   Forced air cooled (vertical finned).

J   Simple installation, adaptable to standard loctal socket.

You will find the 4X150A suited to your requirements, w h e t h e r for wide-band low-efficiency s e r v i c e such as television video and audio or conventional application. For further information on this new, versatile, Eimac tetrode, type 4X150A, write to:

EITEL-McCULLOUGH, INC.
1456 San Mateo Avenue
San Bruno, California

Follow the Leaders to

Eimac TUBES
REG. U. S. PAT. OFF.

PRICE, $31.00

The Power for R-F

EXPORT AGENTS: FRAZAR & HANSEN, 301 CLAY ST., SAN FRANCISCO 11, CALIFORNIA, U.S.A.

Figure 4.21 — Eimac greatly expanded its production capacity during the war. By 1945 the company was shipping 3500 tubes each day. (Apr 1947)

HERE IT IS!

40 WATT INPUT

30 WATT OUTPUT

THE NEW NBFM MOBILE XMITTER

The MB611, Sonar's newest NBFM creation, is a compact, crystal controlled unit incorporating the exclusive Sonar circuit* development for NBFM† used in all Sonar products. Built rugged to withstand shock and vibration, the MB611 is ideal for mounting in any moving vehicle. The pie-network system incorporated in the MB611, which will match any antenna from 30 to 600 ohms impedance, makes it an excellent unit for the shack as well.

With the separate mounting and easy accessibility to the connections, the MB611 is easily removed from the vehicle and "hooked up" anywhere.

The exclusive NBFM circuit development using phase modulation, needs NO EXTRA modulation equipment. This feature permits a definite economy of parts and space, as well as permitting phone operation with full CW rating on the final tube, giving extra power over AM operation.

POWER SUPPLY—Any external supply of 250 to 600 volts at 100 MA.

FREQUENCY RANGE—6 meters or 10 and 11 meters. Specify which when ordering.

PHYSICAL SIZE—10⅛″ x 7″ x 5″.

RECEIVER—ANY AM RECEIVER WILL RECEIVE NBFM SIGNALS. (See QST March, 1947, page 30).

FINISH—Sonar Gray baked enamel, inside and outside (for protection against the weather) with red and white lettering for easy readability.

The MB611 is designed with easy accessibility to the lock-nut screwdriver adjusted condensers, which are tuned by means of a dual tuning eye for the prestages and a jack for the 0–100 MA meter for tuning the final and antenna pie-network. Once the unit is tuned there is no need for any further adjusting.

The many advantages of this rugged unit are unlimited. It can be used aboard ship, aboard a pleasure boat, in a car, in your summer camp or cottage and in the shack as a final or to push a hi-powered final.

SEE THE MB611 AT YOUR DEALERS.

WATCH THESE ADS FOR THE LATEST BY SONAR.

Amateur Net **$72.45**

(Less crystal and power supply)

* Patent Pending.

† NBFM at present permitted on 11 meters and above 29 MEGS. In Canada on 27.395 to 27.455 and 29.5 to 29.7 MEGS.

Representatives for SONAR in Canada: Measurement Engineering, Ltd., Toronto: Frank's Agencies, Alberta

XE-10 AMATEUR NET **$39.45** LESS XTAL

SEE YOUR DEALER OR WRITE US DIRECT

SONAR Radio
NARROW BAND FM

SONAR RADIO CORP. Box 445 BKLYN 1, NEW YORK

VFX 680 AMATEUR NET **$87.45** LESS XTAL

Figure 4.22 — The FCC authorized narrow band frequency modulation (NBFM) on portions of the 75, 20, 10 and 6 meter amateur bands in August 1947 for a temporary one year period. The commission granted a further 12 month extension the following year. (Jun 1947)

Figure 4.23 — Electro-Voice founder Al Kahn, K4FW, received his first license, 9BBI , at age 15 — later becoming W8DUS. He went on to found Ten-Tec in 1969. (Oct 1947)

ANOTHER NATIONAL
FIRST
THE NC-183

EST. 1914

USE THE NC-183
for Narrow-Band FM Reception!

This new NFM-83 adaptor unit plugs into the accessory socket provided for it inside the cabinet of the NC-183.

A flick of the radio-phono switch gives you instant selection of AM or NFM reception.

The NFM-83 employs the new ratio detector for maximum noise suppression and high sensitivity.

For the first time, a ham receiver incorporating *all* the latest innovations demanded by amateurs is now available at a reasonable price.

The NC-183, latest in National's great new line of communications receivers, is a band-switching set covering frequencies from 0.54 to 31 MC plus the 6 meter band. Two r.f. amplifier stages provide remarkable image rejection and the latest crystal filter aids in maintaining the highest degree of selectivity.

In addition, a stabilized voltage regulated circuit makes the NC-183 a truly top-flight performer on the highest frequencies. A push-pull audio output stage with separate 10" speaker affords excellent fidelity of output.

These, plus many other features, combine to make the NC-183 a really "hot" receiver. It will certainly become a strong favorite with those stations that specialize in digging DX out of the background.

See and hear the NC-183 at your nearest National distributor this week.

Amateur Net (Complete with 10" speaker)......$269.00

National
Company, Inc.
Dept. No. 8
Malden, Mass.

MAKERS OF LIFETIME RADIO EQUIPMENT

Figure 4.24 — National's NC-183 offered a plug-in adapter for NBFM reception. (Dec 1947)

AT LAST!
A PERFECT FIST FOR YOU!

MON-KEY
~ ELECTRONIC ~
Monitor and Sending Key

NOTE THESE FEATURES

- Electro-timed rhythm.
- Uniform dots, dashes, intervals.
- Adjustable speed control.
- Variable monitor tone.
- Easy to send . . . easy to read.
- 2 inch dynamic speaker.
- Keying relay with 2 amp. contacts for directly keying transmitter.
- Uses only 3 tubes including rectifier.
- Feather touch aluminum key . . . plastic knob and paddle.
- Fully shielded.
- 110 volt AC or DC.

Only $29.95

Ask your dealer or write for folder

Here's sending rhythm and timing that the best professional can't beat . . . electro-timed rhythm. It's a key that not only makes dashes proportioned to dots but keeps spaces uniform for the speed you're sending. At the same time, it's a monitor, producing a clear tone that can be regulated as to volume and tone or cut out entirely at the twist of a knob.

MON-KEY is easy to use . . . easy to learn . . . easy to read. Press the key to the right and you get dots . . . evenly spaced . . . as long as you hold it there. Press it to the left and you get a series of evenly spaced dashes. Just relax and let the words roll out with the most perfectly timed rhythm you ever heard. Send as fast or slow as you like . . . there's a dial setting to regulate speed.

Remember . . . MON-KEY is a combination automatic electronic sending key, monitor, and keying relay all in one compact unit . . . at a remarkably low price. It's only 11″ long, 4½″ wide, and 4″ high with plastic base, rubber feet, and cast aluminum housing with handsome black crackle finish. A transparent plastic cover protects contacts from dust.

Here is, without question, a most important improvement in sending equipment. Get yours today. Get on the air with a fist near perfect. See your dealer at once. If he can't supply you, write for descriptive folder.

ELECTRIC EYE EQUIPMENT COMPANY • 6 West Fairchild Street • Danville, Illinois

Figure 4.25 — Electric Eye Equipment Company of Danville, Illinois, produced the first commercial electronic keyer. The Mon-Key used a pair of 12AU7 tubes and a keying relay to create automatic dots and dashes. (Feb 1948)

Figure 4.26 — Cameradio's catalog boasted, "If you see it advertised — we have it!" One item in the company's impressive inventory was the Millen Single Side Band Selector, a device developed by J. L. A. McLaughlin for the Office of Strategic Services during the war. (May 1948)

Figure 4.27 — The Suburban Radio Company offered the growing contingent of amateur mobile operators a compact transmitter for the 10 and 11 meter bands. (Aug 1948)

NBFM or CW
VFO or CRYSTAL !

$298⁰⁰
Slightly Higher
West of Rockies

...the New **HT-19** *Transmitter*

- Designed for the modern-minded Ham. Maximum flexibility on 5 Bands — 3.5, 7, 14, 21, and 28 MC. High stability, low FM distortion (measured at less than 5%). Provisions for applying AM from external modulator. 125 watts output. Oscillator—reactance modulator with speech amplifier—buffer—and final. The 4-65A in output stage is air-cooled by a 3000-rpm fan! 5 Tubes plus 2 Voltage Regulators and 3 Rectifiers.

See it at your Hallicrafters Dealers!

●

the hallicrafters co.
4401 W. Fifth Ave., Chicago 24, Ill.

World leading manufacturers of precision radio and television equipment

Figure 4.28 — The HT-19 ran 125 watts out on either CW or NBFM with VFO frequency agility on 80 through 10 meters. AM phone operation required an external modulator. (Oct 1948)

Figure 4.29 — General Electric presented the YRS-1 as the commercial implementation of a single sideband receiving adapter developed by GE engineer Don Norgaard, W2KUJ. In addition to receiving single sideband suppressed carrier signals, it also helped dodge interference on conventional double sideband AM phone. (Nov 1948)

Figure 4.30 — After a quarter century in the radio parts business, E. F. Johnson introduced its first amateur transmitter, the Viking I in 1949. (Oct 1949)

Figure 4.31 — The Harvey-Wells TBS-50 series of transmitters included a number of different models accompanied by a variety of accessories. The Bandmasters covered 80 through 2 meters. (Nov 1949)

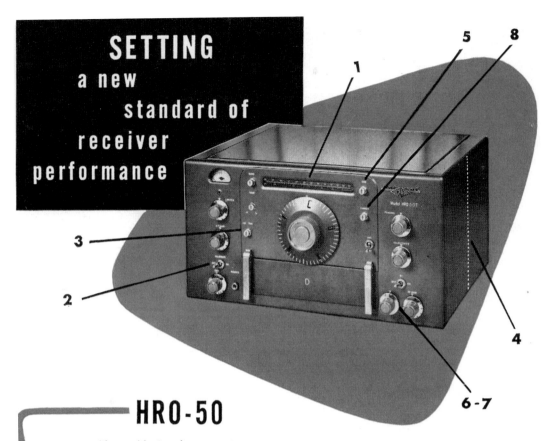

SETTING a new standard of receiver performance

HRO-50

Now, National presents a great new HRO receiver. Retaining such time-tested features as a variable-threshold automatic noise limiter, voltage-regulated oscillator, two tuned R.F. stages with excellent signal/image ratio and micrometer dial with gear drive, the new HRO-50 incorporates 12 "asked for" innovations. Performance tests indicate the HRO-50, the finest National has ever made, will set a new standard of performance for communication receivers.

12 ALL NEW FEATURES

1. Direct frequency reading linear scale with a single range in view at a time. 2. Provisions for using 100 kcs. crystal calibrator unit, switched from panel. 3. Variable front-of-panel antenna trimmer. 4. Built-in power supply with heat resistant barrier. 5. Front-of-panel oscillator compensation control. 6. B.F.O. switch separated from B.F.O. frequency control. 7. Provision for incorporation of NFM adapter inside receiver, switched from front panel. 8. Dimmer control for dial and meter illumination. 9. Miniature tubes in front end and high frequency oscillator. 10. Speaker matching transformer built into receiver with 8 and 500/600 ohm output terminals. 11. High frequency and beat frequency oscillator circuits not disabled when receiver in "send" position. 12. High-fidelity push-pull audio amplifier, 8 watts undistorted output. Ideal for phono attachment.

Shipments will start shortly after January 15. Place your order with your National dealer today for early delivery.

© EST. 1914

NATIONAL COMPANY, Inc.
MALDEN, MASSACHUSETTS

Figure 4.32 — The HRO-50 was the first of its line to include a direct frequency readout scale. Previous HROs used a coil chart in conjunction with the PW dial. (Dec 1949)

Chapter 5

The 1950s

Transistors, SSB, VHF, TVI and the Novice License

In 1951, the FCC implemented a basketful of changes to the Amateur Service known collectively as Docket 9295.[1] Several issues central to the proposed sweeping rules changes had provoked discussion and debate as the docket languished in the federal paperwork pipeline after being introduced in April 1949. The League objected to several changes in the rules governing the Amateur Service with other interested parties joining in as well.

The FCC's Basis and Purpose statement for the Amateur Service and its intention to establish a new Extra Class license ranked at the top of the League's concerns. It also took issue with the privileges to be accorded to holders of the Extra Class license. The new regulations would have required an Extra Class ticket to operate in the 75 and 20 meter phone bands.[2] Other proposals received a more positive reception.

The Commission's intended changes included two new license classes. The first, a Novice Class license, added an entry level to the existing structure. It was designed as an apprenticeship program to add newcomers to the hobby. The Novice license granted CW-only privileges for small portions of the 80 and 11 meter bands along with voice operation on the 145-147 MHz segment of 2 meters. A Novice license limited the holder to a crystal-controlled transmitter with a power input of 75 W. The Novice test consisted of a simple examination on regulations and theory and a 5 WPM code test. The FCC introduced the Technician Class license at the same time. It not only required a 5 WPM code test but also a theory and regulations exam identical to the General Class license.[3] The Technician license permitted operation on all bands and modes allocated to amateurs above 220 MHz. It carried a license term of five years and was renewable. The one-year Novice license could not be renewed.

In addition to adding the two entry-level classes, the commission created another license at the top end of the structure. The Amateur Extra Class required two years' experience at a lower level license, a rigorous theory exam, and a 20 WPM code test. The new regulations also redefined and renamed existing license classes. The old Class A changed to the Advanced Class, while Class B amateurs became General Class licensees. The former Class C license, available to those eligible to take the General Exam via mail, constituted the new Conditional group. The Novice and Technician licensees went into effect July 1, 1951. All others, with the exception of Amateur Extra Class, became available March 1, 1951. The Extra was delayed until January 1 of the following year.

Docket 9295 changed the amateur bands somewhat too. It expanded 75 meter phone from 3800-4000 kHz and restricted it to Advanced Class licensees. Temporary NBFM authorizations on the HF bands became permanent and the 6 meter allocation expanded to include the entire band.[4]

The 21 MHz band, at long last, was officially transferred to amateurs on May 1, 1952. The Commission had initially proposed the allocation seven years earlier. The new band granted Novices CW privileges on 21.1-21.250 MHz in exchange for their previous 27 MHz slot. The thorn in the new 15 meter band, a hazard for all license classes, came in the form of TV sets having 21 MHz IF strips.[5]

Television interference (TVI) was not unique to 15 meters. Harmonic radiation by amateurs, or just simple overload of a TV set's front end, gave amateurs on all

Heath's DX-20 crystal-controlled CW transmitter used a 6CL6 oscillator driving a 6DQ6 final for 50 W input on 80 through 10 meters. ($35.95, 1957)

bands an equal opportunity to become the neighborhood pariah. Responsibility for harmonic suppression fell entirely to the amateur. Many of the overload and other problems lay at the feet of the TV manufacturers. With the exponential proliferation of TVs, the playing field was not a level one and it behooved amateurs to find solutions before the problem put the hobby off the air.

The League adopted a proactive stance, providing education on the subject through its publications and seminars. It encouraged clubs to form TVI committees, putting their resident experts to work. Lew McCoy, W1ICP, conducted demonstrations of TVI cures for ham clubs as well as clinics for TV servicemen. The TVI Tour eventually visited more than 50 cities across the country.[6] Although interference with consumer electronics devices, whether television or radio, would never disappear entirely, the League's prompt and effective action saved the day in the TVI matter.

A few amateurs had succeeded in operating from their automobiles before World War II, but it wasn't until the 1950s that mobile operation really took off. Cars were scarce in the immediate post-war years, then production began to catch up with demand. By the end of the 1950s, automobile ownership more than doubled what it had been at the war's end, and three out of four families owned at least one automobile. It was a natural time for amateurs to take their hobby on the road.

The trend encompassed both HF and VHF operations. *QST* pages were filled with articles on mobile station and antenna projects. Manufacturers such as Gonset, Elmac, Master Mobile, Sonar and Johnson displayed their wares on the ad pages. Cars of the era possessed cavernous space for radio equipment compared to their 21st century counterparts. Plenty of room existed to hang ham gear beneath dashboards, steering columns became a favored place to mount converters, and the heavy chrome bumpers accommodated even large mobile antennas.

Besides providing another facet of the hobby to enjoy, the obvious beneficiaries of mobile operation were emergency and civil defense communications. A vehicle equipped with mobile gear provided the quickest way to get Amateur Radio into the field when and where needed.[7]

In contrast to modern mobile operation using a transceiver, the typical 1950s setup employed a separate transmitter and receiver, especially at HF. Sometimes a tunable converter fed the automobile's broadcast receiver, using it for the IF and audio stages. Prior to the middle of the decade an American automobile was likely to have a 6 V electrical system, sometimes even with the positive side grounded. Even when 12 V, negative ground systems became commonplace, the car's battery still did not directly supply plate voltage for the equipment. Mobile gear required a dynamotor or power supply — some means of furnishing the high voltage. Going mobile was neither easy nor simple.

Experimental in the late 1940s, single sideband operation gained popularity and became commercial in the following decade. *QST* published articles on the technology and a regular column on

The double-conversion RME 4350 succeeded the single-conversion RME 4300 but retained the physical appearance of its predecessor. ($229, 1957)

sideband activity appeared in October 1951.[8]

Single sideband entered the mainstream with the introduction of the first commercial gear. Even while the mode remained the province of the home constructor, sideband generation diverged along two different paths. The first used the phasing method of sideband generation in which a pair of RF signals differing in phase by 90° and a pair of audio signals also 90° apart in phase drove a pair of balanced modulators. The balanced modulators suppressed the carrier frequency and by combining their outputs, one sideband or the other could be selected.[9] The other method employed a filter, typically a crystal lattice design, to eliminate one sideband and, in some cases, the carrier.[10]

In November 1950, Don Norgaard, W2KUJ, described a simple three-tube, 75 meter SSB exciter in *GE Ham News*.[11] Eldico picked up the design for the phasing-type rig and put it into production. It appeared in a "New Apparatus" column in January 1951 *QST* and Eldico ran an ad for the SSB Jr — the first commercial amateur sideband transmitter — in February.[12]

Paul Wright, W9OHM, president of the Electronic Engineering Company (Elenco) in Wabash, Indiana, wrote *QST* articles on both the transmission and reception of sideband, experimenting with transmitters along the way. In early 1952, Wright announced his intention to manufacture his SS-75 transmitter design and within months the filter-type exciter began showing up in sidebanders' ham shacks.[13]

Central Electronics of Chicago, headed up by Wes Schum, W9DYV, entered the market with its Model 10A exciter in September of 1952. The 10A evolved from the basic concepts of Don Norgaard's SSB Jr design. Central Electronics' phasing exciter generated its signal in a 9 MHz IF and heterodyned it to the desired band. The 10A covered 160-10 meters using plug-in coils and featured voice-controlled (VOX) operation.[14]

Ed Harrington, W1JEL, a design engineer for National described his experiences using the final model of the company's tube-type HRO receivers. His description appeared in one of conversational, letter-style ads that National placed in *QST* monthly for more than 20 years — a total of 245 consecutive installments.[15] A full-page

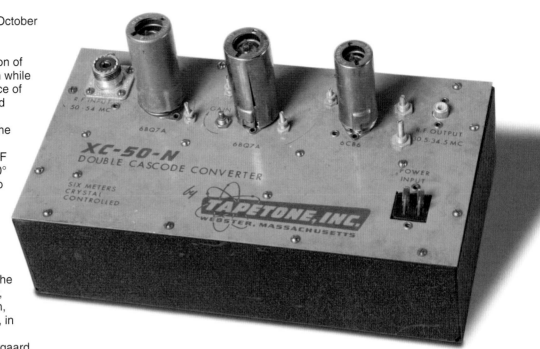

The noise figures claimed in Tapetone's advertising copy seemed so low, they were looked at skeptically by the League's truth-in-adverting staff. Subsequent lab tests affirmed the company's claims and the ads ran as written. ($59.95, 1957)

advertisement for the HRO-60 appeared elsewhere in the same August 1952 issue.

Collins developed the mechanical filter during the war, and first incorporated it into an amateur product in early 1953. A two-page spread in the December 1952 *QST* announced the company's new 75A-3 receiver and described the filter.[16]

1953 proved to be a good year for significant products from other ham companies. After getting its start in the test equipment business, the Heath Company moved into the amateur market with its AT-1 transmitter and AR-2 receiver. The band-switching 35 W CW transmitter and six tube superhet receiver targeted the Novice market.[17] Gotham Hobby Company ran the first of its antenna ads in March 1953 — with many more to follow in the coming years.[18]

Innovation and new equipment development occurred outside the commercial sector as well. The cover photo on the February 1953 *QST* showed the first amateur transistor transmitter. George Rose, K2AH, designed and built the flea power 2 meter transmitter. Power output from the experimental RCA germanium transistor was about 50 microwatts and George's best DX was W2UK, 25 miles away.[19]

VHF interest surged in the 1950s among amateurs and manufacturers alike. Most phone operation was done on AM, with a sprinkling of FM and SSB as well. Some equipment came from longtime manufacturers of HF gear who added VHF products to their existing lines. Other companies, such as Tecraft, Tapetone and Centimeg dealt primarily in VHF/UHF gear.

Riding the mid-decade crest of all-time record high sunspot numbers, 6 meters bustled with unprecedented activity. Cross-country and even worldwide contacts became commonplace. "The World Above 50 Megacycles," a *QST* column conducted by Ed Tilton, W1HDQ, was a meeting place and a must-read for those populating the planet in the column's title line. Amateurs pushed the frequency limits higher and higher. They set and eclipsed distance records again and again.

On the evening of July 8, 1957, W6NLZ and KH6UK established contact over a 2450 mile path on 2 meters to establish a new record for the band. Their persistence rewarded more than nine months of effort.[20] The two operators, John Chambers in California and Ralph Thomas on the Hawaiian end, covered the same path on 220 MHz in June 1959.

VHF activity received another boost

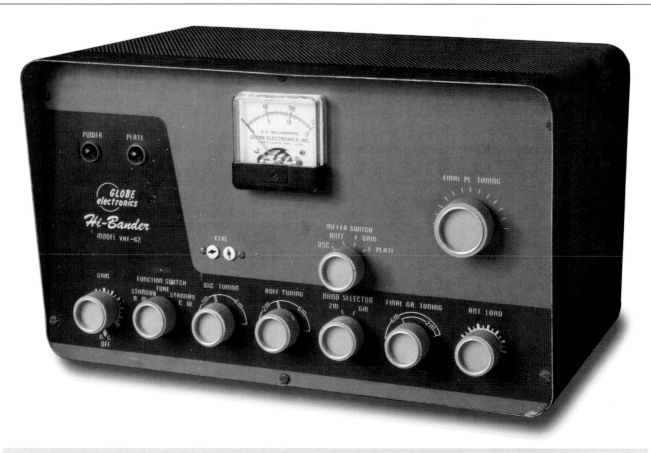

World Radio Labs' Globe Electronics division produced the Hi-Bander 6 and 2 meter, CW/AM transmitter in both factory-wired and kit form. ($119.95 (kit), $139.95 (factory), 1958)

when the FCC granted Technician Class licensees access to the 2 meter band. The Technician allocation was identical to that of the Novice segment, 145-147 MHz.[21] It dispensed with the situation facing those who upgraded from Novice to Technician rather than General Class: the loss of 2 meter privileges as the cost of their upgrade. The move to 2 meters marked the first expansion of Technician privileges since being granted access to 6 meters in April 1955. A Technician allocation on 2 meters had been denied at that time.

After an intense period of regulation and rule changes early in the decade, the process slowed somewhat in the mid-1950s, but did not cease altogether. Back during those Cold War days, there was an expectation that enemy bombers could home in on radio signals emanating from our country's urban areas. The FCC developed what it called a CONELRAD (Control of Electromagnetic Radiations) program to deny the enemy the navigation aid that broadcast signals, or even amateur signals, might provide. In the event of an attack or during a simulated test, the

program required broadcast stations to leave the air, with a selected few moving to either 640 or 1240 kHz to pass along essential emergency information. The CONELRAD rules required amateurs to monitor a broadcast station and likewise leave the air if the broadcaster did in the event of an actual attack or simulated test.[22]

CONELRAD became effective for amateurs January 2, 1957. Ham compliance with the rules meant continuously monitoring a broadcast station, by either manual or automatic means. Automatic monitoring was more appealing and before long construction plans for automatic devices and ads for similar commercial products appeared in *QST.*

In the fall of 1958, the FCC withdrew the 11 meter band from amateur use, allocating it instead to the Citizen's Radio Service.[23] The 11 meter band had always been shared with industrial, scientific and medical electronics. Because of the interference presented by these devices it had failed to attract widespread amateur use.

Interesting and often significant

equipment continued to roll across *QST's* ad pages and into ham shacks. Heath introduced the VF-1 in 1954, adding frequency agility to its AT-1 and similar transmitters.[24] The VFO proved to be the perfect accessory for those upgrading to General Class, gaining freedom from their rockbound Novice license in the process.

Collins Radio Company set a new standard in Amateur Radio equipment with the announcement of its 75A-4 receiver/KWS-1 transmitter pair in March 1955.[25] In addition to being premium amateur equipment, the transmitter and receiver formed part of an air-to-ground communications system Collins was developing for the Strategic Air Command at the time.[26] Not content to stand still for long, Collins trotted out the KWM-1 SSB/CW transceiver in 1957.[27] It had no AM mode and covered only the 14, 21 and 28 MHz bands, but the KWM-1 was the first amateur HF transceiver and set the stage for the way hams would operate in the future.

The single sideband revolution drove development across the ham equipment industry. The R.L. Drake Company of Miamisburg, Ohio, diverged from the bigger-and-heavier-is-better path followed by other manufacturers with its innovative 1-A receiver.[28] It occupied less table space than competitors and weighed only 18 pounds, but the story didn't stop there. Drake advertised it as a *sideband receiver*, a claim supported by its feature set.

Central Electronics furthered its pioneering SSB work with a 1958 announcement of an elaborate transmitter, the 100V. It needed only one tuning control, the permeability tuned VFO, because the other RF circuits used the same broadband couplers developed for the company's 600L linear amplifier.[29]

Transceiver development spread across several product lines. Cosmos Industries' Cosmophone 35 broke new ground. The *bilateral transceiver*, as Cosmos called it, used two separate VFOs and offered conventional transceiver operation or independent control of transmit and receive frequencies.[30] The Hallicrafters FPM-200 transceiver also offered two-VFO operation. Its distinction was being transistorized except for the driver, final amplifier and a pair of voltage regulator tubes.

World Radio Laboratories entered the sideband transmitter market in 1958 with the DSB-100, a rig with double, rather than single, sideband output.[31] It used double sideband (DSB), suppressed carrier as an economy measure. DSB signals are less tolerant of tuning error than SSB but, except for that, an operator using a selective receiver might not realize the transmitting station was on DSB.

Collins introduced its follow-up to the 75A-4/KWS-1 in 1958. The new S/Line, not an evolution but a new development, came in smaller packages with more of a fashion sense than previous Collins gear. The S/Line originally consisted of a transmitter, receiver, power supply,

speaker, control console and a linear amplifier, with a consistent design appearance for all components. Collins rolled out the S/Line with a massive ad campaign in November 1958. It included a full-color insert that was bound into the November *QST*, as well as more than a dozen cooperative ads placed by Collins dealers.[32]

October 4, 1957, marks the day the Space Age began. The Soviet Union launched its Sputnik I satellite, capturing the attention of people everywhere on the planet it orbited. It held a special fascination for amateurs and others with scientific or communications interests. Not long after news of the launch spread in this country W1AW took to the air with a special broadcast advising amateurs how, when and where to monitor the beep-beeps emanating from the Soviet satellite.[33] In the following days, hometown news media across the country contacted amateurs for the latest word on Sputnik.

Collins closed out the decade with yet another achievement. In an October 1959 *QST* ad, the company announced its new KWM-2. In essence the transceiver combined the 75S-1 receiver and 32S-1 transmitter into a single package.[34] Unlike its KWM-1 predecessor, the KWM-2 covered all amateur bands from 80-10 meters and, by installing crystals, any 200 kHz segment between 3.4 and 30 MHz.

Notes

[1]"We Have New Regulations," *QST*, Mar 1951, pp 26-31, 108, 110, 112.
[2]"It Seems To Us — Docket 9295," *QST*, Feb 1950, p 9.
[3]*Ibid*. 1.
[4]*Ibid*. 3.
[5]"Public Notice," *QST*, Sep 1953, p 43.
[6]"On the TVI Front," *QST*, Dec 1954, p 57.
[7]"It Seems To Us — Mobile on 29.6-29.7," *QST*, Jul 1950, p 9.

[8]"On the Air With Single Sideband," *QST*, Oct 1951, pp 51, 126.
[9]W. Rust, W2UNJ, "Single Sideband for the Average Ham," *QST*, Aug 1949, pp 47-50, 88, 90.
[10]F. Edmunds, W1JEO, "A Crystal-Filter S.S.B. Exciter," *QST*, Nov 1950, pp 11-15.
[11]"SSB, Jr.," *G.E. Ham News*, Vol. 5 No. 6, pp 1-9.
[12]"New Apparatus — Single Sideband Transmitter," *QST*, Jan 1951, p 20.
[13]"On The Air With Single Sideband," *QST*, Mar 1952, pp 57, 118.
[14]*Ibid*. 13.
[15]"HRO-60," National ad, *QST*, Aug 1952, cover III.
[16]"Selectivity Never Before Achieved in a Communications Receiver," *QST*, Dec 1952, pp 80-81.
[17]Heath Company ad, *QST*, Dec 1953, p 97.
[18]Gotham ad, *QST*, Mar 1953, p 126.
[19]G. Rose, K2AH, "The Transistor — Or 25 Miles on a Hunk of Germanium," *QST*, Mar 1953, pp 13-15, 138.
[20]E. Tilton, W1HDQ, "The World Above 50 Mc.," *QST*, Aug 1957, p 70.
[21]Happenings of the Month, "Techs on Two," *QST*, Sep 1959, pp 79, 158, 160, 164.
[22]Happenings of the Month, "CONELRAD for Amateurs," *QST*, Oct 1955, pp 47, 148.
[23]Happenings of the Month, "27 Mc. Band Deleted," *QST*, Oct 1958, pp 78-79.
[24]Heath Company ad, *QST*, Dec 1954, p 85.
[25]Collins Radio Company ad, *QST*, Mar 1955, pp 80-81.
[26]J. Miller, KK5IM, *A Pictorial History of Collins Amateur Radio Equipment* (1999: Dallas, Texas), p 91.
[27]B. Goodman, W1DX, "Recent Equipment — The Collins KWM-1 Transceiver," *QST*, Apr 1958, pp 23-27.
[28]R.L. Drake ad, *QST*, Dec 1957, p 153.
[29]Central Electronics ad, *QST*, Jun 1958, p 127.
[30]B. Goodman, W1DX, "Recent Equipment — Cosmophone 35 Bilateral Transceiver," *QST*, Jun 1958, pp 44-47.
[31]B. Goodman, W1DX, "Recent Equipment — Globe Sidebander DSB-100," *QST*, Dec 1958, pp 40-41.
[32]*Ibid*. 26, p 105.
[33]"It Seems To Us — Sputniks and Mouses," *QST*, Dec 1957, pp 9-10.
[34]Collins ad, *QST*, Oct 1959, p 2.

Figure 5.1 — At a quick glance, it looked as if Lettine Radio Manufacturing Company ran the exact same ad every month for more than a decade. The small Valley Stream, New York, company offered a handful of transmitters with a similar appearance and their ads maintained a consistent format. (Jul 1950)

Simple · Complete · Amazingly Effective!

ELDICO'S SINGLE SIDEBAND XMTR-XCTR

The Eldico SSB Jr. is patterned after the amazingly effective unit developed by Don Norgaard, W2KUJ, and described in the November-December 1950 G-E Ham News. It is available in either kit form or completely wired and tested.

Everyone can now enjoy *all* the benefits of single sideband transmission. Tremendous effectiveness of low power; QRM minimized or eliminated entirely; QSB has less effect . . . complete phone contacts with "c. w. reliability."

Eldico's SSB Jr. is a complete 7-tube 5-watt single side-band transmitter. Tube complement consists of 12AU7 combination speech amplifier-oscillator; 12AT7 twin-channel amplifier; 6AG7 final; 12AT7 twin-speech pre-amplifier; 6H6 bias; 5Y3G rectifier.

Each kit comes complete with all parts, punched chassis, cabinet, tubes, power supply components and full instructions for assembly and operation. Audio phase-shift network comes fully assembled-preadjusted, eliminating necessity for elaborate test equipment. Less difficult to construct and adjust than many conventional transmitters . . . practical SSB at amazingly low cost is now a reality. The Eldico SSB Jr. may be used as a transmitter, as a driver for high-power linear amplifier, or in conjunction with a v.f.o. The transmitter provides 40-db. sideband suppression by using a simplified phasing method which because of Eldico's laboratory assembled phase-shift network, requires only standard components and no special technical skills. A pre-amplifier is included as an integral part of the Eldico SSB Jr. kit to enable the use of any low-level microphone such as crystal or dynamic.

SSB Jr. complete kit with instructions....................$69.95
SSB Jr. Wired and tested.........................$99.95

Signals of Distinction

WRITE
W2UOL
FOR FREE--
TVI CAN BE
CURED.

ELDICO
OF NEW YORK
INCORPORATED

44-31 DOUGLASTON PARKWAY · DOUGLASTON, L. I., NEW YORK · BAyside 9-8686

Figure 5.2 — Eldico led the way with the first commercial single sideband transmitter, the SSB Jr. The design, based on work by General Electric engineers, used the phasing method of sideband generation. (Feb 1951)

Figure 5.3 — The band switching Millen 90711 VFO incorporated oscillator, buffer/doubler and amplifier stages, yielding output sufficient to drive a low-power transmitter. It possessed excellent mechanical and electrical stability. (Jun 1951)

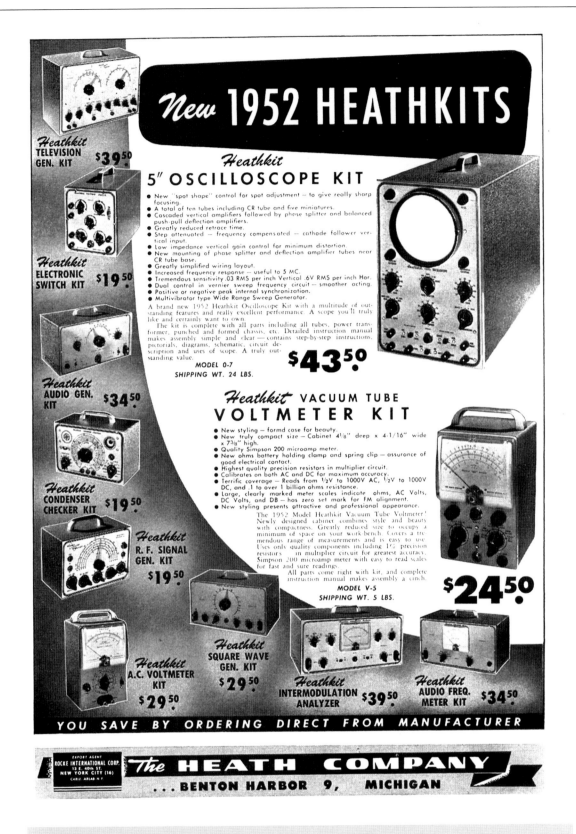

Figure 5.4 — Beginning with its initial offering, an oscilloscope, the early Heathkit line consisted mainly of test equipment. (Sep 1951)

Figure 5.5 — Gonset's 2 meter Communicator, an AM transceiver, helped increase VHF activity and also proved an asset for emergency and public service work. The Communicator's superhet receiver tuned 144-148 MHz; the transmitter was crystal controlled. (Dec 1952)

NOW YOU CAN TRY TRANSISTORS

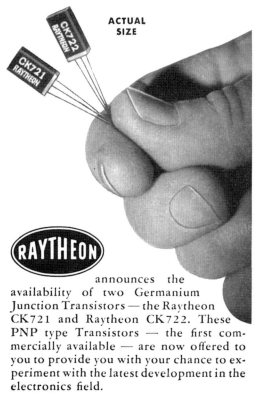

ACTUAL SIZE

RAYTHEON announces the availability of two Germanium Junction Transistors — the Raytheon CK721 and Raytheon CK722. These PNP type Transistors — the first commercially available — are now offered to you to provide you with your chance to experiment with the latest development in the electronics field.

See these Raytheon Germanium Junction Transistors at your Raytheon Tube Suppliers or write for Data Sheets.

RAYTHEON
®
Excellence in Electronics
RAYTHEON MFG. CO.
Receiving Tube Division
Newton 58, Massachusetts
RELIABLE SUBMINIATURE AND MINIATURE TUBES
GERMANIUM DIODES AND TRANSISTORS
NUCLEONIC TUBES
RECEIVING AND PICTURE TUBES • MICROWAVE TUBES

Figure 5.6 — Raytheon announced the availability of its germanium transistors to the general public in early 1953. The best performing transistors went to hearing aid manufacturers, with the remainder — designated CK-722 — sold to amateurs and other hobbyists. (Jan 1953)

Figure 5.7 — The Walter Ashe Radio Company did a national business from its headquarters in St. Louis, Missouri. This ad features products targeting holders of the Novice license. (Jan 1953)

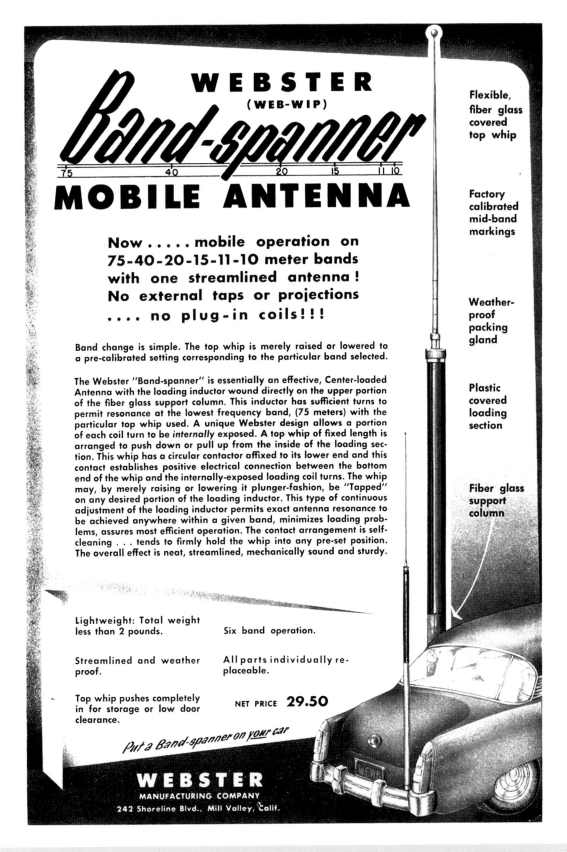

WEBSTER
(WEB-WIP)
Band-spanner
MOBILE ANTENNA

Now ..... mobile operation on 75-40-20-15-11-10 meter bands with one streamlined antenna! No external taps or projections .... no plug-in coils!!!

Band change is simple. The top whip is merely raised or lowered to a pre-calibrated setting corresponding to the particular band selected.

The Webster "Band-spanner" is essentially an effective, Center-loaded Antenna with the loading inductor wound directly on the upper portion of the fiber glass support column. This inductor has sufficient turns to permit resonance at the lowest frequency band, (75 meters) with the particular top whip used. A unique Webster design allows a portion of each coil turn to be *internally* exposed. A top whip of fixed length is arranged to push down or pull up from the inside of the loading section. This whip has a circular contactor affixed to its lower end and this contact establishes positive electrical connection between the bottom end of the whip and the internally-exposed loading coil turns. The whip may, by merely raising or lowering it plunger-fashion, be "Tapped" on any desired portion of the loading inductor. This type of continuous adjustment of the loading inductor permits exact antenna resonance to be achieved anywhere within a given band, minimizes loading problems, assures most efficient operation. The contact arrangement is self-cleaning . . . tends to firmly hold the whip into any pre-set position. The overall effect is neat, streamlined, mechanically sound and sturdy.

Flexible, fiber glass covered top whip

Factory calibrated mid-band markings

Weather-proof packing gland

Plastic covered loading section

Fiber glass support column

Lightweight: Total weight less than 2 pounds.

Streamlined and weather proof.

Top whip pushes completely in for storage or low door clearance.

Six band operation.

All parts individually replaceable.

NET PRICE **29.50**

Put a Band-spanner on your car

WEBSTER
MANUFACTURING COMPANY
242 Shoreline Blvd., Mill Valley, Calif.

Figure 5.8 — Webster's Band-Spanner enabled mobile operation on any frequency from 75 through 10 meters with one antenna, although it was still necessary to get out of the car to change bands. (Sep 1953)

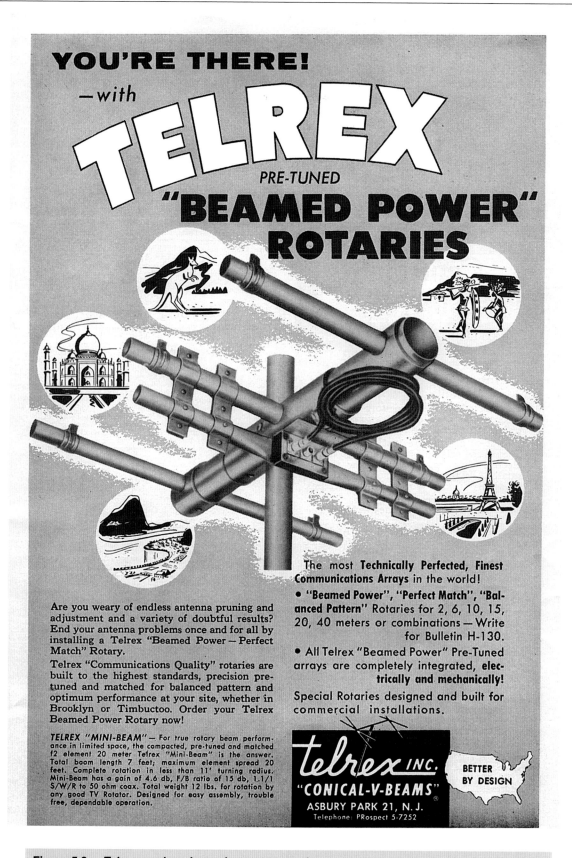

Figure 5.9 — Telrex produced premium antennas, from monobanders and tribanders all the way to multiband stacked Christmas tree arrays. (Aug 1954)

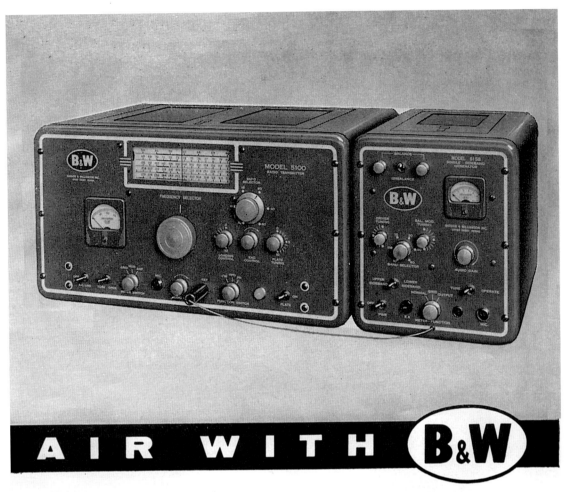

SINGLE SIDEBAND GENERATOR — Model 51SB

For Use With B&W Model 5100 Transmitter

Now, for the first time, you can get really sparkling performance on either SSB, AM phone, or CW. This B&W Single Sideband Generator teamed up with the famous Model 5100 Transmitter gives you outstanding SSB operation on all frequencies provided in the 5100. Tuning and operation are a breeze. No test equipment is required. Single sideband signal is generated by a simple and efficient method perfected after two years of extensive research and testing by B&W engineers. No stone has been left unturned to give you such extras as voice operated and push-to-talk controls, a speaker deactivating circuit, TVI suppression, and unitized construction for quick and easy removal of any major section. Completely self-contained, the 51SB requires no more external accessories than a microphone.

Combine this Single Sideband Generator with the features of your Model 5100—150 watts peak envelope power input (100 watts peak envelope power output) on SSB, 150 watts on CW, 135 watts on AM phone; VFO or crystal operation; pi-network final—and you've got a combination that will flutter the heart of the most critical operator. The 51SB cabinet is made to bolt right onto the 5100 cabinet, extending the 22-inch length to 32 inches. Distinctive panel styling and appointments are the same for both. Easy to install, the 51SB comes factory wired and tested, complete with tubes and all necessary components to convert your Model 5100 Transmitter to SSB. This combination provides a superlative driver for *any* hi-powered linear amplifier.

Write for Bulletin

Figure 5.10 — The 51SB enabled the B & W 5100 AM and CW transmitter to operate on single sideband as well. The 51SB, when connected electrically and mechanically to the 5100, took output frequency RF from the transmitter and generated SSB at the output frequency using audio and RF phase shifts. (Nov 1954)

Collins for NEW EASE in OPERATION

75A-4 Receiver

KWS-1 Transmitter

The new Collins 75A-4 Receiver, 32W-1 Exciter, and the KWS-1 Kilowatt Transmitter are expressly designed for SSB, AM and CW. Like all Collins Amateur equipment, they meet the same high standards as Military and Commercial equipment.

The 75A-4 Receiver features passband tuning, AVC on SSB, bridged T rejection notch filter, built-in crystal calibrator circuit, separate detectors for AM and SSB, a new noise limiter, and provision for three Mechanical Filters together with time-proven features such as good image rejection, and an accurate linear dial with calibration of 1 kc per division.

Transmitter features include a SSB generator using Collins Mechanical Filters, selectable sideband, band switching from 3.5 to 30 mc, voice control or push-to-talk, automatic load control, and dual conversion with crystal controlled high-frequency oscillator and stable, linear, permeability-tuned low frequency oscillator resulting in a linear dial similar to the 75A-4 Receivers.

Power input is one kw peak envelope power on SSB, one kw on CW, and equivalent to one kw AM when received on narrow-bandwidth receiver.

Several versions of the transmitting equipment are available. The 32W-1 Exciter is capable of driving a kw linear amplifier. With exception of the power supply, which is housed in a separate cabinet, it is complete in a receiver-type cabinet and can be converted into a KWS-1. The KWS-1 is also complete in a receiver-type cabinet except for power supplies, which are mounted in an attractive desk-high cabinet. As an alternate, the KWS-1 is available without the high voltage power supply as type number KWS-1K, and kits are available for converting a 32W-1 or a KWS-1K into a KWS-1.

AMATEUR NET PRICES ARE AS FOLLOWS:

32W-1 Exciter complete	$ 895.00
KWS-1 Transmitter complete	$1,995.00
KWS-1K Transmitter less H.V. power supply and P.A. tubes	$1,225.00
428A-2 H.V. Power supply kit for KWS-1K	$ 545.00
428A-1 Power supply for KWS-1K, wired and tested	$ 700.00
367A-2 P.A. Kit to convert 32W-1 to KWS-1K	$ 215.00

See your nearest Collins distributor for delivery information.

Figure 5.11 — Amateurs called the Collins 75A-4/KWS-1 duo the Gold Dust Twins with good reason. In the mid-1950s, the pair sold for $2600 — about $22,000 today. (Apr 1955)

IT'S A PLEASURE TO "WORK THE WORLD"
with a
Full-Size GOTHAM ROTARY BEAM

FULL SIZE GOTHAM BEAM
A BASIC NEED

A basic need on today's crowded bands is a good beam. Thousands of satisfied users attest the value of the Gotham rotary beam — the full value that no midget beam can supply. *Full value* is inseparable from *full size.*

DECREASES QRM

The Gotham beam radiates in the desired direction, creating minimum interference with other stations and extending the range of your transmitter and improving your reception appreciably.

LOW PRICE, HIGH PERFORMANCE

Yet the Gotham beam's price is 25% to 75% lower than toy-like midget beams with "midget performance." The Gotham beam will out-perform even the highest-priced midget, and will compare favorably with any full-size beams, at any price.

ENGINEERED FOR SIMPLICITY, STRENGTH, PERFORMANCE

Simplicity of design is the key to Gotham's performance. No link coupling; no complicated mounts; no tuning stubs. It comes to you completely fabricated, made (except for the polystyrene insulator) entirely of rustless, new (not surplus) first-quality mill stock aluminum. The simple design structure and the top quality castings used provide maximum strength. There is no substitution of flimsy wire for good, solid tubing. No wood to rot or require weather-proofing, no complicated assembly or struggle with color coding, no pretuning. Matching of line to antenna is simple and quick, so getting power from transmitter into antenna poses no problems. No pre-drilling, no pre-fitting, with Gotham. A tried and tested beam, not an experiment.

GET ON THE BEAM,
GET GOTHAM

Get the most enjoyment from your hobby. Get range and performance greater than you ever thought possible. Get the only beam guaranteed unconditionally. Get the Gotham beam.

See sample beams and literature at your local Gotham distributor listed below.

——— 2 METER BEAMS ———
Deluxe 6-element	$ 9.95
Deluxe 12-element	16.95

——— 6 METER BEAMS ———
Deluxe 3-element (Gamma match)	21.95
Deluxe 3 element (T match)	24.95
Standard 4 element (Gamma match)	16.95
Standard 4 element (T match)	19.95

——— 10 METER BEAMS ———
Standard 3 element (Gamma match)	16.95
Standard 3 element (Γ match)	18.95
Deluxe 3 element (Gamma match)	22.95
Deluxe 3 element (T match)	25.95
Standard 4 element (Gamma match)	21.95
Standard 4 element (T match)	24.95

——— 15 METER BEAMS ———
Standard 2 element (Gamma match)	$19.95
Standard 2 element (T match)	22.95
Deluxe 2 element (Gamma match)	29.95
Deluxe 2 element (T match)	32.95
Standard 3 element (Gamma match)	26.95
Standard 3 element (T match)	29.95
Deluxe 3 element (Gamma match)	36.95
Deluxe 3 element (T match)	39.95

——— 20 METER BEAMS ———
Standard 2 element (Gamma match)	21.95
Standard 2 element (T match)	24.95
Deluxe 2 element (Gamma match)	31.95
Deluxe 2 element (T match)	34.95
Standard 3 element (Gamma match)	34.95
Standard 3 element (T match)	37.95
Deluxe 3 element (Gamma match)	46.95
Deluxe 3 element (T match)	49.95

California: Offenbach & Reimus Co., 1569 Market St., San Francisco.
Florida: Kinkade Radio Supply, Inc., 402 W. Fortune St., Tampa.
Indiana: Graham Electronic Supply, Inc., 102 S. Pennsylvania St., Indianapolis.
Iowa: Radio Trade Supply Co., 1224 Grand Ave., Des Moines.
Iowa: World Radio Laboratories, 3415 W. Broadway, Council Bluffs.
Kentucky: Universal Radio Supply, 533 S. 7th St., Louisville.
Louisiana: Radio Parts, Inc., 807 Howard Ave., New Orleans.
Michigan: M. N. Duffy & Co., 2040 Grand River, Detroit.
Michigan: Purchase Radio Supply, 605 Church St., Ann Arbor.
Minnesota: Lew Bonn Co., 67 South 12th St., Minneapolis.
Missouri: Henry Radio, Butler

New Hampshire: Evans Radio, Concord.
N. Carolina: Allied Electronics, 411 Hillsboro St., Raleigh.
N. Dakota: Fargo Radio Service, 515 Third Ave. North, Fargo.
Ohio: Mytronic Company, 2145 Florence Ave., Cincinnati.
Ohio: Selectronic Supplies, Inc., 1320 Madison Ave., Toledo.
Ohio: Srepco, Inc., 135 E. 2nd St., Dayton.
Pennsylvania: Radio Electric Service Co., 7th & Arch Sts., Phila.
S. Dakota: Burghardt Radio Supply, Inc., Watertown, Aberdeen.
Virginia: Radio Equipment Co., 819 W. 21st St., Norfolk.
Virginia: Radio Supply Co., 3302 West Broad St., Richmond.
Washington: Western Electronic Supply Co., 717 Dexter Ave., Seattle.
Canada: Louis Desrochers, P.O. Box 688, Amos, Quebec.

HOW TO ORDER: Order through your local distributor or direct from GOTHAM. Remit by check or money-order. Immediate shipment made by Railway Express . . . charges collect; foreign shipment sent cheapest way. 10-DAY MONEY-BACK GUARANTEE.

GOTHAM HOBBY CORPORATION · 107 East 126th Street · New York 35, N. Y.

Figure 5.12 — New York City's Gotham Hobby Company sold a variety of simple vertical, Yagi and quad antennas. They were available mail order via Railway Express, or through a national network of dealers. (Jun 1955)

Quality, Style and Beauty

THE *ALL NEW* COMMUNICATIONS RECEIVER

GPR 90

THE TECHNICAL MATERIEL CORPORATION, and TMC CANADA, LIMITED, have for many years been engaged in the manufacture and sale of high quality precision communications equipment such as, high stability direct reading oscillators, radio teletype frequency shifters and converters, broadband transformers, tone telegraph systems and diversity and fixed tuned receivers. Millions of dollars worth of this equipment is in use in twenty or more countries throughout the world. Three of our receivers, the DDR, the DRP and the FFR are now in regular use by the United States and Canadian Air Forces and Navies, so we felt we could produce a really good communications receiver containing many of the high priced requirements of the military and yet keep medium price range for the amateur.

In our work, both consulting and manufacturing, we have tested practically every receiver in the field and have included every basic feature inherent in a good unit but have added some new ones of our own. Compare our features to any receiver in any price range. Bulletin 179B for complete details.

Complete receiver - Amateur Net **$395**⁰⁰

Matching Speaker $16.00 extra

THE TECHNICAL MATERIEL CORPORATION

MAMARONECK, NEW YORK.   OTTAWA, ONT., CANADA

Figure 5.13 — The Technical Materiel Corporation manufactured equipment mostly for military, commercial and government users but also marketed their high quality gear to amateurs. (Aug 1955)

Save Money

BUILD YOUR OWN
ENGINEERED-QUALITY
Ham Gear

LOW COST knight-kit
50 WATT CW TRANSMITTER KIT
- Pi-Type Antenna Matching
- For 80 Through 10 Meters
- Bandswitching
- TVI Suppression

Model SX-255

$42.50

Built-in Pi-Type Antenna Coupler
Check the features packed into this new transmitter kit and you'll see why it's one of the greatest Amateur values ever offered. Compact and versatile, it is the perfect low-power rig for the beginning Novice or seasoned veteran. Features: 50 watts input to 807 final; high-efficiency 6AG7 modified-Pierce oscillator takes crystal or VFO without circuit changes; bandswitching coverage of 80, 40, 20, 15, 11-10 meters; pi-section antenna output matches line impedances from 50 to 1200 ohms—permits use with any type of antenna. Crisp, clean, cathode keying of oscillator and final. Power take-off plug supplies filament and B-plus voltages for other equipment. Copper-finished chassis and cabinet interior, filtering, shielding, bypassing, and coaxial SO-239 antenna connector provide excellent TVI suppression. Meter reads either plate or grid current of final. Jacks for VFO, crystal, and key. Supplied with all parts, tubes and step-by-step instructions. Less crystal and key. Size, 8⅜ x 11⅜ x 8¾". For 110-120 volts, 50-60 cycle AC. Shpg. wt., 18 lbs. **$42.50**

SX-255. 50-Watt Transmitter Kit. Net **$42.50**

knight-kit
SELF-POWERED
VFO KIT

Model S-725

$27.50

Complete with built-in power supply! Careful design and voltage regulation assure high stability. Excellent oscillator keying characteristic for fast break-in with clicks or chirps negligible. Full TVI suppression. Has plenty of bandspread: separate calibrated scales for 80, 40, 20, 15, 11 and 10 meters; vernier drive mechanism. 2-chassis construction keeps heat from frequency determining circuits. Output cable plugs into crystal socket of transmitter. Output on 80 and 40 meters. With Spot-Off-Transmit switch for "no swish" tuning. Extra switch contacts for operating relays and other equipment. Complete kit for easy assembly. Shpg. wt., 8 lbs.

Model S-725. Self-Powered VFO Kit. Net **$27.50**

knight-kit
CODE PRACTICE
OSCILLATOR KIT

Model S-239

$4.95

Transistorized—
Powered by Flashlight Battery

An ideal new code practice oscillator. Uses transistor circuit. Extremely low current consumption—powered by single penlight battery. Provides crisp, clear tone (400 to 600 cps). Has input jack for earphone; screw-type terminal strip for key. In compact bakelite case (2⅜ x 3¾ x 1½") with anodized aluminum panel. Complete with all parts, battery and easy-to-follow instructions. Shpg. wt., 1 lb.

Model S-239. Code Practice Oscillator Kit **$4.95**

Figure 5.14 — Allied Radio, a long-time Chicago industrial and consumer electronics vendor greeted amateurs with a well-equipped ham shack in their Western Avenue store. Along with equipment from major manufacturers, the company sold build-it-yourself ham gear under the house brand Knight-Kit label. (Jan 1956)

Figure 5.15 — Uncle Dave's Fort Orange Radio Distributing Company ad shows a blending of equipment from the AM and SSB eras as the old and new modes began to trade places in the mid-'50s. (Feb 1956)

NOW!

world's first and only
TRANSISTORIZED
Amateur Band Converter

Regency
ATC-1

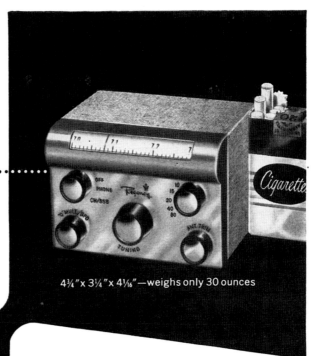

4¾" x 3¼" x 4¹⁄₁₆"—weighs only 30 ounces

a tiny self-powered
converter that connects
INSTANTLY
to any receiver

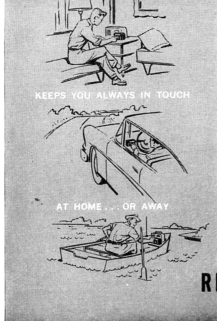

KEEPS YOU ALWAYS IN TOUCH

AT HOME . . . . OR AWAY

● No other converter like it! REGENCY's new ATC-1 is truly portable. Hooks up in seconds to *any receiver* (including car radios)—only connections are to an antenna and to receiver's antenna input.

The ATC-1 takes no power from the receiver. It is self-powered by three tiny Penlight cells which have a current drain of only 450 to 600 micro-amperes.

World's Smallest Converter. Use of transistors instead of bulky vacuum tubes makes this remarkable unit as easy to carry as a candid camera—it's actually less than half the size of this page!

The ATC-1 provides AM, CW and SSB reception on the 80, 40, 20, 15 and 10 meter amateur bands. Sensitivity is 5 to 10 mv for 6 db signal-noise ratio. A modified "Q" multiplier circuit improves sensitivity and selectivity for phone operation. Smartly styled aluminum cabinet is covered in dark grey tweed with satin finished aluminum front.

With features that can't be duplicated at any price, the transistorized REGENCY ATC-1 is available now at just....**$79.50**
amateur net

See and hear this miniature marvel at your local distributor.

Bulletin giving complete details and specifications yours on request.

REGENCY Division • I.D.E.A., Incorporated

Dept. Q, 7900 Pendleton Pike, Indianapolis 26, Indiana

Figure 5.16 — In the fall of 1954, a joint venture between Texas Instruments and Regency Electronics produced the world's first transistor radio for the consumer market. A little less than two years later, Regency announced its ATC-1, a transistorized 80 to 10 meter converter, the first all solid state product in the amateur market. (Aug 1956)

New _heavyweight_ champion!

Hallicrafters new SX-101 receiver employs heaviest chassis in industry...incorporates V.F.O. feature*...has 2000° disc logging counter.

SX-101
amateur net
$395.00

It's all amateur—and as rugged as they come! Hallicrafters presents the complete answer to ham reception, with every essential needed for today and for the future.

First—built like a battleship. Bigger. Heavier. Second—a marvel of stability—the result of 22 years of experience and development. Third—it brings you a long list of new features:

- Complete coverage of 7 bands—160, 80, 40, 20, 15, 11-10 meters.
- Special 10 mc. pos. for WWV, plus coverage of major MARS frequencies.
- Exclusive Hallicrafters upper/lower side band selection.
- S-meter functions with A.V.C. off.
- Tee-notch filter.
- *Local oscillator output available for use in heterodyne V.F.O.

PLUS: Band in use individually illuminated...built-in crystal calibrator...antenna trimmer...dual conversion...full gear drive from tuning knob to gang condensers...five steps of selectivity from 500-5000 cycles...sensitivity—less than 1 microvolt on all bands...direct coupled series noise limiter...50 to 1 tuning knob ratio...and many more.

For full specifications see it at your Radio Parts Supplier today!

NEW
FROM
hallicrafters
CHICAGO 24, ILLINOIS

WHERE THE BEST IDEAS IN COMMUNICATIONS ARE BORN

EXPORT SALES: Philips Export Co.
100 East 42nd Street, New York 17, New York

Figure 5.17 — Among major manufacturers the bigger-and-heavier-is-better philosophy still reigned supreme in 1956. Hallicrafters advertised its SX-101 as "Built like a battleship." The 70 pound, ham band only receiver offered a host of features, many of them tailored expressly for SSB reception. (Oct 1956)

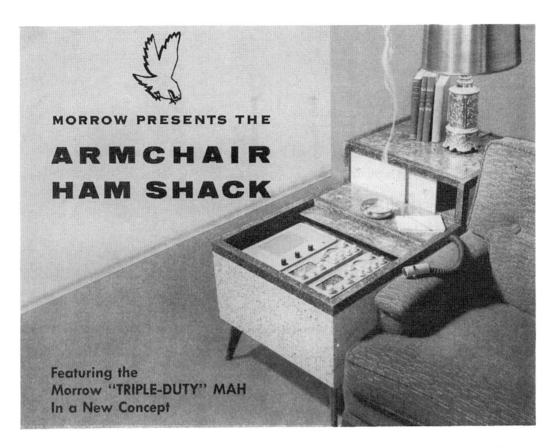

MORROW PRESENTS THE

ARMCHAIR HAM SHACK

Featuring the
Morrow "TRIPLE-DUTY" MAH
In a New Concept

Just imagine the extra fun this outfit offers you ... and the saving in equipment investment! The "Armchair Ham Shack" is an idea made possible by the new Morrow MAH ... a complete outfit occupying less than a cubic foot of space ... so compact it comes mounted in an end table, or you can mount it in your car, carry it anywhere. Transmitter is extremely stable, 90-watts CW, 60-watts phone, covers 80, 40, 20, 15 and 10 meters. Features simplified tune-up procedure and push-to-talk convenience. Receiver has exclusive Morrow "squelch circuit" to eliminate interstation noise, is sensitive to $\frac{1}{2}$ microvolt, SSB, CW, AM reception on all bands. Matching AC Power Supply has built-in 8-inch speaker. All units beautifully finished in grey hammertone. The MAH "Armchair Ham Shack" includes MBR-5, MB-560A, RTS-600S, mike, cables, end table with fiberglassed mahogany top and blending zolotone finish. Amateur net $595.00

One compact outfit

for fixed station,

portable or

mobile operation

FREE DATA SHEETS — WRITE TODAY!

If bought separately, above units would total $644.90. Mobile power supply and antennas not included. Maple flakewood table top, $5 extra.

For easy terms — see your jobber.

MORROW
radio manufacturing co.

2794 MARKET STREET • SALEM, OREGON
801 Dominion Bldg., Vancouver, B. C.
Prices and specifications subject to change without notice.

Figure 5.18 — Morrow, a Salem, Oregon, company, made equipment compact enough for mobile and portable use, as well attractive enough for a home living room station. The end table enclosure shown here illustrates the latter purpose. (Oct 1956)

A Ham's Best Friend...
The New RME 4350 Receiver

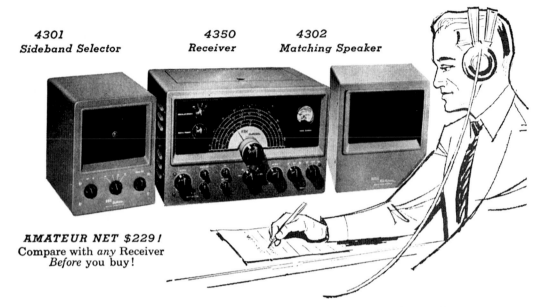

4301
Sideband Selector

4350
Receiver

4302
Matching Speaker

AMATEUR NET $229!
Compare with *any* Receiver
Before you buy!

Dual Conversion for all Amateur Bands

At last, your long-standing desire for better controls to complement your judgment and skill has been achieved in a receiver that sells at a sensible price. Yes, all the design features you want and need for present conditions in amateur bands, and usually found only in expensive receivers, are available to you in the RME 4350. It's laboratory-engineered to give maximum performance for SSB, CW, phone DX, Traffic and contests.

Superior Design Features Cost Less . . . with the RME 4350

• **Dual Conversion.** Maximum performance results through the use of crystal-controlled dual conversion; images on all amateur bands are down 54 db or more.

• **High Selectivity and Rejectivity.** Even at high frequencies, you can precisely tune the signal you want.

• **Easy, Pinpoint-Precision Tuning . . . Velvet-Smooth Operation** with the E-V exclusive, new two-speed tuning control. With it, you can tune to any part of the band and then micro-scan the area or the whole dial range by means of a 75 to 1 differential planetary reduction mechanism. This mechanism is an integral part of the tuning knob.

• **A High Degree of Mechanical and Thermal Stability** has been achieved by a 6-pound, die-cast panel, welded chassis and case, widely-spaced tuning condenser plates, voltage regulation and temperature compensation of thermal-sensitive elements. As a result, there is negligible frequency shift or drift.

• **Sensitivity** is between 1 and 2 microvolts throughout the tuning range.

• **Low Noise Factor**—between 3.5 and 6, formerly unheard of in communications receivers.

Meet "Your Best Friend" at Your
EV-RME Distributor! Write for
complete details, Dept. Q73.

RME RADIO MFG. ENGINEERS, INC.
DIVISION OF **ELECTRO-VOICE, INC.** BUCHANAN, MICHIGAN
Canada: E-V of Canada, Ltd., 73 Crockford Boulevard, Scarborough, Ontario

Figure 5.19 — The long history of Radio Manufacturing Engineers in Peoria, Illinois, came to an end when it became a division of Electro-Voice and moved to Buchanan, Michigan. The company changed hands again, becoming a division of Textron, before disappearing for good in the early 1960s. (Mar 1957)

FIXED STATION PERFORMANCE

IN A MOBILE

The features of Collins KWM-1 Transceiver make it the finest mobile rig available. The permeability-tuned precision VFO and mixer crystal oscillators provide the stability; the Mechanical Filter and high Q permeability-tuned circuits provide the selectivity; 175 watts PEP input provides the talk power. It occupies very little space — only 6¼″ high, 14″ wide and 10″ deep. Mounting tray folds out of the way when not in use. VOX circuits permit operation without holding mike button. Only $770 net. Power supplies and other accessories extra. See your Collins distributor for full details about the KWM-1 and its accessories.

Collins CREATIVE LEADER IN COMMUNICATION

Figure 5.20 — Designed for mobile use, the Collins KWM-1 also took a step into the future. As the first amateur transceiver, it looked ahead to the way nearly all amateur operating would one day be done. (Jul 1957)

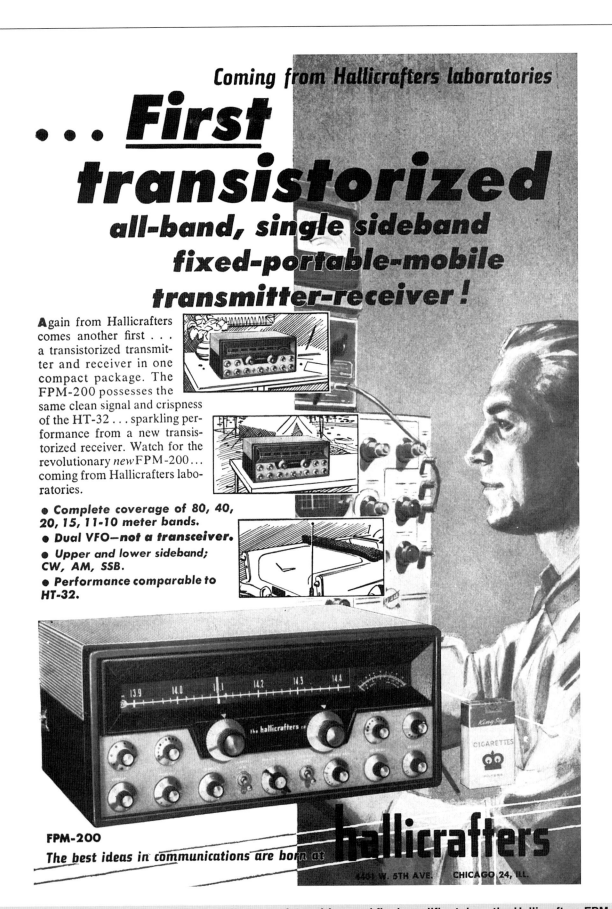

Coming from Hallicrafters laboratories

... *First* transistorized

all-band, single sideband fixed-portable-mobile transmitter-receiver !

Again from Hallicrafters comes another first . . . a transistorized transmitter and receiver in one compact package. The FPM-200 possesses the same clean signal and crispness of the HT-32 . . . sparkling performance from a new transistorized receiver. Watch for the revolutionary *new* FPM-200 . . . coming from Hallicrafters laboratories.

- **Complete coverage of 80, 40, 20, 15, 11-10 meter bands.**
- **Dual VFO—not a transceiver.**
- **Upper and lower sideband; CW, AM, SSB.**
- **Performance comparable to HT-32.**

FPM-200

The best ideas in communications are born at **hallicrafters**

4401 W. 5TH AVE.   CHICAGO 24, ILL.

Figure 5.21 — Except for the transmitter's voltage regulator, driver and final amplifier tubes, the Hallicrafters FPM-200 boasted all-transistor circuitry. The ambitious project, announced in August 1957, did not reach limited production until late 1960. (Aug 1957)

≡NEW≡

A SIDEBAND RECEIVER

FEATURES for best SSB and CW........

- **CRYSTAL-CONTROLLED, HIGH FREQUENCY CONVERTER.** Seven "ham" band tuning ranges—80, 40, 20, 15, 10, 10, 10. Same tuning rate and stability on all bands. Each band 600 kc wide.
- **HIGH STABILITY VFO**—New circuit does not need voltage regulator or filament ballast.
- **TRIPLE CONVERSION**—2900-3500, 1100, & 50 kc IFs.
- **SIDEBAND TUNING**—2.3 kc sideband filter tunes with front panel control through both sidebands.
- **SIDEBAND A. V. C.**—Fast charge—slow discharge—full A. V. C. without pumping and clicking. Full tuning meter action on sideband.
- **MUTING AND SPEAKER CONNECTIONS** arranged for best sideband and "patch" operation.
- **PRODUCT DETECTOR** provides distortion-free sideband reception.

MODEL 1-A

$259.00 AMATEUR NET

PLUS...

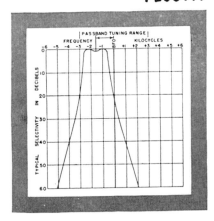

- **AM RECEPTION BY EXALTED CARRIER METHOD.**
- **AUDIO LOW PASS FILTER** is built in for best signal-to-noise ratio.
- **INVERSE FEEDBACK AUDIO** gives better low frequency response and minimum distortion.
- **BUILT IN THE SHAPE OF A "SCOPE" FOR PORTABILITY AND MINIMUM DESK SPACE.** Set it beside that old general purpose receiver.
- **ELEVEN TUBES**—6DC6 1st R. F.—6BY6 1st mixer—6BY6 2nd mixer—6BY6 3rd converter—12AU7 product detector—6BF6 A. V. C. amplifier and rectifier—6AB4 crystal oscillator—6BQ7A V. F. oscillator—12AU7 L. F. oscillator and 1st audio—12AQ5 output audio—12X4 rectifier.
- **WEIGHT**—18 pounds   **SIZE**—6¾ x 11 x 15"
- **POWER CONSUMPTION**—45 watts at 115V A. C.

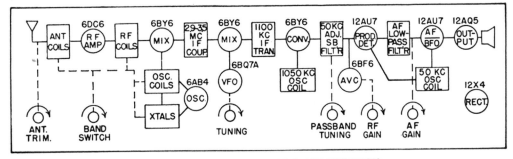

AVAILABLE FROM LEADING ELECTRONIC PARTS DISTRIBUTORS

R. L. DRAKE COMPANY, MIAMISBURG, OHIO

Figure 5.22 — Bob Drake, founder of R.L. Drake took the opposite fork from companies making the bigger, heavier receivers. He designed his compact, 18 pound 1-A receiver with sideband reception in mind. It featured triple conversion and passband tuning, and it occupied minimal desk space. (Dec 1957)

We can't hold back any longer!

Figure 5.23 — Central Electronics, a pioneer in amateur sideband equipment, dazzled everyone with the features of its new 100V transmitter. Modes included SSB, AM, PM, FSK and CW. It had a built-in waveform monitor scope and a 1 kHz readout PTO. Thanks to patented broadband couplers, its RF circuits needed no tuning controls other than the VFO knob. (Jan 1958)

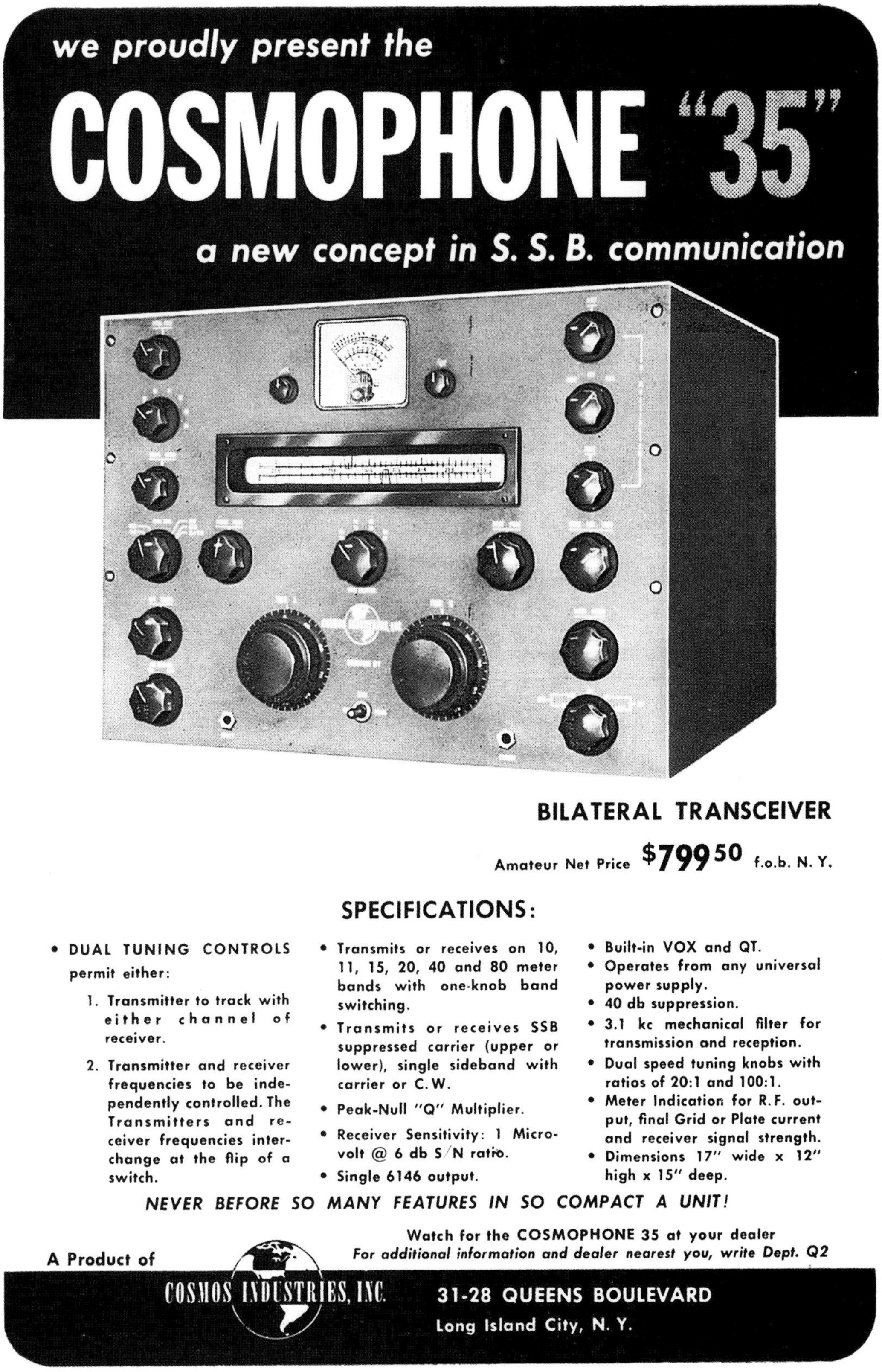

Figure 5.24 — Not to be outdone by other innovators, Cosmos Industries introduced what it called a bilateral transceiver. The Cosmophone 35 could transceive on either of its two VFOs or split transmit and receive using any combination of the two. Cosmophone's station-in-a-box operated on CW and AM in addition to SSB. (Feb 1958)

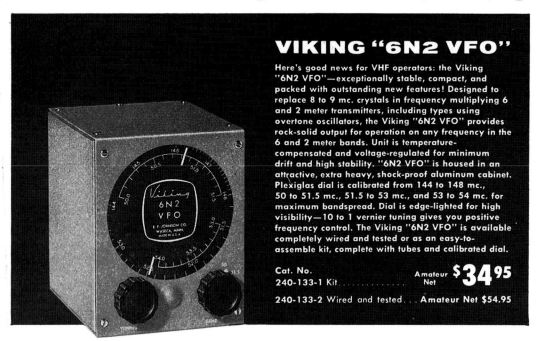

Figure 5.25 — E.F. Johnson rode the rising tide of interest in amateur VHF operation in the 1950s. The 150 W CW, 100 W AM 6N2 transmitter covered the 50 and 144 MHz bands. The companion VFO provided the 8-9 MHz signal required by the transmitter. (Aug 1958)

Figure 5.26 — Hammarlund's late 1950s receiver offerings exhibited a true family appearance. Features and functions as well as price points varied across the lineup, but they were unmistakably related. (Aug 1958)

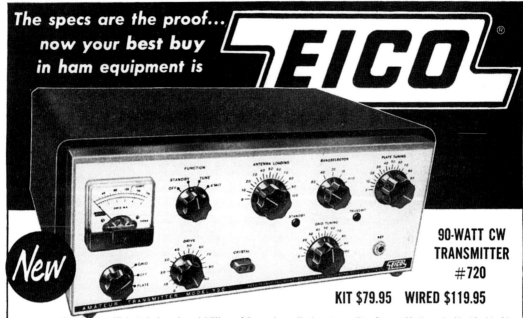
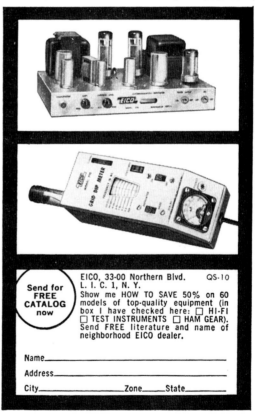
Figure 5.27 — Founded in New York City right after WW II, the Electronic Instrument Corporation initially sold test instruments in kit form. In the 1950s, the product line expanded to include amateur gear. The model 720 transmitter shown in this ad starred as the communications equipment for the Mayberry sheriff's department on the old Andy Griffith TV show. (Oct 1958)

TAPETONE'S NEW

Sky Sweep....

Model 345
Price **$279**.95

Single Conversion   **High Frequency IF.**   **Crystal Lattice Filter**   **No Secondary Image**

Tapetone, specialists in frequency conversions, now brings to the air waves an amazing, new six-meter receiver that will give you consistent top performance.

● **RECEIVER FEATURES:**

    ★ Noise figure less than 3.6 db (0.5MV signal produces 10 db signal to noise).
    ★ Long linear slide rule dial with smooth inertia tuning.
    ★ Dial calibrated for 6, 2, 1¼ and ¾ meter bands.
    ★ Power available from receiver for future companion 2, 1¼ and ¾ meter converters.
    ★ Cascode RF amplifier.
    ★ Linear detector for SSB and CW with AVC on or off.
    ★ Coverage — 49.0 — 54.0 mc.

● **CRYSTAL LATTICE FILTER ACHIEVES THESE FEATURES:**

    ★ Band width at 6 db: 3.5 KC.   ★ Image rejection 60 db down.
    ★ Band width at 60 db: 12.5 KC.   ★ Rejection of all other spurious and unwanted
    ★ Band pass flat to ±½ db for 3.0 KC. band width.   signals 70 db down.

We are specialists in frequency converters.
We offer over 30 different models.
Write for descriptive literature on all units.

TAPETONE, INC. 10 ARDLOCK PLACE, WEBSTER, MASS.

Figure 5.28 — Long a major player in the VHF/UHF transmitter and converter field, Tapetone took a step up with its dedicated 6 meter receiver. The Sky Sweep offered calibrated dial scales for use with accessory 144, 220 and 420 MHz converters. (Dec 1958)

S LINE

SYSTEM ENGINEERED — Engineered as a communication *system*, Collins new S/ Line offers exceptional SSB performance and operating convenience. Incorporated are such time-proven features as Mechanical Filter sideband generation and detection; stable, permeability-tuned VFO; crystal controlled high frequency oscillator; RF inverse feedback, and automatic load control. Simplified SSB design promises minimum maintenance. Operate transmitter and receiver separately or as a transceiver with the receiver VFO controlling. Operated with maximum legal power on SSB with the 30S-1 Linear Amplifier (available soon).

See the S/Line now, on display at your Collins distributor.

COLLINS

Figure 5.29 — In addition to its usual attention to technical and performance details, Collins graced the S/Line with an attractive appearance. Legend has it that the S/line's textured front panels were inspired by the covering on Art Collins' Hasselblad (or Leica, depending upon who is relating the tale) camera. (Jan 1959)

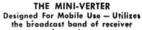

Figure 5.30 — VHF/UHF operation in the 1950s often used the station HF communications receiver as a tunable IF for a converter. A transmitter for the band of interest completed the setup. Tecraft of River Edge, New Jersey, supplied both. (Sep 1959)

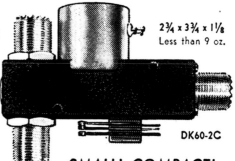

Figure 5.31 — The Dow-Key name became synonymous with coaxial antenna relays in the amateur world when separate transmitters and receivers were the norm. The company made conventional mechanical relays as well electronic TR switches. (Oct 1959)

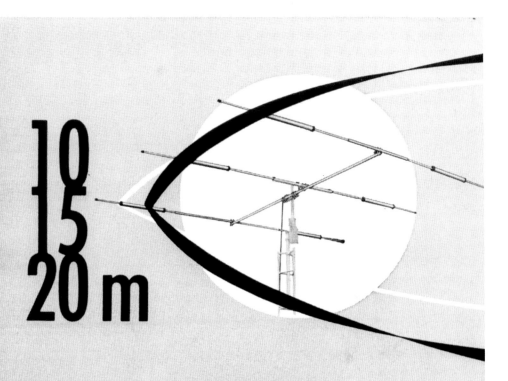

MOSLEY TRAPMASTER BEAMS

Streamlined grace combines with the look of rugged strength to make **MOSLEY** Trap Master Antennas pleasing to the eye and completely acceptable to your neighbors.

Trap Master Antennas *perform*, too . . . thousands of Amateurs in the U.S.A.—and almost every corner of the globe—are glad *they* bought a **MOSLEY** Trap Master!

(Illustrated, is the world-famous TA—33. Rated to maximum legal power, this 3 element beam performs wonderfully on 10, 15 and 20 meter bands. Factory pre-tuned for quick, easy assembly without tedious measuring. AMATEUR NET, $99.75)

AT YOUR FAVORITE AMATEUR EQUIPMENT DEALER

8622 St. Charles Rock Road • St. Louis 14, Mo.

Export Department: 15 Moore St., New York 4, N.Y.

Figure 5.32 — The Mosley TA-33 Trapmaster antenna provided a solution for the amateur wanting three elements on three bands on the same boom. Even with the trap losses and element spacing compromises inherent in such a design, the Mosley and other trap tribanders gained wide popularity in the ham community. (Dec 1959)

Chapter 6

The 1960s

Offshore Equipment, Channelized FM, OSCAR, Incentive Licensing and ICs

Congratulations poured in to the OSCAR Association (Orbital Satellite Carrying Amateur Radio) on December 12, 1961, and the days to follow. Everyone from Vice President of the United States Lyndon B. Johnson, to ARRL President Goodwin L. Dosland, to FCC Chairman Newton Minow, to Air Force Chief of Staff (and fellow amateur) General Curtis Lemay added to the growing pile of accolades. Amateurs worldwide celebrated the successful launch of the first OSCAR satellite as it orbited the Earth.[1]

More than 80 amateurs worked on the satellite itself, pre-launch testing, preparations for the launch, logistics, communications, the launch into space, and the myriad other things necessary for such an endeavor to succeed.[2] Thousands of other amateurs involved themselves in listening for OSCAR's 144.98 MHz Doppler shifting signal and reporting to the project's headquarters in Sunnyvale, California.[3]

The cover of February 1962 *QST* displayed a photo of the missile launch that carried the amateur satellite into space. That issue devoted 16 pages to OSCAR. Satellite articles and information appeared in the magazine during the months to follow. Even amateurs with no connection to the project looked at the sky and took pride in one of the hobby's signature achievements.

Back on Earth, ads in the February *QST* included Heathkit's new HX-10 Marauder SSB transmitter, VHF gear from Clegg and Polytronics, an explanation of the Drake 2-B's passband tuner and VFO, and a 6 meter transceiver named the Solar System VI. As if to bookend the rocket launch front cover, RCA ran a back cover ad for a device known as the Nuvistor.

Developed by RCA and introduced in 1959, the Nuvistor represented one of the last steps in the evolution of the vacuum tube. The tiny devices soon lost the battle to the even tinier transistor, but a few pieces of amateur equipment

The Class B grounded-grid Drake L-4 ran 2000 W PEP SSB and 1000 W dc input on CW, AM and RTTY. It used a pair of 3-400Z or 8163 tubes. ($695, 1966)

used them — notably receiver preamps and converters.[4] The August 1961 *QST* cover showed a pair of Nuvistor preamps built by W1HDQ and his article inside described their construction.[5]

In response to a petition filed by ARRL, the FCC amended its amateur regulations to expand the 20 meter amateur band to 14.0-14.35 MHz. The Commission noted the crowded conditions on the 20 meter phone band and allocated 14.2-14.35 MHz to the voice modes (and CW).[6]

Barker & Williamson announced its synthesized model 6100 transmitter in September 1962. E.F. Johnson also introduced a new transmitter line. The Invader and Invader 2000 departed from their earlier equipment in the appearance and concept departments. Hallicrafters' new receiver, the SX-115, also differed from the company's earlier products but fit well cosmetically with

the HT-32 transmitter line. Hallicrafters diverged from business-as-usual with its new HT-40K and HT-140LK transmitter and receiver Halli-Kits. In an era when building it yourself was popular with hams, Hallicrafters decided to offer the pair in kit form. They sold the same equipment — without the K at the end of the model number — wired and tested.[7]

Introductory products from companies new to the ham market included the Swan 140 and Sideband Engineers SB-33 transceivers. SBE was a new name on the scene, but its founder, Faust Gonsett, W6VR, first entered the ham business manufacturing Gonset equipment in the late 1940s.

Sonar, another veteran manufacturer, brought out its SSB monoband transceiver, and Drake entered the transceiver race with the TR-3. With its PTO tuning, 300 W PEP finals, and compact dimensions, the TR-3 fathered a long line of similar-appearing transceivers, transmitters, receivers and accessories.

VHF receivers, transmitters, transceivers and amplifiers appeared alongside HF offerings in advertisements as well as on dealers' shelves. Ameco produced a 6 and 2 meter transmitter as well as preamps and converters for the VHF bands.[8] Allied/ Knight sold VHF gear in kit form.[9] A California company, Centimeg, made a transmitter for 432 MHz as well as receive converters for 144 and 432 MHz.[10] Heath VHF gear covered the range from simple to sophisticated, with its famous Benton Harbor Lunchbox holding down the simple end of the line. The low power transceivers paired a crystal-controlled transmitter with a tunable super-regenerative receiver. Heath made models for 10, 6 and 2 meters.[11]

Hallicrafters VHF gear included the HA-6 and HA-2 transverters that worked in conjunction with its HF gear. They also made dedicated VHF transceivers, the SR-42 and SR-46.[12] Gonset joined the VHF SSB gang with the 900 and 910 Sidewinders, later called the GSB-2 and GSB-6. A pair of amps for 2 and 6 meters rounded out their VHF line.[13]

Collins Radio also tried the VHF market. The 62S-1 transverter worked in conjunction with an S/Line transmitter and receiver or with a KWM-2 transceiver. The HF gear was tuned to the 14 MHz band. The 62S-1 covered the 6 and 2 meter bands in 200 kHz segments. The transmitter ran about 65 W output on the VHF bands.[14]

The FCC turned the Amateur Radio world upside down in 1967 much as it had done 15 years earlier. Its Report and Order, dated August 24, 1967, announced the Commission's Incentive Licensing Program.[15] The reactivation of the long-dormant Advanced Class license and phone band allocations restricted to Advanced and Extra Class licensees formed the core of the new regulations. The Report and Order called for the changes to go into effect on November 22, 1968, with an additional expansion of the restricted segments a year later. The changes granted the Extra Class exclusive phone and CW segments in a similar manner.[16]

Putting it mildly, the changes generated controversy in the amateur ranks! Many felt that privileges for which they had already qualified were being suddenly yanked from them.

Both the ARRL and FCC favored some form of incentive license structure as being necessary to encourage the advancement of technical proficiency.[17] Depending upon whom one surveyed and who conducted the survey, the amateur fraternity split about 50/50 on the incentive licensing matter.[18]

As a sideshow to licensing changes, the FCC added nine new questions to the Novice exam, bringing the total to 50, and denied a petition to eliminate the code requirement for the Technician license.[19] The Commission also extended the Novice license term from one year to two years.[20] In the midst of all the other regulatory commotion, the FCC renumbered its rules governing the Amateur Service, changing the designation from Part 12 to Part 97.[21]

Even Commission regulations for other services brought sweeping changes to Amateur Radio. An FCC requirement for commercial FM users to move to narrower channel spacing made their cast-off equipment available to amateurs. Hams soon found themselves busy converting gear from fire and police departments, taxi cabs and other commercial services to the 2 meter band.[22] The former

The nine tube G.4 general coverage receiver tuned from 510 kHz to 30.5 MHz in six bands. It was manufactured in Milan, Italy, and enjoyed a brief presence in the North American marketplace. ($175, 1961)

commercial and public service gear brought with it another change to the way amateurs operated: the repeater. A repeater retransmits received signals, providing increased range and coverage, particularly for mobile stations.[23] The cover of October 1969 QST showed a repeater site and an interior view of the repeater itself.

When the supply of surplus commercial gear began to dry up, manufacturers saw an incentive for getting into the amateur VHF FM market. Japan's Inoue Communications tested the waters early on with its FDFM-2 transceiver.[24] Varitronics in Phoenix, Arizona, imported the gear, running its first ad in the December 1969 QST. Inoue Communications would one day be known as ICOM and become a major player in the American amateur market.

The initial US market penetration by imported gear was not limited to VHF and FM equipment. Spectronics, a California importer, advertised a Yaesu HF transceiver in 1968. Lafayette sold the HA-350, a receiver made in Japan by Trio (Kenwood). Lesser known import names such as Sommerkamp and Star advertised and sold HF gear here in the mid and late 1960s as well.

New American manufacturers joined the imports in the ham market. Swan led off its long line of amateur gear with a single-band transceiver in 1961. Al Kahn, K4FW, founder and president of Electro-Voice, co-founded TEN-TEC (with Jack Burchfield, K4JU) after retiring from Electro-Voice.[25] In September 1969 an ad for TEN-TEC's first amateur products — modular circuit boards for a QRP transceiver — appeared. The company became famous for solid state gear that found favor with CW and phone operators alike.

Heathkit took aim at the Novice market with the HW-16 in 1968. The Benton Harbor, Michigan, company's ad called it a Novice transceiver. The same year, Drake added the FF-1 fixed frequency adapter to its line of accessories, suggesting it could be used for Novice operation of its TR-4 transceiver — as

long as input power stayed below 75 watts. National's VX-501 external VFO gave owners of the NCX-5 transceiver crystal control of transmit frequencies, complying with Novice regulations. The same input power cautions applied.

Radioteletype (RTTY) operation in the 1960s required much more mechanical equipment than current day computerized setups. In addition to an HF or VHF transmitter and receiver, a typical RTTY station used a demodulator, printer, reperforator and tape reader. A basic setup could function without the two latter items.[26] Some Teletype machines combined two or more of those functions in one piece of equipment.

Amateur RTTY operation began on the East and West Coasts shortly after World War II, spreading inland over time.[27] Most amateurs using the mode equipped their stations from stocks of military surplus gear or obtained used equipment from commercial operations. The bulk of the hardware came from these sources and only a few manufacturers advertised demodulator (converter) units for amateurs in the 1960s, among them Alltronics-Howard and Frederick Electronics.

Toward the end of the decade a new device arrived on the scene, bringing with it another round of technological change. An article in March 1968 QST titled "A Look at Integrated Circuits" asked, "What are they?" and "How Can They Be Used in Ham Radio?"[28] Author Doug DeMaw, W1CER, answered those questions. In short order, construction projects for keyers, frequency standards, regulated power supplies and audio amplifiers using the devices showed up in QST.

Integrated circuits (ICs) also began to populate the circuit boards of commercial gear at the close of the 1960s. The design and manufacture of ICs gave birth to an entire industry. They made it easier to use digital technology in communications gear and placed a significant mark on radio's history timeline.

Notes

[1] "Oscar Congratulations," QST, Feb 1962, pp 16-17.
[2] W. Orr, W6SAI, "The Honor Roll: Oscar Participants," QST, Feb 1962, p 18.
[3] "It Seems To Us — Oscar," QST, Feb 1962, p 9.
[4] Ameco ads, QST, Feb 1962, pp 128, 130.
[5] E. Tilton, W1HDQ, "Nuvistor Preamplifiers for 50 and 144 Mc.," QST, Aug 1961, pp 44-45.
[6] "Happenings of the Month — 14 Mc. Phone Expanded," QST, Mar 1960, pp 68-69.
[7] P. Williams, W1UED, "Recent Equipment — Hallicrafters HT-40 Transmitter and HT-40K Kit, and Hallicrafters SX-140K," QST, Dec 1961, pp 56-60.
[8] Ibid. 4.
[9] Allied Radio Ad, QST, Oct 1966, p 163.
[10] E. Tilton, W1HDQ, "Recent Equipment —The Centimeg 432-Mc. Transmitter," QST, Feb 1960, pp 46-47.
[11] Heath ad, QST, Jun 1960, p 93.
[12] E. Tilton, W1HDQ, "Recent Equipment — Hallicrafters HA-2 Transverter," QST, Sep 1962, pp 43-45; "Recent Equipment — Hallicrafters SR-42 and SR-46," QST, Jul 1965, pp 85-87.
[13] "Recent Equipment — Gonset 903A and 913A V.H.F Amplifiers and The Gonset Sidewinder 6-Meter Transceiver," QST, Aug 1965, pp 74-77
[14] E. Tilton, W1HDQ, "Recent Equipment — Collins 62S-1 VHF Converter," QST, Nov 1963 pp 52-54.
[15] "Happenings of the Month — Incentive Licensing Adopted by FCC," QST, Oct 1967, pp 78-85.
[16] Ibid.
[17] "It Seems To Us — League Goals," QST, Jun 1963, pp 9-10.
[18] "It Seems To Us — Incentive Licensing," QST, Oct 1967, pp 9, 152.
[19] "Happenings of the Month — More New Novice Questions," QST, Jul 1967, p 73.
[20] "Happenings of the Month — Two Year Novices Now Issued," QST, Nov 1967, p 79.
[21] "Happenings of the Month — FCC Rules Renumbered," QST, Feb 1964, p 64.
[22] L. Cobb, W6TEE and J. O'Brien, W6GDO, "Amateur FM and Repeaters," QST, Oct 1969, pp 11-15.
[23] Ibid. p 13.
[24] E. Tilton, W1HDQ, "Recent Equipment — The Inoue FDFM-2 2-Meter FM Transceiver," QST, Nov 1969, pp 46-48.
[25] "Happenings — Ten-Tec Co-Founder Al Kahn, K4FW, SK," QST, Sep 2005, p 81.
[26] I. Hoff, K8DKC, "Operating the RTTY Station," QST, Nov 1965, pp 44-50, 164.
[27] I. Hoff, K8DKC, "The Teletype Machine," QST, Jan 1965, pp 14-19.
[28] D. DeMaw, W1CER, "A Look at Integrated Circuits," QST, Mar 1968, pp 11-16.

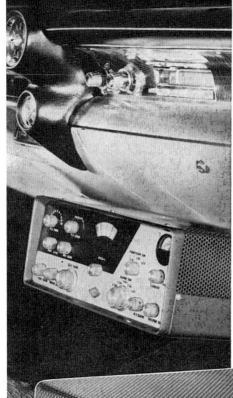

Figure 6.1 — After pioneering mobile operation with its converters in the late 1940s and early 1950s, Gonset entered the 1960s with the compact MSB-1 mobile SSB transceiver. The feature-laden rig used a transistorized 12 V dc power supply. (Jan 1960)

The Stradivarius of electronic keyers

new HA-1 $7995
T. O. Keyer

♩ In every field of human endeavor, there is a group of strong-minded individuals whose goal is perfection. They settle for nothing less in the equipment with which they pursue their hobby or profession.

And inevitably, one manufacturer with similar goals produces a product so strikingly superior that overnight it becomes—like the Stradivarius—*not only the ultimate standard of performance but a symbol of perfection.*

Whatever your communications experience, if you are among that group who insist on the finest, you will recognize in the new T.O. Keyer a technological stride that will bring you greater personal satisfaction, and clearly advance the art of CW.

HA-1 ADVANCED FEATURES

- Employs digital techniques. Advanced circuitry assures constant ratio of dot-to-space-to-dash over entire speed range.

- All timing circuits electronic—not affected by relay variations. Dots and dashes are self completing.

- Employs four dual-purpose triodes, two voltage regulators, two neons, three semi-conductor diodes. Transformer-operated.

- Plug-in, vacuum-sealed, mercury-wetted relay used only to key transmitter and sidetone signal. Capable of dot speeds up to 100 dots per sec. Life span over 10 billion operations.

- Monitor or sidetone may be heard via built-in speaker, or fed through receiver audio.

FRONT PANEL: Function control: off; low speed, hold (key down), high speed. Speed control: calibrated in range 10-30 and 25-65 WPM. Keyjack; neon keying and balance indicator.

REAR CHASSIS: D.C. Balance (factory set); Weight (dot duration); Sidetone Level; Head Set Jack; Octal socket for transmitter connections; Aux. Paddle Input; Monitor Tone Output; extra contacts.

The new ideas in communications are born at . . . **hallicrafters**

Chicago 24, Ill.

Figure 6.2 — The T.O. Keyer, designed by Jim Ricks, W9TO, employed digital technology, even though a quartet of 12AU7 tubes did the work of creating CW characters. Ironically, the ad copy for the keyer includes an invitation to an annual SSB dinner in New York City. (Mar 1960)

ACTUAL SIZE OF METER SCALE WHICH
READS % MODULATION AND R.F. OUTPUT

*T*he LW-51 DeLuxe is the well known 50 watt
LW-51 that you've been seeing in QST (May, page
136, for example) with these added features:
Meter, meter switch, VFO input, front panel final
amplifier tuning, cabinet 5″ wide x 6″ high x 9″
deep. The Kit prices are

$69.50 with tubes and crystal

$57.50 without tubes and crystal

and we'll furnish it factory wired and tested for an
additional $15.00.

Please Add **60¢** shipping charges for
East Coast, **$1.25** for West Coast

**ELECTRONIC
LABORATORY**

ROUTE 2.   JACKSON, MICHIGAN

**Figure 6.3 — Lester Willis, W8PYY, owned L.W. Electronic Laboratory
in Jackson, Michigan. The company manufactured 6 and 2 meter
gear that was sold either factory wired or in kit form. (Mar 1960)**

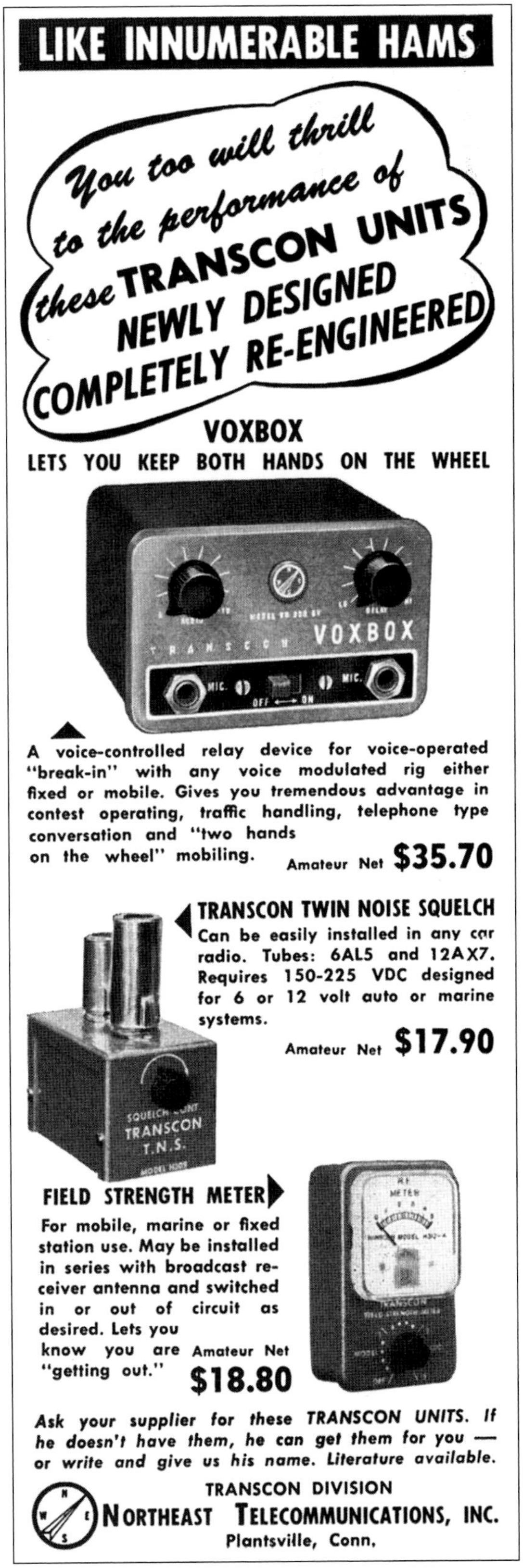
LIKE INNUMERABLE HAMS
You too will thrill to the performance of these TRANSCON UNITS
NEWLY DESIGNED
COMPLETELY RE-ENGINEERED
VOXBOX
LETS YOU KEEP BOTH HANDS ON THE WHEEL
TRANSCON VOXBOX
MIC.
OFF ⟷ ON
A voice-controlled relay device for voice-operated "break-in" with any voice modulated rig either fixed or mobile. Gives you tremendous advantage in contest operating, traffic handling, telephone type conversation and "two hands on the wheel" mobiling.
Amateur Net $35.70
TRANSCON TWIN NOISE SQUELCH
Can be easily installed in any car radio. Tubes: 6AL5 and 12AX7. Requires 150-225 VDC designed for 6 or 12 volt auto or marine systems.
Amateur Net $17.90
TRANSCON
T.N.S.
FIELD STRENGTH METER
For mobile, marine or fixed station use. May be installed in series with broadcast receiver antenna and switched in or out of circuit as desired. Lets you know you are "getting out."
Amateur Net $18.80
TRANSCON
Ask your supplier for these TRANSCON UNITS. If he doesn't have them, he can get them for you — or write and give us his name. Literature available.
TRANSCON DIVISION
NORTHEAST TELECOMMUNICATIONS, INC.
Plantsville, Conn.

Figure 6.4 — The Transcon brand of mobile accessories belonged to Creative Electronics in Stamford, Connecticut. Their lineup included power supplies, noise squelch units, converters, and a combination transmitter/converter for 6 or 2 meters. (Mar 1960)

Introducing the **NEW** *Globe* ✴ *Electronics*

Mobiline Six...

6 METER MOBILE OR FIXED STATION TRANSCEIVER
CRYSTAL OR VFO CONTROLLED WITH 20 WATTS INPUT

The smartly styled new Mobiline Six is a compact transmitter and receiver combination for equal 6 meter adaptability to a fixed or mobile installation, operating from 115v AC, 12v DC or 6v DC, all with the power supply provided. It weighs only 20 pounds. Sized only 5″ x 12″, the unit takes little space in either home or car.

The receiver portion utilizes 7 tubes, including an RF stage delivering better than 1 μv sensitivity. A squelch control is also provided in the Mobiline Six.

In the transmitter section, the internal VFO is voltage regulated and shock mounted to provide the utmost stability under adverse mounting conditions. The 2E26 amplifier stage is conservatively operated to handle 20 watts input power.

VFO or XTAL control; "S" meter, tuning meter, slide rule dials, VFO spotting and Class B modulation are a few of the other feature highlights. Available August, 1960. $229.95.

...and the **NEW** *Citizens Band CB-200 Deluxe and Pocketphone*

CB-200 DELUXE

Two-way radio. Five channels. One tunable channel for receiving. Dual conversion. Pi net. $179.95.

POCKETPHONE

Transistorized two-way radio 1⅝″ x 2⅜″ x 6¼″. 13 ounces. No license required. Range ½-1 mile. Rechargeable battery. $125.00.

GLOBE ELECTRONICS
A DIVISION OF TEXTRON ELECTRONICS, INC.
22-30 SOUTH 34TH ST. COUNCIL BLUFFS, IA.

Figure 6.5 — About the time this ad appeared, Textron had purchased the Globe Electronics brand from World Radio Laboratories. The new company continued the cosmetic style of the Mobiline Six transceiver in its future products. (Jul 1960)

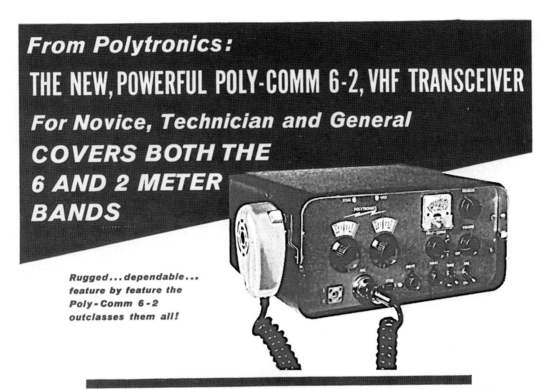

From Polytronics:

THE NEW, POWERFUL POLY-COMM 6-2, VHF TRANSCEIVER

For Novice, Technician and General

COVERS BOTH THE 6 AND 2 METER BANDS

Rugged...dependable... feature by feature the Poly-Comm 6-2 outclasses them all!

This is it! Built for continuous heavy-duty service, the Poly-Comm 6-2 has a V.F.O. or crystal controlled transmitter plus a triple conversion superheterodyne receiver!

All weatherproof steel cabinet and chassis . . . equipped with weatherproof fittings and teflon wiring for operation under the toughest conditions.

LOOK AT THESE ADDITIONAL FEATURES! 18 watt power input . . . S meter doubles as tune-up meter . . . 100% plate modulation . . . V.F.O. or 2 crystal positions for transmitter control . . . built-in 115 V AC/12 V DC power supply . . . triple conversion with second and third conversion oscillators crystal controlled . . . squelch and automatic noise limiter . . . sensitivity: better than 1 microvolt for 10 db S/N/N ratio . . . selectivity (6 Kc @ 6 db pt.) and stability assured by triple conversion and Hi-Q IF stages utilizing 12 tuned circuits... single knob bandswitching . . . B and filaments regulated on oscillators . . . complete with under-the-dash bracket and ceramic microphone.

$299.50 amateur net COMPLETE

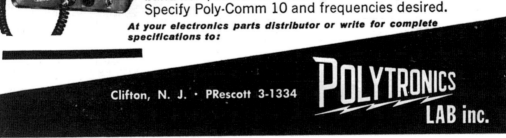

NOW AVAILABLE!

THE POLY-COMM 10—10 meter transceiver. 10 meter version of the Poly-Comm II, "workhorse" of the citizens band field, now available as an amateur band transceiver. Specify Poly-Comm 10 and frequencies desired.

At your electronics parts distributor or write for complete specifications to:

Clifton, N. J. · PRescott 3-1334

POLYTRONICS LAB inc.

Figure 6.6 — Polytronics manufactured well-designed 6, 2 and 10 meter AM transceivers. The New Jersey company was active in the amateur market from 1960 until 1965. (Aug 1960)

HIGH POWER IN SMALL PACKAGES

A COMPLETELY NEW DESIGN CONCEPT IN MOBILE COMMUNICATIONS... Here is a LINEAR AMPLIFIER package that takes low exciter power, converts it to 1000 watts PEP and delivers the RF directly into a conventional whip antenna.

The DM1000A is a single tube liquid cooled Linear Amplifier operating in Class AB$_2$. Cooling is accomplished by a small amount of recirculating coolant. Pump and heat exchanger are an integral part of the base and no external liquid connections are required. Normally supplied in a passive grid configuration, it is also available as a grounded grid amplifier where use of more exciter power is desired. The output circuit is unique—there is no tank tuning in the ordinary sense. The antenna working through the ground system provides the required capacity. Peak antenna adjustment is made possible through use of a Jennings variable vacuum capacitor. The Amplifier is sufficiently broadband to cover a wide range without retuning and with little attenuation. A conventional 96-inch whip antenna is satisfactory on all frequencies. The system requires no base loading and puts the RF power where it is most useful. Multiband operation from 6 to 60 MC is attained through easily interchangeable plug-in units.

The DMP1012A is a highly efficient solid state inverter that operates from a 12 volt DC source and supplies the plate, screen and bias voltages for the DM1000A. It is capable of 1000 watts output ICAS and has many applications. Test points are provided as part of the inverter for monitoring plate voltage, plate current, screen voltage and bias.

The package consists of a Linear Amplifier model DM1000A; a DC to DC inverter model DMP1012A and all power and signal cables necessary for normal installation.

TECHNICAL INFORMATION

DM1000A Linear Amplifier	DMP1012A	Inverter
Plate: 2500V.	Output:	2500V. at 400MA
Screen: 350V.		350V. at 100MA
Bias: —60V.		—40 to —80V. adjustable

RF Bandwidth: Flat for 100KC at 7MC. Input: 11 to 13V. DC
Frequency Range: 6-60MC with plug in units. Efficiency: 85% at 1 KW
Excitation: Any good exciter providing a peak signal of 80 volts.
High power exciters should be terminated in characteristic loads.

PRICE AND ORDERING INFORMATION

Complete package consisting of DM1000A Linear Amplifier, DMP1012A DC to DC
Inverter and all power and signal cables for normal installation $995.00
Additional plug-in units DM1000A . . . . $ 27.50 each

YUBA

Contact your nearest dealer or write:

YUBA-DALMOTOR DIVISION
1375 El Camino Real, Santa Clara, California
YUBA CONSOLIDATED INDUSTRIES, INC.

Figure 6.7 — Want a kilowatt mobile? Don't have room for the amp in the vehicle? The Yuba DM-1000A installed a 4CX300 final in the mobile antenna's base. (Sep 1960)

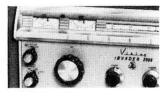

Figure 6.8 — Johnson made its Invader transmitter in 200 and 2000 W PEP versions. The two shared a filter-type SSB exciter. The higher power Invader moved the power supply components to an external cabinet to make room for its final amplifier. (Nov 1960)

Figure 6.9 — DeWald Radio Company built Allied's Lincoln 6 meter transceiver. DeWald also produced a similar radio with its own name as well as a version for Lafayette (HE-35). (Feb 1961)

You can't miss hearing this!

CLEGG ZEUS

TRANSMITTER for 6 & 2

...185 Watts of Solid "Talk Power" Tops the Band!

Again . . .

Clegg Laboratories brings VHF'ers a new power packed performer . . . A new beauty that's guaranteed to produce more carrier output and a higher level of modulation power than any other commercially built VHF amateur transmitter now available.

Put a *Zeus* on 6 and 2 and watch the QSO's roll in. If you like DX, listen to this! — You'll have 185 solid watts on *both* AM and CW . . . and you'll have *automatic* modulation control that will actually let you "out-talk" many kilowatt rigs!

CHECK THESE FEATURES AND SEE WHY A NEW ZEUS WILL PUT YOUR CALL ON THE "MOST WANTED LIST"

- High Level Plate and Screen Modulation
- Highly Efficient Type 7034 Final Amplifier
- Self-Contained Stable VFO
- Built-In Automatic Modulation Control
- Simple Band Switching and Tune-Up

- Two Unit Construction with Remote Modulator and Power Supply Conserves Space at Operating Position

Amateur Net Price: Only $595. Completely wired and tested with all tubes, Modulator, Power Supply, VFO, cables, etc.

Clegg LABORATORIES

502 RT. 53, MT. TABOR, N. J. • OAkwood 7-6800

Ask your Clegg Distributor (listed below) for full information. He'll be glad to serve you.

California
Henry Radio, Los Angeles, Severns, Hemet
Connecticut
Kaufman Electronics, Bridgeport
Delaware
Delaware Electronics Sup., Wilmington
Florida
Amateur Radio Center, Inc., Miami
Electronic Equipment Company, Inc., Miami
Indiana
Brown Distributors, Fort Wayne
Van Sickle Radio Supply, Indianapolis
Iowa
World Radio, Council Bluffs
Kansas
Acme Radio & T. V., Hutchinson

Maryland
Key Electronics, Wheaton
Massachusetts
De Mambro Radio Supply, Boston
Michigan
Purchase Radio Supply, Ann Arbor
Radio Parts, Inc., Grand Rapids
Missouri
Henry Radio, Butler
Walter Ashe, St. Louis
New Mexico
Car Parts Depot, Roswell
Valley Engineering, Los Alamos
New Jersey
Federated Purchaser, Mountainside
New York
Terminal Electronics, New York
Harrison Radio Corp., New York

Ohio
Universal Service, Columbus
Sternbergs, Inc., Cincinnati
Oklahoma
Radio, Inc., Tulsa
Pennsylvania
Tydings Company, Pittsburgh
Eugene G. Wile, Philadelphia
South Carolina
Dixie Radio Supply Company, Sumter
South Dakota
Dakota Supply, Yankton
Virginia
Key Electronics, Arlington
Washington
Radio Supply Company, Seattle

Figure 6.10 — Clegg Laboratories principal Ed Clegg, W8LOY, put many amateurs on the air with AM, CW and SSB gear for the VHF bands. Clegg products included receivers, transmitters, transceivers, amplifiers and accessories. (May 1961)

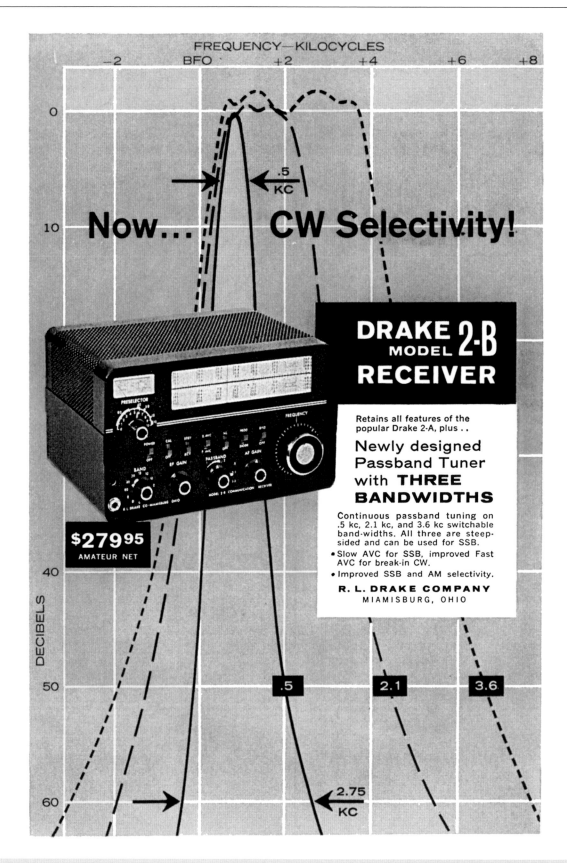

Figure 6.11 — Drake's 2 series receivers changed appearance from the company's initial 1-A but retained the compact size and passband tuning. The 2-B offered improved selectivity over earlier models. (Jul 1961)

IMAGINATIVE DESIGN CONCEPT

PRODUCES COMPACT, LOW COST SSB, AM, CW COMMUNICATIONS RECEIVER WITH FINE RECEIVER PERFORMANCE

Now the leading manufacturer of quality amateur radio antennas offers you tried and proved components in the new Mosley CM-1 Communications Receiver. But – FOR THE FIRST TIME –

Clean, functional panel layout and compact cabinet of receiver and speaker will compliment the finest Amateur Station. Baked on dukane grey and black enamel over heavy gauge steel. Receiver: 10½" x 7½" x 8" deep. Speaker: 7½" x 7½" x 8" deep.

these have been combined so as to result in performance equal to or better than that of receivers selling for several times the price.

Ask for demonstration of the CM-1 at your favorite dealer. Prove to yourself that you need not spend more to get fine receiver performance!

FEATURES and PERFORMANCE DATA:

- Double conversion with crystal controlled first oscillator.
- Diode detector for AM and product detector for SB and CW.
- Covers complete range of all amateur bands – 80 meters through 10 meters. Ten meter band segmented in three overlapping increments of 650 kc. each. Each band and each segment covers full 12" dial scale.
- Calibration every 5 kc. WWV reception at 15 mc.
- S-meter functions on AM, CW or SB, with or without BFO.
- Five dual-purpose tubes plus two semi-conductor diodes provide functions of 12 tube sections. TUBE and DIODE LINEUP: One 6AW8A, triode mixer and crystal oscillator; one 6AW8A, 2nd mixer and tunable oscillator; one 6AW8A, 1st IF and 1st Audio; one 6AW8A, 2nd IF and product detector; one 6AW8A, 2nd audio and BFO; 1N34, AM detector; 2F4, power rectifier.
- SELECTIVITY: 2.5 kc. at -6 db.
- SENSITIVITY: ½ microvolt for 10 db. signal-to-noise ratio on ten meters.
- STABILITY: Less than 500 cycles drift after one-minute warm-up. Less than 200 cycles change for 10% line voltage change. Temperature compensated and voltage regulated.
- IMAGE and IF REJECTION: 35 db. minimum.
- AUDIO OUTPUT: ½ watt at 6% distortion.

REAR CHASSIS ACCESSORY FACILITIES: Transmitter Relay Terminals, Accessory Power Socket, External Speaker/VOX Terminals.

POWER CONSUMPTION: 33 Watts. (117 volts AC, 50 to 60 cps.)

Net Price, only $169.95

Matching Speaker, Model CMS-1. Net Price, $16.95

(slightly higher west of the Rockies and outside the U.S.A.)

Mosley *Electronics, Inc.* – 4610 North Lindbergh Blvd. – Bridgeton, Mo.

Figure 6.12 — The Mosley CM-1 made stocking replacement tubes simple: each of the receiver's five tubes is a 6AW8. It used solid state devices for the AM detector and power rectifier. Mosley used two different front panel paint schemes during its production run. The antenna manufacturer's venture into the receiver business played out after about a year. (Sep 1961)

ANNOUNCING!!

FOR THE PROFESSIONAL . . . FOR THE AMATEUR

RELiant® L-103 1 KW LINEAR AMPLIFIER

Here is a piece of commercial gear . . . to fascinate the discriminating amateur. Brilliantly designed—as modern as tomorrow—the REL L-103 1 KW Linear Amplifier sets new standards of performance and achieves the distinction of proven. power input of 1000 watts PEP, SSB, CW and FSK.

This completely self-contained, two-tube grounded grid linear amplifier measures only 7″ high, 15″ wide and 12″ deep—yet gives you the **big** signal you want—consistently.

Matching power supply provides plate power and regulated screen voltage for the amplifier.

® Registered

CHECK THESE FEATURES!

* Complete Coverage 3.4 MC to 30 MC.
* Built to MIL Specifications
* VSWR and Power Output Meter
* Peak Limiter Indicator
* Hi-Lo Antenna Output Switch
* High Efficiency Grounded Grid Circuit
* 4CX300A Beam Power Tubes
* RF Wattmeter for Simplified Tuneup
* Top Performance on CW, SSB, and FSK Operation

Figure 6.13 — The RELiant name harkens back to Radio Engineering Laboratories, a manufacturer and *QST* advertiser with roots in the 1920s. Along the way, Eldico came under the REL umbrella. The parent organization produced equipment under both the Eldico and RELiant brands. (Apr 1962)

HERE IS THE SENSATIONAL NEW SINGLE SIDEBAND TRANSCEIVER YOU'VE BEEN HEARING ABOUT!!

- One Band, High Efficiency Design
- Rugged High Quality Construction
- 120 watts PEP Input, 6DQ5 Final
- High Frequency Crystal Filter
- Mobile, Portable, Fixed Station

Models for 20, 40, and 75 Meters Now In Production

$275

NET PRICE, from authorized dealers only

Matching 12 Volt Power Supply $99.50

For Additional Information See Your Dealer, or write:

Swan Engineering Company OCEANSIDE, CALIFORNIA

Figure 6.14 — Herb Johnson, W7GRA, made Swan a major player in the amateur market. He designed and manufactured his first radios in Benson, Arizona, before moving the company to Oceanside, California. (Jul 1962)

Figure 6.15 — Sonar, a supplier of NBFM equipment in the post-war years, introduced a line of single-band SSB transceivers for 80 to 10 meters in 1962. A four band model covering 80 to 15 meters followed. (Jul 1962)

Figure 6.16 — Amateur Electronic Supply, a longtime *QST* advertiser, was founded by Terry Sterman, W9DIA. Sterman entered the amateur business selling ham gear in a corner of his father's Fond Du Lac, Wisconsin, radio and TV shop. For a long time, a photo of Terry, with a hand-drawn crown displaying a "King of Traders" label, graced each ad. AES moved to Milwaukee and later expanded to locations around the country. (Aug 1962)

Figure 6.17 — Barker & Williamson broke new ground with the synthesized 6100 transmitter. Setting the frequency accurately and quickly proved as easy as dialing it up with three little knobs on the front panel. (Sep 1962)

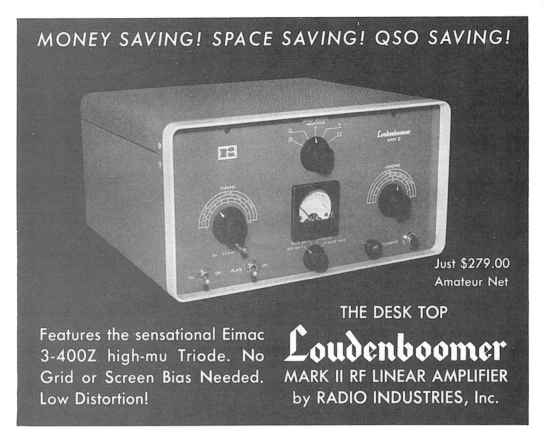

Figure 6.18 — The Loudenboomer Mark II amplifier from Radio Industries ran the legal limit with a 3-400 tube in grounded grid. Hallicrafters acquired the company in 1963 and rechristened the amp as the HT-45. (Nov 1962)

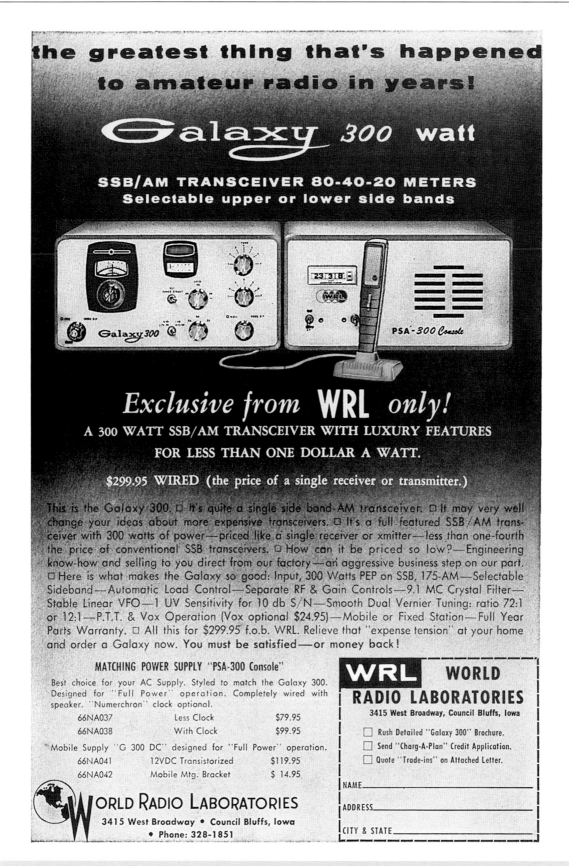

Figure 6.19 — The Galaxy 300 from WRL covered the phone portions of the 80, 40 and 20 meter bands. With 300 W PEP on SSB, the transceiver cost an economical dollar per watt. (Apr 1963)

DRAKE MODEL *TR-3*
SIDEBAND TRANSCEIVER

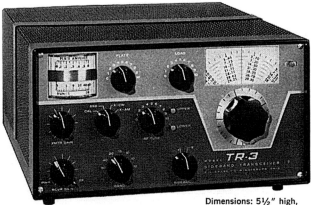

Dimensions: 5½" high, 10¾" wide, 14⅜" deep.

$495⁰⁰
AMATEUR NET

FULL FREQUENCY COVERAGE all amateur bands 10 thru 80 meters

UPPER and LOWER SIDEBAND on all bands

VOX or PTT

OUTPUT IMPEDANCE ADJUSTABLE with pi-network

300 WATTS P.E.P. on SSB

CONTROLLED CARRIER SCREEN MODULATOR for AM built-in

SHIFTED CARRIER CW, 260 watts input

TWO SPECIAL 9 Mc CRYSTAL FILTERS for sideband selection

LINEAR PERMEABILITY TUNED VFO

SEPARATE RF and AF GAIN CONTROLS

FULL AGC with Drake dual time constant system

2.1 KC PASSBAND

100 KC CRYSTAL CALIBRATOR built-in

SEPARATE RECEIVER S-METER and TRANSMITTER PLATE AMMETER

ONLY ONE DPDT RELAY USED — RF switching limited to antenna

Due to the 300 watt P.E.P. input rating, the TR-3 will require a power supply capable of low voltage at high current with very good dynamic regulation.

REMOTE RECEIVING VFO

Model RV-3 . . . $99.95

Used with the TR-3 to permit reception on frequencies other than your transmitting frequency. Complete ham band coverage 10 through 80 meters. Uses same linear permeability tuned VFO, dial calibration, and tuning assembly as TR-3. Cabinet styled to match TR-3, includes 5-inch speaker and space for AC power supply.

Dim: 5⅜" h, 10¾" w, 10¾" d.

RV-3 makes an ideal all-band transmitting VFO for 10B, 20A, and similar 9 MC exciters.

TR-3 ACCESSORIES

MATCHING SPEAKER

Model MS-3 . . . $19.95

Contains a 5 x 7 inch heavy magnet speaker.
Styled to match TR-3 Transceiver.
Dim.: 5⅜" h, 10¾" w, 10¾" d.

POWER SUPPLIES

AC Power Supply
Model AC-3   **$79.95**

Will mount in rear of MS-3 and RV-3 cabinets.

Dimensions: 5" x 5" x 10¼".

DC Power Supply
Model DC-3   **$129.95**

TR-3
Operating and Instruction
MANUAL
Price **$2.00**
SPECIAL OFFER
Limited time only **$1.00** Postpaid in U.S.A.

Write for Free TR-3 Brochure and list of Authorized Distributors.

R. L. DRAKE COMPANY
BOX 185-A · MIAMISBURG, OHIO

Figure 6.20 — R. L. Drake followed up the series 2 receivers with an 80 to 10 meter transceiver. A trio of 12JB6 sweep tubes in the TR-3's final ran 300 W input. The transceiver's PTO tuning provided linear dial calibration. (May 1963)

Figure 6.21 — Legendary contester Larry Le Kashman, W9IOP, created the Second Op circular slide rule back before computers assumed logging and other functions in ham shacks. Le Kashman served as a sales executive and also Vice President at Electro-Voice. (Jul 1963)

SB-33

without question... **SB-33**

one of the biggest...and best ssb transceiver values!

Compare SB33 price-wise. The 115 volt AC power supply and the loudspeaker are built-in—**are included in the low 389.50 price!** And in addition, SB-33 gives you **four bands**—selectable sidebands—a **Collins mechanical filter** that is used both on transmit and receive.

Compare SB-33 circuit-wise. 20 transistors—13 diodes—1 zener diode—virtually all solid-state with exception of the two husky linear amplifier tubes and that in the RF driver. The transistors are all in low-level applications—consume very low power—have very long life expectancy. And of course, **no heaters** so that cabinet temperature is lower, equipment size can be smaller, stability higher. Much of the advanced transistorized circuitry is **bilateral**—two directional—operates both transmit and receive. This means fewer components, less assembly and wiring. These savings are passed on to you in the form of a low selling price.

4-BANDS: 80-40-20-15 meters

POWER INPUT: 135 watts P.E.P. maximum. (Speech waveform)

RECEIVER SENSITIVITY: Better than 1 μv for 10 db signal/noise ratio

SIDEBAND SELECTION: Upper or lower sideband selectable by panel switch without change in frequency

TUBE AND SEMICONDUCTOR COMPLEMENT:
2—PL-500 beam power tetrodes
1—12DQ7 driver
20—Transistors
13—diodes, 1—zener diode.

POWER SUPPLY: Built-in 115V AC supply.

LOUDSPEAKER: Built-in

SIZE: 5½"H, 11¾"W, 10¼"D. 15 lbs.

Take your SB-33 along on vacation. Functional, luggage-type carrying case has thick foam rubber nesting for SB-33 also felt-lined accessory compartment. SB-33 carrying case.......39.50

SB-33 **Special Inverter**
12V DC/115V AC............59.50

SB-33 **De Luxe VOX/Compressor** 39.50

SB-33 **Mobile mounting base,** locking type 12.50

389⁵⁰

SBE
Sideband Engineers Inc.
Faust Gonsett, W6VR, President.
Rancho Santa Fe, Calif.

Figure 6.22 — Faust Gonsett, of Gonset fame, left that company to form Sideband Engineers. The new company's first effort, a compact (½ cubic foot) transceiver, was solid state except for the driver and final amplifier. The SB-33 covered the phone portions of 80, 40, 20 and 15 meters. The built-in 115 V ac power supply required an inverter for mobile operation. (Sep 1963)

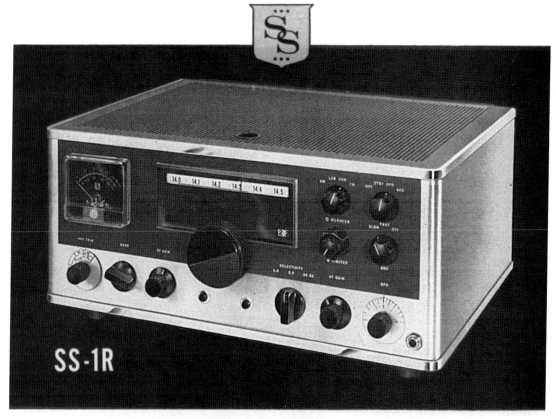

The New Standard of Performance

The SS-1R sets a new standard of performance for amateur band communication receivers. A completely new front end design[1] provides superb freedom from cross modulation and overload, while the low noise balanced mixers deliver superior sensitivity — with *no r.f. stage*. Steep-skirted crystal bandpass filters and newly developed high-Q IF circuits provide optimum selectivity with greater than 80 db ultimate attenuation. Extreme linearity, double loop AGC and front end freedom from cross modulation make this selectivity as effective as though it were *at the antenna terminals*. Frequency precision and stability exceed that of most frequency meters; frequency is read directly on a *digital* display.

There are many new operating conveniences not found in other amateur equipment. The unique SS-1R design, plus fixed tuned WWV positions at 10.0 and 15.0 MC (and an auxiliary 5.0 to 5.5 MC band), permits autocalibration of the amateur bands — *with no cursor lines to twiddle*. The manual tuning rate is slow enough for easy and exact sideband tuning — 10 kc. per knob revolution — while pushbutton motor tuning gives fast traverse. An optional noise silencer accessory with spectacular performance[2] is available, as will be a Video Bandscanner. The SS-1R may be operated in transceiver mode with the SS-1T transmitter.

[1] "A New Approach to Receiver Front-End Design", W. K. Squires, W2PUL, QST, Sept. 1963. [2] "A Pre-I.F. Noise Silencer", *ibid.*, Oct. 1963.

SPECIFICATION PROFILE

- **Frequency Coverage:** 80 through 10 M (eight 500 kc. segments). Fixed tuned WWV at 10.0 and 15.0 MC; 5.0-5.5 MC auxiliary (WWV 5.0 MC). Two general coverage 500 kc segments
- **Selectivity:** 5 kc./2.5 kc./0.35 kc.
- **Stability:** Less than 500 cps warmup drift (typically in less than 5 min.); less than 100 cps thereafter including low to high line variation
- **Sensitivity:** ½ μv, or better, for 10 db S/N on 10 M with 5 kc. bandwidth

- **I.F. and Image Rejection:** Greater than 60 db
- **Cross Modulation:** Example: Receiving a **10 μv** signal with 2.5 kc. selectivity, an unwanted **0.1 volt** signal 20 kc. away produces negligible cross modulation
- **Internal Spurious:** None at stated sensitivity
- **AGC:** Attack — **1 ms.**, **Slow** release — 1.0 sec., **Fast** release — 0.1 sec. Audio rise less than 2 db from 5 μv to 0.3 volt
- **ANL:** I.F. type; operates on AM, SSB, and CW
- **Size:** 7¾" H x 16¼" W x 13" D, 25 lb.

Squires–Sanders, Inc.

475 WATCHUNG AVENUE, WATCHUNG, N.J. • 755-0222

Figure 6.23 — A front end designed to exhibit greater immunity to overload and cross-modulation than contemporary receivers led off the list of the Squires-Sanders SS-1R's high performance features. Just prior to the receiver's introduction, William K. Squires, W2PUL, published a *QST* article explaining the circuit's operation. (Nov 1963)

THE DAYTON AMATEUR RADIO ASSOCIATION

Cordially Invites You To Attend

THE 13th ANNUAL

Dayton HAMVENTION

SATURDAY, APRIL 25, 1964

WAMPLER'S BALLARENA

Dayton, Ohio

- **Exhibits**
- **Technical Sessions**
- **Forums—DX, VHF, SSB, RTTY, ARRL, MARS**

- **Awards**
- **FCC Exams**
- **Women's Activities**

Send name and address to:

DAYTON HAMVENTION

P.O. BOX 426

DAYTON, OHIO   45401

for attractive brochure, map, and list of accomodations.

Figure 6.24 — The Dayton Amateur Radio Association put on its first Hamvention in 1952. Twice the anticipated number of amateurs attended. This ad from 1964 indicates that, then and now, it is the *Big Show*. (Apr 1964)

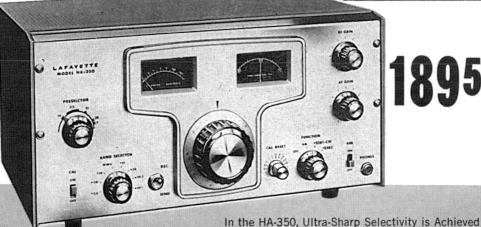
Figure 6.25 — "Imported" is the last item in the bullet list beneath the HA-350 — in a barely visible type size. Japan's Trio (Kenwood) manufactured the receiver for Lafayette. This tiny trickle of imported gear into the US ham market became a flood in only a few years. (Sep 1964)

DESIGNED FOR THE AMATEUR WHO IS
ACTIVE ON SIX

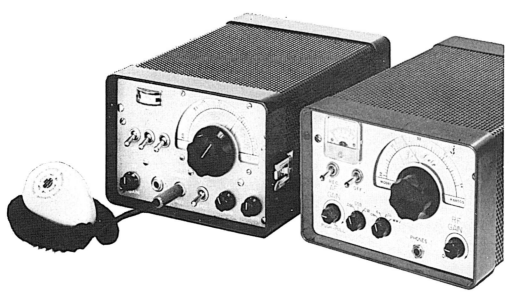

COMPLETE, SELF-CONTAINED STATION FOR FIXED, PORTABLE, OR MOBILE OPERATION.

LI'L LULU TRANSMITTER FOR 6

Special gang-tuned circuits in Li'l Lulu let you QSY instantly — there's no buffer tuning and final dipping needed when the frequency is changed. And the rig is really TVI proof! By keeping the VFO grid circuit in the 25mc range, TVI is eliminated.

• 117 vac, 12 vdc integral power supply. Class A high level modulation. Carbon dynamic or crystal mic input. Push-to-talk, or use panel switch • Built-in cw keying filter • VFO spotting switch • VFO control • 12 DQ7 final.

LI'L LULU RECEIVER FOR 6

Specially developed to complement the famous Li'l Lulu one-knob-controlled transmitter for 6 meters, the new Li'l Lulu receiver is unmatched for performance.
• AM, CW, SSB • Product detector for SSB • BFO crystal controlled • Delayed AGC operates on AM, CW, SSB • Integral front-end filter • Tunes 50-54 mc, and 10 mc for WWV and converter input • Critical components are temperature compensated • 10 mc crystal filter ahead of 3 IF amplifiers • Built-in CW monitor • ANL operates in all modes • S meter controlled by non-delayed AVC • Front panel control for companion transmitter — 80 to 1 drive reduction for precise tuning • Matches the Li'l Lulu transmitter.

WHIPPANY LABORATORIES, INC.
1275 BLOOMFIELD AVENUE, WEST CALDWELL, N. J.

Figure 6.26 — Ed Ladd, W2IDZ, designed the L'il Lulu 6 meter transmitter, a popular homebrew project in the 1950s. He manufactured a commercial version in the early 1960s and planned to pair it with a matching receiver. The transmitter sold well but receiver production amounted to only a half-dozen prototypes. (Mar 1965)

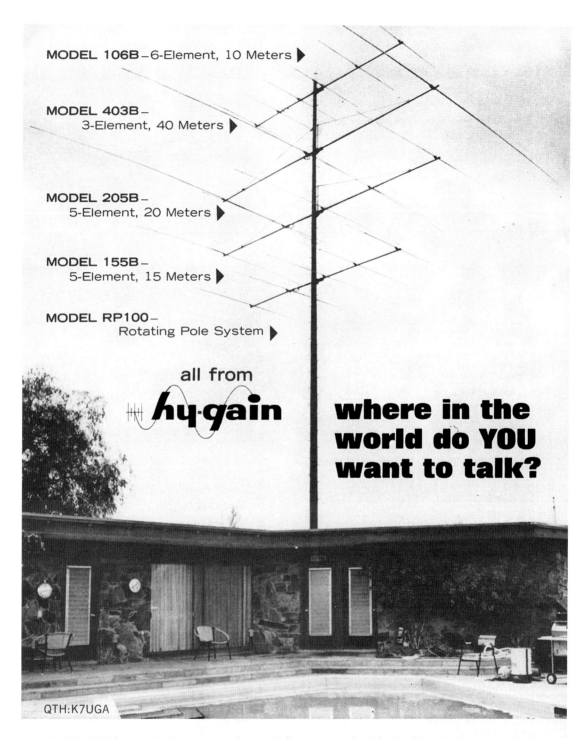

Figure 6.27 — Stacked on a rotating tower, Hy-Gain's DX Long John Yagis constituted a formidable antenna array. The installation shown belonged to Senator Barry Goldwater, K7UGA (SK) in Scottsdale, Arizona. (Jun 1965)

Introducing...
The HEATHKIT® SB-100

180-Watt, 80-10 Meter SSB Transceiver......$360.00

- Full five band transceive SSB & CW operation, 80-10 meters
- 180 watts P.E.P. SSB-170 watts CW • Switch selectable Upper/Lower sideband/CW operation • Operate PTT & VOX
- VOX-operated CW with built-in sidetone • Can operate crystal control in the transmit mode with variable tuning of receiver or can operate crystal-controlled transceive mode—excellent for net control • Separate offset CW carrier crystal for clear, pure CW note • Triple Action Level Control™ • Built-in 100 kc crystal caibrator • Enclosed relays for quiet, trouble free operation • Heath SB-Series LMO (Linear Master Oscillator) provides truly linear tuning with 1 kc dial calibration—less than 100 cps per hour drift after warm-up—400 cps accuracy • Perfect companion for HA-14 KW Kompact or SB-200 final amplifiers • Fixed station operation with HP-23 power supply—mobile with HP-13 & SBA-100-1 mobile mount for quick plug-in/quick disconnect mobile installation • Fast circuit board assembly • Simple alignment—requires only a VTVM with RF probe, a dummy load and a broadcast receiver

If you are considering the purchase of an SSB transceiver, we urge you to read every word on the next two pages before deciding.

Figure 6.28 — The SB-100's front panel shared an appearance with other members of Heath's SB equipment series and, some thought, the Collins S/Line. The SB family evolved into large collection of receivers, transmitters, amplifiers and accessories. (Dec 1965)

DAVCO DR-30 COMMUNICATIONS RECEIVER

New, compact, high performance solid-state receiver for amateur applications

Featuring FIELD-EFFECT TRANSISTORS

Figure 6.29 — Everest McDade, W4DYW, and James Lovette, K4BXO, designed the Davco DR-30 receiver and built the first few examples. Lovette and McDade sold out to a Florida company that produced fewer than 600 receivers before the business failed. (Sep 1966)

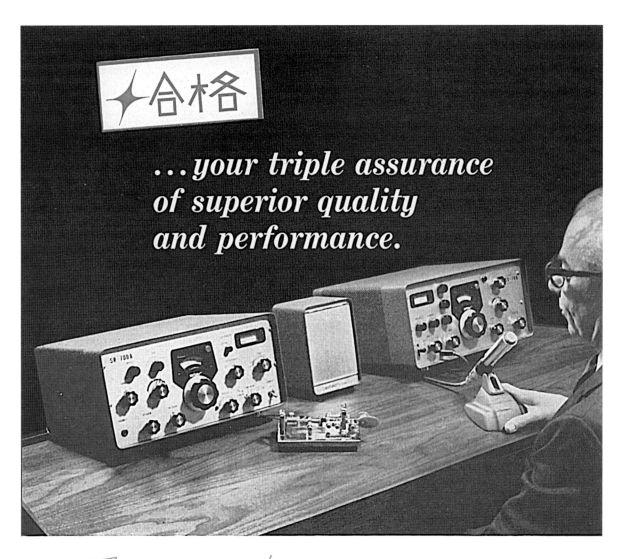

Figure 6.30 — The InterStar Corporation in Brooklyn, New York imported this transmitter and receiver pair manufactured by Star Radio in Japan. The ST-700E and SR-700E not only operated independently but also could transceive when cabled together. An August 1967 *QST* review said their construction had "a clean appearance," and that they were "orderly and well-built." (Nov 1966)

Figure 6.31 — Waters manufacturing made a variety of station accessories including dummy loads, wattmeters, coax switches, mobile antennas, speech compressors and keyers. Some Waters products later appeared bearing the Barker & Williamson name but with the same model number designations. (Dec 1966)

The world's finest 5-band transceiver
NATIONAL'S NEW 1967 NCX-5...$549
The <u>only</u> change is the price!

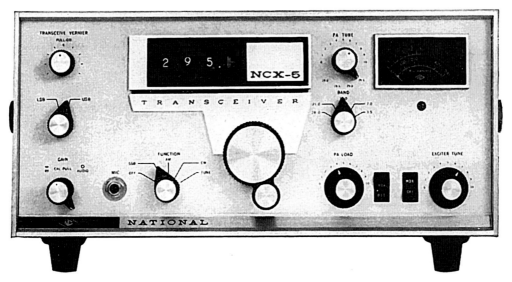

You can pay much more, but you'll never find another 5-band transceiver to match National's top-quality NCX-5. Here are the features and performance figures that have made the NCX-5 the most wanted transceiver on the market: ■ Amazing frequency stability . . . virtually no warm-up drift ■ Incomparable selectivity . . . 8-pole high-frequency lattice filter exhibits a 1.7:1 shape factor ■ Two RF stages in receiver section for matchless sensitivity ■ Transceive Vernier control for 5 kHz of receiver offset ■ Digital counter read-out accurate to 1 kHz on each band with additional counter calibration to 100 cycles ■ Conservative 200 Watts PEP rating ■ Fast attack-slow decay AGC ■ S-meter ■ Full VOX or PTT operation ■ Break-in CW keying with adjustable release time ■ ALC and external ALC input for use with the NCL-2000 linear amplifier ■ Mobile mount included. See the NCX-5 at your National dealer's today. Enjoy National quality . . . National features . . . National's full One Year Warranty . . . at National's 1967 price . . . only $549.

◇ National Radio Company, Inc.
37 Washington Street, Melrose, Massachusetts 02176

Figure 6.32 — In 1967, National lowered its 1964 introductory price of the NCX-5 from $585 to $549. The transceiver covered 80 through 10 meters using a mix of semiconductors and tubes. The mechanical digital tuning dial set it apart from other equipment of the era. (Jun 1967)

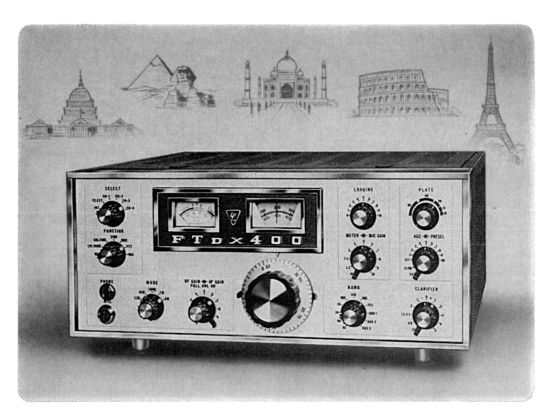

TOMORROW'S TRANSCEIVER TODAY BY YAESU

FTdx-400

Latest arrival on the American scene, Spectronics presents the FT dx 400. Yaesu engineers have looked into the future to provide the present day amateur with a complete station in one package.

The usual "accessories" are standard equipment in the FT dx 400. Features built-in power supply, dual calibrators — 100KC and 25KC, break in CW with sidetone, fully adjustable VOX system, four switch selected crystal controlled transmit channels in addition to VFO positions, and varactor controlled clarifier offers receiver offset tuning capability.

Remember, all these extras are included in this new imported transceiver. Check the specs and ask your local dealer for a demonstration dx trip with the FT dx 400.

$599.95 including power supply and all accessories except speaker.

SP-400 matching speaker **$14.95**

DEALER INQUIRIES INVITED

SPECIFICATIONS

FREQUENCY RANGE: 3.5-4Mc, 7-7.5Mc, 14-14.5Mc, 21-21.5Mc, 28-30Mc (3 more 500KC receiver bands can be added).
FREQUENCY STABILITY: Less than 100 c/s drift in any 30 minute period after warm up.
ANTENNA IMPEDANCE: 50 to 120 ohm unbalanced.
MAXIMUM INPUT: 500W P.E.P. SSB, 440W CW, 125W A.M.
CARRIER SUPPRESSION: —40db
SIDE BAND SUPPRESSION: —50db (at 1,000 c/s)
DISTORTION PRODUCT: Down at least 25db
AUDIO BANDWIDTH: 300-2,700 c/s
RECEIVING SENSITIVITY: 0.5uV, S/N 20db (14Mc SSB)
SELECTIVITY: 2.3Kc (—6db), 3.7Kc (—55db)
IF AND IMAGE RATIO: More than 50db
AUDIO OUTPUT: 1 watt @ 5% distortion
OUTPUT IMPEDANCE: 8 ohm, 600 ohm
TUBES AND SEMICONDUCTORS: 18 tubes, 9 transistors and 33 diodes
POWER SOURCE: AC 117 volts, 50/60 c/s
DIMENSIONS: 15¾" wide x 6¼" high x 13¾" deep
WEIGHT: 50 Pounds

SPECTRONICS

BOX 356 • LOS ALAMITOS, CALIFORNIA 90720

Figure 6.33 — Spectronics of Los Alamitos, California, was an early importer of Japanese transceivers. The Yaesu FTDX-400 arrived on our shores with an impressive feature set. It covered 80 through 10 meters with an input power of 500 W PEP on SSB. (Jan 1968)

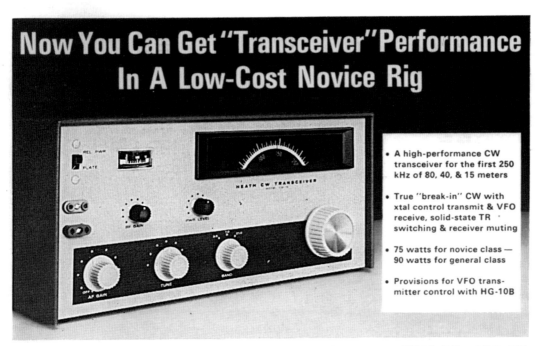

Now You Can Get "Transceiver" Performance In A Low-Cost Novice Rig

- A high-performance CW transceiver for the first 250 kHz of 80, 40, & 15 meters
- True "break-in" CW with xtal control transmit & VFO receive, solid-state TR switching & receiver muting
- 75 watts for novice class — 90 watts for general class
- Provisions for VFO transmitter control with HG-10B

New! Heathkit® Novice CW Transceiver . . . HW-16 $99.50

Not Just For The Novice, But a High-Performance 3-Band Transceiver For All CW Operators. Use the HW-16 at your beginning code speed — the built-in sidetone lets you hear what you send, helps you build up speed, helps you develop a near-perfect fist. And through the added gain of the dual conversion circuit, plus an RF amplifier stage, the HW-16 has the high sensitivity you need for working DX. That RF amplifier means excellent image rejection for "clean" reception and superior weak signal capability. Crystal controlled first conversion oscillators and a low frequency VFO provide maximum frequency stability. You'll appreciate the sharp (500 Hz) selectivity for peeling through crowded nighttime amateur bands provided by the built-in crystal lattice filter. Better than 1 microvolt sensitivity plus a solid state TR switch for automatic antenna change over and receiver muting means real performance. You'll never outgrow your HW-16. You can work fast "break-in" rag chews and high speed traffic nets with ease. Your HW-16 will even outperform many of the "expensive" rigs on CW.

Easy Assembly Gets You On The Air Fast! Layout is open, uncluttered. Solder points are easy to get at. The HW-16 goes together with a combination of circuit board construction and rugged chassis mounting of components that makes simple, straight-forward assembly — assures electrical and mechanical stability. It's a rig you'll be proud of, and want to show to your friends. The assembly manual leads you carefully, step-by-step through the assembly and checkout procedures. Checkout requires only a VTVM, dummy load, and crystals for the bands in which you intend to operate. Headphones, a key, and an antenna are all you need to get on the air. Who said getting a good start in amateur radio is expensive? Order your HW-16 today.

Kit HW-16, 25 lbs.	**$99.50**
GD-396, Headphones (not a kit), 1 lb.	**$3.50**
Kit HS-24, Speaker, 4 lbs.	**$7.00**
Kit HD-10, Electronic Keyer, 6 lbs.	**$39.95**
Kit HG-10B, VFO, 2 lbs.	**$37.95**

HW-16 SPECIFICATIONS — TRANSMITTER: RF Power input: 50 to 90 watts (adjustable). **Frequency control:** 80-meter crystal or VFO on 80-meter band. 80 or 40-meter crystal, or VFO on 40-meter band. 40-meter crystal or VFO on 15-meter band. **Keying:** Grid-block. Break-in with automatic antenna switching and receiver muting. **Output impedance:** 50 ohm unbalanced. **Sidetone:** Neon lamp relaxation oscillator. **RECEIVER:** Sensitivity: Less than 1 microvolt for 10 db signal-plus-noise to noise ratio. **Selectivity:** 500 Hz at 6 db down. **Intermediate frequency:** 3396 kHz. **Antenna impedance:** 50 ohm unbalanced. **External speaker**

impedance: 8 ohms. **GENERAL: Frequency coverage:** 3.5 to 3.75 MHz. 7.0 to 7.25 MHz. 21.0 to 21.25 MHz. **Power:** 120 VAC 50-60 Hz. **Transmitter tube complement:** 6CL6 Crystal Oscillator; 6CL6 Driver; 6GE5 Final. **Receiver tube complement:** 6EW6 RF amplifier; 6EA8 Heteroydne mixer-oscillator; 6EA8 VFO mixer-oscillator; 6EW6 IF amplifier; 12AX7 Product detector-oscillator; 6HF8 1st audio and audio output. **Transistor complement:** 2N1274 muting circuit. **Dimensions:** 13¾" W. × 11½" D. × 6½" H.

Figure 6.34 — Heath's HW-16 covered the Novice bands as they existed at the time of its introduction. The transceiver label stretched the definition a bit. The HW-16 contained a tunable receiver and separate, crystal-controlled CW transmitter in the same box. Electronic TR switching gave it break-in keying. (Jan 1968)

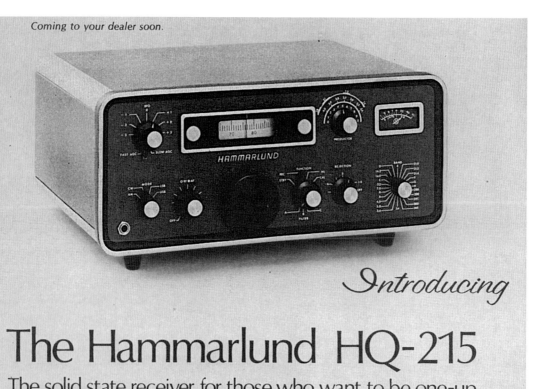

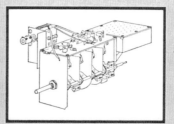

Figure 6.35 — The ad for Hammarlund's HQ-215 receiver states, "Transceive Operation: Provided." It does not identify the transmitter part of the pair as a Collins S/Line unit. Similar IF and oscillator frequencies led made this compatibility possible. Hammarlund never produced a companion transmitter for the HQ-215. (Mar 1968)

A NEW Thoroughbred in Solid-State Receivers

NOW—a **Competitively Priced** **Receiver** for the **most exacting** Professional **Performance!**

Phase-locked Frequency Synthesizer for Maximum Stability!

The superb, new R-530 by GALAXY

Designed for the exacting requirements of *laboratory, broadcast* and *HF monitoring* and *point-to-point* complex system *communications*, the R-530 is an advanced *solid-state* communications *receiver*. Its unsurpassed performance is the result of over three years of exhaustive research.

It receives selectable Upper and Lower Sideband, CW AM and RTTY signals...provides *accuracy of 1 KHz* tuning throughout the 0.5 to 30 MHz frequency spectrum.

Unique front end design and crystal lattice filters insure *optimum sensitivity and selectivity.* An adjustable *noise blanker* minimizes interference ...background noise. Frequency stability is amazing...less than 100 Hz drift after turn-on!

Complete transistorization and *modular construction* provide *maximum stability.* Minimum heat generation and power requirements allow the R-530 to be used in field applications now impractical with vacuum tube equipment. The new Galaxy R-530 is compatible with existing systems. *Beautifully styled,* compact, weighing only 25 pounds.

(Priced in the $700 range) Write for free brochure and complete specifications.

GALAXY ELECTRONICS

"Pacesetter in Commercial/Amateur Equipment Design"
10 South 34th Street, Dept. QST-f31, Council Bluffs, Iowa 51501

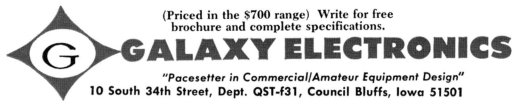

Figure 6.36 — Galaxy Electronics' solid-state and synthesized R-530 covered 0.5 to 30 MHz in 500 kHz ranges. The receiver came with a standard 2.1 kHz filter with optional 0.5, 1.5 and 5 kHz filters available. It sold for $795 when introduced. (Jul 1968)

Figure 6.37 — Comdel engineered its speech processor to provide instantaneous limiting action while eliminating the harmonic distortion of conventional speech clippers. The company sold a variety of station accessories, such as directional wattmeters and high dynamic range receiving preamplifiers. (May 1969)

to help the beginner
Begin Right!
(on a beginner's budget)

$7⁹⁵ Each!

MODEL MX1. Synchrodyne detector-converter. Eliminates need of IF strip. Uses dual gate MOSFET for high sensitivity, low noise and effective reduction of overload. Selectivity, 1 KHz. Price $7.95

MODEL AA1. Integrated circuit audio amplifier has 100 db gain. Frequency response shaped for optimum intelligibility, 200-2,500 Hz. Drives high impedance headphones. Price $7.95

MODEL VO1. Two stage oscillator - buffer. Drift less than 100 Hz. Covers 7.0-7.3 and 3.5-4 MHz. Output 2 volts R.M.S. For receiving with Novice and transceiving with General or higher class license. Price $7.95

MODEL TX1. Crystal oscillator and power amplifier. 2 watts input. Requires 12 volt, 250 ma. supply. Toroidal coils used in both stages for high efficiency. Covers 7.0-7.3 and 3.5-4 MHz. Price $7.95

POWER-MITE MODULES, consist of modules MX1, AA1, VO1 and TX1. Complete with instructions for assembly. Model MR1 Price $29.95

The basic modules supply the elements for 40-80 meter reception and transmission. Merely connect them, attach a 12 volt DC supply (such as a lantern battery), headphones and antenna. A crystal will be required for Novice class license. Key not included.

POWER-MITE 1. Power-Mite modules wired into a band switching 80-40 meter transceiver. With accessories AC-1, flywheel tuning, slide rule dial, front panel band changing controls, VFO-crystal switch and aluminum chassis. Model PM1 Price $49.95

CONVENIENCE KIT FOR **POWER-MITE.** Amplifier current meter, antenna switch, knob and connector. Model AC1 Price $7.95
MONITOR FOR KEYER. Side-tone for normal keying also ideal for code practice. Model AC2 Price $5.95
ELECTRONIC KEYER, with integral paddle. Requires 6 volt DC supply. Model KR5 Price $34.95
15 METER CONVERTER. Covers 21-21.45 MHz. Requires tunable IF 3.5-4.0 MHz such as MR1 or PM1. Model AC3 Price $8.95
LOW POWER SWR METER. Usable from ½ watt. Model AC4 Price $14.95
LOW POWER ANTENNA TUNER, matches random length, twin-lead or open-wire-line fed antennas. Model AC5 Price $8.95

FOR FURTHER INFORMATION, WRITE:

TEN-TEC
INCORPORATED
HWY. 411 EAST, SEVIERVILLE, TENN. 37862

Figure 6.38 — TEN-TEC entered the amateur market with wired circuit boards for constructing a direct conversion receiver and crystal-controlled transmitter. They sold the Power-Mite modules separately and also with an AC-1 Convenience Kit for combining them into a PM-1 transceiver. (Sep 1969)

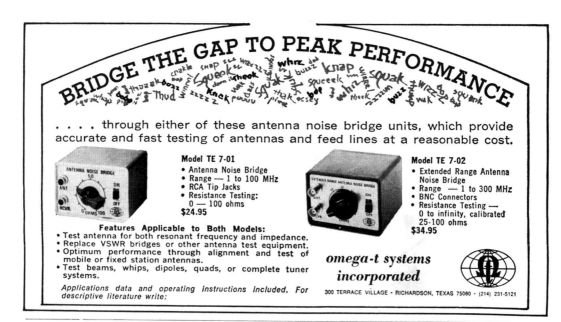
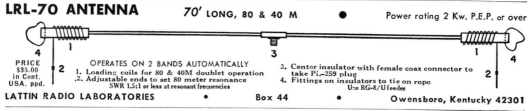

Figure 6.39 — The Pickering KB-1 keyboard included Morse prosigns. A diode matrix generated the CW characters. The noise bridges from Omega-T Systems helped test and tune antennas at a time when amateur ownership of more sophisticated analyzers was uncommon. Lattin Radio Laboratories advertised a reduced size antenna for 80 and 40 meter operation. (Sep 1969)

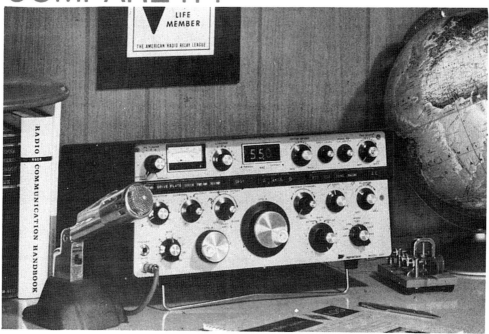

Figure 6.40 — Signal/One preferred the term Deluxe Integrated Station, rather than transceiver, for its CX-7. The company took a cost-is-no-object approach to a design with features such as 100 Hz digital readout, 16-pole filters, full QSK with a built-in keyer, high dynamic range, and 300 W input. (Oct 1969)

Chapter 7

The 1970s

Old Companies Disappear, Solid State, FM & Repeaters and Digital Readouts

Even though they managed to stay alive in one form or another for a while, veteran companies National, Hallicrafters and Hammarlund were all effectively out of the ham business by the mid-1970s. After Rockwell International gained control of Collins Radio, Arthur Collins resigned from the company in January 1972.[1] For the first time since he ran an ad for his radio transmitters in January 1932 *QST*, there was no Arthur Collins at the radio company bearing his name. The brand remained active with the introduction of the final Rockwell Collins amateur product, the KWM-380, in 1979.

French oil services company Schlumberger had acquired Heath when it bought parent company Daystrom

The KB-107 CW keyboard's reed-relay output made it suitable for use with any type of transmitter. ($344, 1979)

An ad for the SB35 ran in the October 1970 issue of *QST*, but no transceivers (beyond a few prototypes) were ever manufactured.

in the mid-1960s and would sell the Heath operation to Zenith before the 1970s ended.[2] Stanley, a New Britain, Connecticut, hand tool manufacturer, snapped up Multi-Elmac, more for Elmac's garage door opener business than its line of Amateur Radio gear.

US companies such as Drake, Varitronics, Henry Radio, Spectronics and Allied Radio took on distributorships or did house branding of equipment made by Japanese ham companies.[3,4,5,6] In only a few years those Japanese companies, including Yaesu, Trio-Kenwood and ICOM, became major players in the US market under their own names.

KW Electronics, located in the United Kingdom, advertised and sold equipment in the US.[7] The KW gear bore a faint cosmetic resemblance to the Collins S/line or Heath SB series of equipment. KW made transmitters, receivers, transceivers and station accessories. It was active in the US market during the 1960s and early 1970s using a Canadian distributor.

In 1972, Martin F. Jue, K5FLU, fabricated active filters in a rented room in downtown Starkville, Mississippi.[8] His first *QST* ad for the filter in April 1973 occupied a fraction of one column.[9] In time, the MFJ ads would grow to fill multiple pages in the magazine.

Fully solid state 100 W HF transceivers from companies such as TEN-TEC, Atlas, Yaesu and Heath appeared in the 1970s. Commercial amateur gear using transistors had become commonplace in the 1960s, but it was not completely solid state in the case of transmitters. This hybrid equipment employed a mix of tubes and solid state devices. Transistors performed adequately in many receiver circuits and low-level transmitter RF stages, but designers assigned the workload to tubes in the driver and amplifier stages. The arrival of power transistors capable of 50 or 100 W output changed the game.[10] The solid state amp's broadband output circuit made for no-tune band switching. The 12 V dc power requirement of most solid state gear made operation using the same equipment both at home and mobile an easy proposition.

Changing operating styles had many amateurs — and manufacturers — moving to transceivers. Some companies with separate transmitter/receiver products continued to produce them, and others even introduced new separates.[11] Kenwood led the parade in 1971 with the introduction of its R-599 and T-599 pair. The all solid state receiver and tube final transmitter shared the appearance of identical twins and worked in the transceive mode if desired. Swan joined with its 600-T/600-R transmitter and receiver.[12] The Swan separates could also be used together with single VFO control.

Yaesu announced its FT-901DM to the world as a "Competition Grade" transceiver in 1978. The 160 through 10 meter rig sold for $1299.

Henry Radio marketed a matching transmitter and receiver pair made by Kenwood in 1971. The R-599 receiver was all solid-state, while its T-599 transmitter sibling was solid state except for the driver and final amplifier stages. The pair could operate in transceive mode or be used separately. The transmitter and receiver were priced at $350 and $300, respectively. The original designs were succeeded by '599A and '599D versions.

Digital frequency readouts began to replace mechanical dials in the 1970s. The readout technology changed from nixie tubes to LED arrays, then to fluorescent displays at the end of the decade. Whichever technology the digital dials employed, they overcame some of the problems inherent in their mechanical counterparts. Digital readouts easily displayed resolutions finer than 1 kHz, and linearity in oscillator tuning was no longer the critical issue it had been with mechanical dials.

Heathkit discovered an antidote for amateurs infected with the back-to-basics fever when it introduced the HW-7 QRP transceiver in 1972. The rig covered portions of 80, 40 and 20 meters, using a direct-conversion receiver and a 2 to 3 watt (depending on the band) transmitter.

Extraterrestrial Amateur Radio continued to develop with the launch of OSCAR 6, the first long lifetime amateur communications satellite, on October 15, 1972.[13] OSCAR 6 performed successfully from its first orbit as amateurs in Europe and North America heard its beacon and transponder signals immediately after launch. The first slow-scan television contact occurred when W9NTP and WA9UHV exchanged pictures via the satellite three days later, a difficult feat given the fading and Doppler shift present on OSCAR's signal. The satellite stayed busy with SSB and CW activity as well. Some stations reported more than 100 QSOs in less than a week of operation.

With the January 1976 issue, *QST* changed from the familiar 6½ by 9½ inch format used since the first issue to the size it is printed in today.[14] Why 6½ by 9½ to begin with? That was the size press *QST's* first printer owned. Why the new larger size? There are layout and legibility benefits, but economics played the biggest role. Newer presses and printing technology meant trimming more than an inch of blank space from each printed page in the older size, amounting to hundreds of pounds of waste paper per issue. Nearly monthly increases in paper costs dictated printing in a size that resulted in less wasted paper. Many other magazines changed size during this era as well.

It is safe to say that FM and repeater operation powered the major wind of change blowing through Amateur Radio in the 1970s. Hams who had not earlier ventured onto the VHF bands suddenly found themselves operating on 2 meters. Channelized repeater operation gave local amateurs a sense of community in a way the wide open spaces of the HF bands could not. Ownership and operation of repeater

The KR-5A single-lever keyer was given a new cabinet paint scheme and a manual key/tune-up button to update the earlier KR-5. ($38.50, 1975)

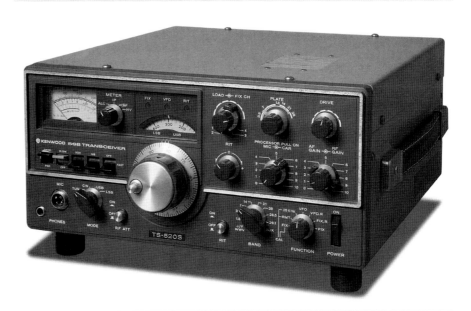

The Kenwood TS-520 80 to 10 meter SSB and CW transceiver was first imported and distributed by Henry Radio. When Trio-Kenwood brought out the TS-520S, it included 160 meter coverage. ($650, 1978)

equipment galvanized clubs, increasing attendance at meetings and participation in club events. The portability of mobile rigs and handheld transceivers enabled amateurs to better fulfill emergency and public service obligations. Manufacturers produced a range of new products to meet the demand.[15]

All this repeater activity did not escape the FCC's notice. The Commission mandated special WR prefix call signs for repeaters and limited their effective radiated power to a range of 25 to 800 W, depending upon height above average terrain and frequency used.[16] The regulatory package also granted Technician licensees access to the 145-148 MHz portion of 2 meters, giving

Kenwood's TS-700 2 meter transceiver added SSB and CW to the already popular FM mode for that band. ($700, 1975)

Venus Scientific of Farmingdale, New York, was among the few companies that made commercial equipment for amateur slow-scan television (SSTV). ($349, 1973)

During Inoue Communications' (later ICOM) early days in the US, its equipment was distributed by Varitronics, a Phoenix, Arizona, company. The HT-2 VHF handheld transceiver covered the 2 meter FM band. ($269.95, 1970)

The Tempo 2000 grounded-grid linear amplifier played companion piece to the Tempo One HF transceiver. The band switching amp ran the legal limit input on 80 through 10 meters. ($395, 1971)

them expanded repeater privileges.[17] The 40 meter Novice allocation shifted downward to 7,100-7,150 kHz and the allocation on 15 meters shrank to 21,100-21,200 kHz. Novices lost access to the 2 meter band entirely.[18]

The regulatory storm did not end with repeater matters and frequency allocations. The FCC proposed granting a petition submitted by the Electronic Industries Association that would require transfer of 224-225 MHz from the Amateur Service to a new Class E Citizens Radio Service (CB).[19] The ARRL encouraged individual amateurs to make their voices heard and its General Counsel, Robert Booth, Jr., filed a reply to the proposal. The Commission essentially forgot the whole Class E thing in 1977 but a new threat to the 220 MHz amateur band reared its head briefly in 1979 in an FCC proposal to find spectrum for a maritime mobile phone service.[20]

In an almost concurrent round of spectrum negotiating at the international level, planning for the 1979 World Administrative Radio Conference (WARC) dealt with matters destined to affect Amateur Radio for the remainder of the 20th century. At the conclusion of the conference in late November 1979, amateurs found much to cheer about. Perhaps most significant was the allocation of spectrum that came to be known as the "WARC Bands." The new bands at 10, 18 and 24 MHz have proven to be both popular and useful. It was, however, not instant gratification. On October 28, 1982, nearly three years after completion of the conference, the FCC granted US amateurs temporary authorization to use portions of the 10 MHz band. Such use was on a shared, non-interference, basis and covered only the 10,100 to 10,109 kHz and 10,115 to 10,150 kHz parts of the band.[21] The 24 MHz band followed in June 1985, and in January 1989 the Commission opened 18 MHz to US hams.[22]

An article in December, 1977 QST announced, "A New Era in Voice Communications."[23] A May 1979 Henry Radio ad called it, "...the most important innovation in Amateur Radio since SSB."[24] What were they talking about?

Narrow Band Voice Modulation (NBVM) used an amplitude compandor and frequency compandor to reduce a signal's bandwidth, improve signal

Henry Radio touted the VBC 3000 Narrow Band Voice Modulation system as, "The most important innovation in Amateur Radio since SSB." The self-contained unit was available from Henry and other Tempo dealers. ($349, 1979)

to noise ratio, and minimize adjacent channel interference. An amplitude compandor compresses a signal's amplitude on transmission and expands the amplitude on reception. A frequency compandor compresses the transmitted signal's bandwidth, expanding it again on reception.

Several articles on NBVM appeared in QST in 1977 through 1979 and Henry Radio advertised its VBC-3000 adapter, advising hams to "Get in on the ground floor."[25] Unfortunately, the elevator never went any higher as the new voice mode failed to gain adherents and interest dwindled.

Notes

[1] J. Miller, KK5IM, A Pictorial History of Collins Amateur Radio Equipment (1999: Dallas, Texas), p 22.

[2] C. Penson, WA7ZZE, Heathkit: A Guide to the Amateur Radio Products (Hicksville, New York: 2003) pp 26, 35.

[3] L. Campbell, W1CUT, "Recent Equipment — Drake ML-2 Marker Luxury FM Transceiver," QST, Sep 1971, pp 50-52.

[4] D. DeMaw, W1CER, "Recent Equipment — Varitronics-Inoue IC-2F FM Transceiver," QST, Jan 1971, pp 48-51.

[5] R. Myers, W1FBY, "Recent Equipment — The Henry Radio Kenwood Pair," QST, Jun 1971, pp 46-50.

[6] D. Mix, W1TS, "Recent Equipment — The Yaesu FT-DX-400 Transceiver," QST, Jun 1968, pp 40-43, 128.

[7] M. Godwin, W4WFL/1, "Recent Equipment — The KW Electronics KW107 Supermatch," QST, Jul 1972, pp 48-49.

[8] S. Nally, Starkville Daily News, 4 Oct 2012.

[9] "MFJ ad," QST, Apr 1973, p 167.

[10] A. Mathiesen, OZ1AM, "100 Watts PEP Output with Power Transistors," QST, Jan 1975, pp 34-39.

[11] R. Myers, W1FBY, "Recent Equipment — The Henry Radio Kenwood Pair," QST, Jun 1971, pp 46-50.

[12] R. Niswander, WA1PID and J. Nelson, W1GNC, "Recent Equipment — Swan Twins (600-T and 600-T)," QST, Jan 1973, pp 44-48.

[13] "Oscar News," QST, Dec 1972, pp 58-60.

[14] R. Baldwin, W1RU, "It Seems to Us — A New Look," QST, Jan 1976, p 9.

[15] W. Silver, Ed., The ARRL Handbook (Newington: 2013), p 18.1.

[16] "It Seems To Us — 1972 Retrospect," QST, Jan 1973, p 9, 73, 79.

[17] "New Repeater Rules!," QST, Oct 1972, pp 100-111.

[18] Ibid. 16.

[19] "Flash!! New Class E Citizens' Radio Service Proposed by FCC," QST, Jul 1973, p 51.

[20] D. Sumner, K1ZZ, "FCC WARC Proposals Finalized," QST, Feb 1979, pp 55-58.

[21] D. Sumner, K1ZZ, "It Seems to Us — The WARC Bands," QST, Oct 1989, p 9.

[22] J. Hennessee, KJ4KB, "Happenings — 17 Meter Band Open!!," QST, Apr 1989, p 58.

[23] R. Harris and J. Gorski, "A New Era in Voice Communications," QST, Dec 1977, pp 24-27.

[24] Henry Radio ad, QST, May 1979, p 1.

[25] R. Harris and J. Cleveland, WB6CZX, "A Baseband Communications System," QST, Part 1 Nov 1978 pp 11-18; Part 2, Dec 1978, pp 14-21.

Just Getting Started In Ham Radio?

If your interest in ham radio has only recently developed you already know by now that there are hundreds of brands of equipment from which to choose, some costly . . . some not too costly. For years, Ameco equipment has appealed to the beginner because of its modest cost, yet with engineering and manufacturing quality you would expect to find in really expensive gear. Read about our All-Wave Receiver and Novice Transmitter below, then write for our new Ameco catalog to get complete specifications on these and other moderately priced items.

Model R-5A Allwave Receiver

An exceptionally fine receiver for the short wave listener and beginning amateur operator. Fully transistorized-solid state. Covers .54 Mc through 54.0 Mc in five continuous bands. Includes standard broadcast band, all foreign broadcast bands, all amateur bands from 160 through 6 meters, all 27 Mc CB channels, all 2 way radio frequencies from 30 to 50 Mc including many police and fire departments. Controls include Beat Frequency Oscillator, Noise Limiter, Bandspread. Provisions for external "Q" multiplier. Compare with tube-type units costing as much!

Wired and tested $99.95
Battery adapter kit. (permits operation
from 12 VDC or eight "D" cells) ....$ 3.95

Model AC-1 Novice CW Transmitter Kit

The ideal kit for the beginner who requires a reliable TVI suppressed transmitter. Keying is clean and chirp-free. Crystal controlled, PI-network Output Circuit. Includes AC Power Supply. For 40 and 80 meters, CW. Fifteen watts input. Kit is simple to build and easy to operate.

Kit with coil for any 1 band, including tubes $24.95
Extra coil kit for any 1 band, CK-1 .... 1.10

Ameco Books and Records

Radio Amateur Theory Course: Gives sufficient information to pass the FCC exams for the Novice, Technician, General and Conditional Classes of Amateur Licenses. The Ameco Theory Course is the shortest path to getting a ham ticket.
No. 102-01, Over 300 pages $3.95

Radio Amateur License Guide: A study guide for those preparing for the Novice, Technician, Conditional and General Classes of Amateur licenses. Contains over 200 questions and answers.
No. 5-01, 32 pages ....50¢

Mastering the Morse Code: Teaches the beginner how to learn the International Morse Code.
No. 6-01, 32 pages ....50¢

Ameco Jr. Code Course: Fastest, simplest way to learn code. Contains 10 lessons and one 12" record in the 33 rpm series. Sample FCC-type exams included.
Complete Jr. Code Course (100 series) $3.95

 Division of Aerotron, Inc.
P. O. Box 6527   Raleigh, North Carolina 27608

Figure 7.1 — The 1970 Ameco beginner's station paired a basic crystal-controlled CW transmitter for 80 and 40 meters on a bare chassis with a transistorized general coverage receiver. Ameco became a division of Aerotron in late 1966 and moved its operations from New York to North Carolina the following year. (Mar 1970)

At last—Drake quality in a
VHF FM Transceiver

DRAKE

Marker Luxury

The best of the Japanese, the Marker Luxury VHF FM Transceiver
is built for and distributed and backed by the R. L. Drake Co.

- **Exceptional receiver**
- **Backed by R. L. Drake**
- **Complete package for . . .**

329^{95}

Includes transceiver,
two channels supplied,
mobile mount, microphone,
coax cable and antenna.

SPECIFICATIONS

General

Frequency Coverage	144-148 MHz

Number of Channels	12 Channels, 2 supplied
	Channel 1
	   Receive 146.94 MHz
	   Transmit 146.34 MHz
	Channel 2
	   Simplex 146.94 MHz

Modulation	Frequency Modulation
Transmitter Control	Push-to-Talk

Power Drain	AC: Receive 6 Watts
	   Transmit 50 Watts
	DC: Receive 0.5 Amps
	   Transmit 4 Amps

Power Source	AC: 117 Volts Factory Wired 220/240 Volts 50-60 Hz DC: 13.5 Volts ±10%.
Dimensions	7⅞″ W x 2¾″ H x 10¼″ D.
Weight	8¼ lbs.
Standard Accessories	Dynamic Microphone, Antenna, Connector Plug, AC/DC Cord

Transmitter

RF Output Power	10 Watts
Frequency Deviation	15 KHz maximum
Frequency Stability	±.001% or less
Spurious Radiation	Greater than —80 dB below Carrier
Frequency Multiplication	12

Receiver

Receiver Circuit	Crystal-controlled Double Conversion Superheterodyne
Intermediate Frequencies	1st 10.7 MHz, 2nd 455 kHz
Input Impedance	50 to 75 Ohms

Sensitivity	0.5 uV or less for
	   20 dB S+N/N ratio
	1 uV or less (30 dB S+N/N
	   ratio at 10 kHz deviation
	   with 1 kHz modulation)

Intermodulation	Greater than 80 dB
Spurious Sensitivity	At 40 kHz separation

Audio Output	Greater than —80 dB 0.5
	   Watt with 10% or less
	   distortion.

See at your distributor, or write for details . . .

R. L. DRAKE COMPANY
540 RICHARD ST., MIAMISBURG, OHIO 45342

Figure 7.2 — Kuranishi Keisokuki, a Japanese company based in Tokyo, manufactured the first VHF FM transceiver sold by R.L. Drake. The Marker Luxury ML-2 used a 6360 vacuum tube in its final amplifier, with both sections of the dual tetrode connected in push-pull. (Nov 1970)

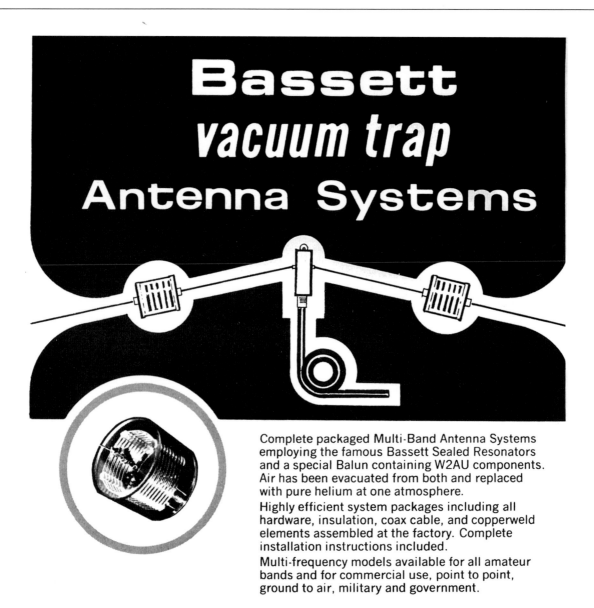

Figure 7.3 — Savoy distributed antennas made by Rex Bassett Electronics. This multiband trap dipole, and others of the era, drew heavily upon the classic designs of *QST* author Chester Buchanan, W3DZZ. (Jun 1971)

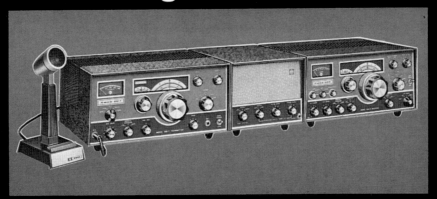

Figure 7.4 — Bucking the transceiver trend, Swan introduced its new separate transmitter and receiver pair in 1971. They could be hooked together for transceive operation, using either VFO for frequency control. (Apr 1971)

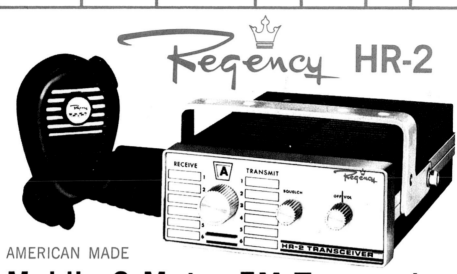

Figure 7.5 — An outline drawing of Regency's HR-2 appeared life-size in its *QST* ad so that prospective buyers could judge the amount of space the 2 meter rig would occupy in their automobiles. (Jan 1971)

the proven 'ONE'

a transceiver by Tempo

MORE THAN A YEAR AGO THE TEMPO 'ONE' WAS INTRODUCED TO THE AMATEUR WORLD AS THE NEW 'ONE'. NOW WITH THOUSANDS IN USE IT'S THE PROVEN 'ONE'. LOOK AT ITS PRICE AND THEN LOOK AT ITS SPECIFICATIONS. ADD TO THIS ITS RECORD OF RELIABILITY AND THE RESULT CAN BE SUMMED UP IN ONE WORD . . . VALUE.

SPECIFICATIONS

FREQUENCY RANGE: All amateur bands 80 through 10 meters, in five 500 khz. ranges: 3.5-4 mhz., 7-7.5 mhz., 14-14.5 mhz., 21-21.5 mhz., 28.5-29 mhz. (Crystals optionally available for ranges 28-28.5, 29-29.5, 29.5-30 mhz.)

SOLID STATE VFO: Very stable Colpitts circuit with transistor buffer provides linear tuning over the range 5-5.5 mhz. A passband filter at output is tuned to pass the 5-5.5 mhz. range.

RECEIVER OFFSET TUNING (CLARIFIER): Provides ± 5khz variation of receiver tuning when switched ON.

DIAL CALIBRATION: Vernier scale marked with one kilohertz divisions. Main tuning dial calibrated 0-500 with 50 khz. points. Each revolution of tuning knob covers approximately 15 khz.

FREQUENCY STABILITY: Less than 100 cycles after warm-up, and less than 100 cycles for plus or minus 10% line voltage change.

MODES OF OPERATION: SSB upper and lower sideband, CW and AM.

INPUT POWER: 300 watts PEP, 240 watts CW

ANTENNA IMPEDANCE: 50-75 ohms

CARRIER SUPPRESSION: -40 dB or better

SIDEBAND SUPPRESSION: -50 dB at 1000 CPS

THIRD ORDER INTERMODULATION PRODUCTS: -30 dB (PEP)

AF BANDWIDTH: 300 -2700 cps

RECEIVER SENSITIVITY: 1/2 μv input S/N 10 dB

AGC: Fast attack slow decay for SSB and CW.

SELECTIVITY: 2.3 khz (-6dB), 4 khz (-60dB)

IMAGE REJECTION: More than 50 dB.

AUDIO OUTPUT: 1 watt at 10% distortion.

AUDIO OUTPUT IMPEDANCE: 8 ohms and 600 ohms

POWER SUPPLY: Separate AC or DC required. See AC "ONE" and DC "ONE" below.

TUBES AND SEMICONDUCTORS: 16 tubes, 15 diodes, 7 transistors

DIMENSIONS: 13 1/4"W, 5 1/2"H, 11"D

WEIGHT: 17.5 lbs.

TEMPO "ONE" TRANSCEIVER	$315.00*
AC/ONE POWER SUPPLY 117/230 volt 50/60 cycle . . .	$104.00*
DC/1-A POWER SUPPLY 12 volts DC	$107.00

Prices subject to import surcharge

Figure 7.6 — When Henry Radio imported the Yaesu FT-200, they sold it as the Tempo One. In Europe it wore the Sommerkamp label. (Dec 1971)

WORLD RADIO HAS THEM

The New Galaxy FM-210 Transceivers!

• The one the Amateurs have been waiting for! A 2-Meter FM Transceiver with Galaxy's well-known fine quality and performance! This American-made, solid state, FET front end transceiver offers no compromise performance for direct or repeater communications. A full 5 watts of Power (or 10 watts with the optional AC-DC Power Booster!) Check these specs and you'll agree — it's a lot of Transceiver for only $199.95!

SPECIFICATIONS

General: Frequency Range: 143-149 MHz. • Antenna Impedance: 50 Ohms Nominal Power Req'mts: 12-14 VDC (or optional power booster) • TRANS/REC. Crystals: 146.94 MHz included.

Transmitter: Power Input: 5 watts (10 W. with pow. booster)• Freq. Control: 3 Chan. crystal controlled • Microphone: High Impedance (PTT) required • Deviation: Adj. narrow or wideband with clipper filter also adjustable for optimum clipping level.

Receiver: Sensitivity: SINAD .5uv for 12db, 1uv provides 20db quieting. • Adjustable squelch • Modulation Acceptance: FM wideband (narrow band available) • Type: Dual Conversion, FET front end for minimum cross modulation and overload • IF Frequencies: 10.7 MHz and 455 KHz • Frq. Control: 3 chan. crystal controlled • Audio Output: 3 watts (internal 3.2 speaker)

Power Booster: Provides high power operation from either 12-14VDC or 117 VAC. Makes an ideal fixed station accessory. ($39.95)

─── WHEN ORDERING, SPECIFY: ───

66MAO13—GALAXY FM-210 ....$199.95
66MAO15—GALAXY AC-210 Power Booster........$ 39.95

WE ACCEPT

 **WORLD RADIO**

"THE HOUSE THE HAMS BUILT"

3415 WEST BROADWAY
COUNCIL BLUFFS, IOWA 51501

QST-HH49

BANKAMERICARD
master charge
THE INTERBANK CARD

Figure 7.7 — After selling Globe Electronics to Textron, WRL founder Leo Meyerson, WØGFQ, reentered retail business with a new name, World Radio, and a new logo. Galaxy Electronics, also owned by Meyerson, manufactured the FM-210 transceiver. (Jan 1970)

25 Watts isn't everything, but with everything else it's GREAT!

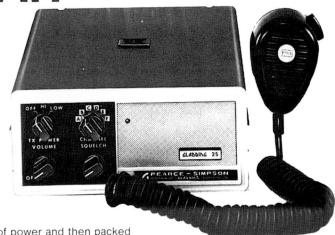

GLADDING 25™

- 25 WATT • FM
- 6 CHANNEL
- 2 METER
- TRANSCEIVER

We loaded this rugged, new, two-meter radio with 25 watts of power and then packed it with desirable features that make it the most wanted two-meter amateur radio on the market. It's the Gladding 25™ from Pearce-Simpson, Division of Gladding Corporation and the World's largest manufacturer of marine communications equipment. Best of all, because of our unmatched marine volume, we could add a price tag to it that can't be matched by anyone, anywhere, and still give it custom quality. Great! 25 watts and a lot more, from Pearce-Simpson.

- 25 watts output • 0.3uv sensitivity for 12db SINAD • built in 12 volt power supply • matching AC power supply accessory • 6 separately switchable transmit and receive channels • Economical vacuum tube driver and final.

- Plus • 8 pole crystal lattice filter • Transistor sockets • Glass epoxy printed circuit boards • Quick disconnect power plugs • Mounting cradle • 1 watt output switch

$249⁹⁵
mobile unit

$295⁹⁵ •
with accessory
AC Power Supply

Suggested List Price

GLADDING HI-SKAN™
8 Channel VHF Monitor

- Automatically scans 8 preselected channels • Switch for manual selection of channel • Priority channel • Bypass channel • 115VAC/12VDC built in power supply • Mounting cradle • Can be tuned to 2 meters.

$99⁹⁵ •

*Suggested List Price

PEARCE-SIMPSON
DIVISION OF **GLADDING** CORPORATION
P.O. Box 800, Biscayne Annex, Miami, Florida 33152

Figure 7.8 — Pearce-Simpson, a major supplier of marine radio equipment, manufactured the Gladding 25 2 meter FM transceiver. It ran 25 watts using a vacuum tube driver and final amplifier. (Jan 1972)

Figure 7.9 — Herb Johnson, W6QKI (ex-W7GRA), started the Swan Company in 1961 and also founded Atlas Radio in 1974. The 210/215 series followed the first Atlas transceiver, the 180. The Atlas rigs shared compact size, great selectivity, audio quality and solid state circuitry. (Mar 1975)

REPEATERS

144 MHz

220 MHz

Why make do with a converted Mark II Gizwachi when you can get a complete repeater designed for Hams by Hams, AT A PRICE YOU CAN AFFORD. The RPT 144 and RPT 220 are self-contained—all solid state machines. Conservatively rated, high quality, components deliver EXCELLENT RELIABILITY. Careful consideration has been given to both interfacing and control flexibility.

Factory wired and tested $595.95

Kits available   Write for details

Figure 7.10 — VHF Engineering, located in Binghamton, New York, sold VHF/UHF gear both factory-wired and as kits. Their range of products included simple transmitters and receivers, handheld transceivers, amplifiers, repeater components, and complete repeaters. (Mar 1975)

Figure 7.11 —Murch Electronics sold a commercial version of the transmatch described in a *QST* article by Lew McCoy, W1ICP. The Murch antenna is similar to the multiband dipole design of Louis Varney, G5RV. The Mini-Products Hybrid Quad provided some gain and directivity to amateurs unable to put up full-size arrays for the 20, 15, 10 and 6 meter bands. (Jun 1974)

A NEW CONCEPT
IN HIGH POWER . . .

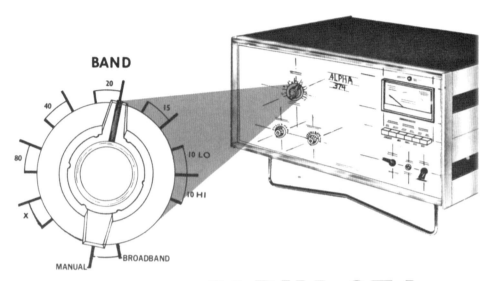

BAND

THE "HANDS OFF" **ALPHA 374**
. . . BY ETO, OF COURSE!

Figure 7.12 —The Alpha 374 offered the option of no-tune band changes when operated in the bandpass mode. Alpha rated its three 8874 tubes for continuous service at legal limit power. (Feb 1974)

What are we handing you?

The most exciting 2-meter, hand-held on the market...
2-watt, 6-channel

Now Midland — for years one of the top names in communication equipment — brings you a high performance hand-held transceiver with a suggested price of just $229.95. What do you get? A full 2 watts output power with automatic deviation control. 6-channel capability with crystals installed for .16/.76, .34/.94 and .94/.94. High performance receiver with mechanical filters, IC and MOSFET front end. Built-in battery/S meter. Compact 9″ x 3″

x 1⅞″ size. Jacks for external speaker, microphone, antenna and charge/power. Operation on 8 "AA" cells, ni-cad battery pack or AC power supply (optional). With carrying case, less batteries. Model 13-520

Write for Midland's full-line amateur radio brochure: P.O. Box 19032, Kansas City, MO 64141

DEALERS: inquire about an exclusive Midland amateur radio area franchise

ELECTRONICS COMPANY
"Coming on Strong in Amateur Radio"

Figure 7.13 — In the early 1970s, most companies selling VHF FM gear brought out a handheld transceiver. Midland's model 13-520, a 2 meter transceiver, featured six crystal-controlled channels and 2 W output. (Mar 1973)

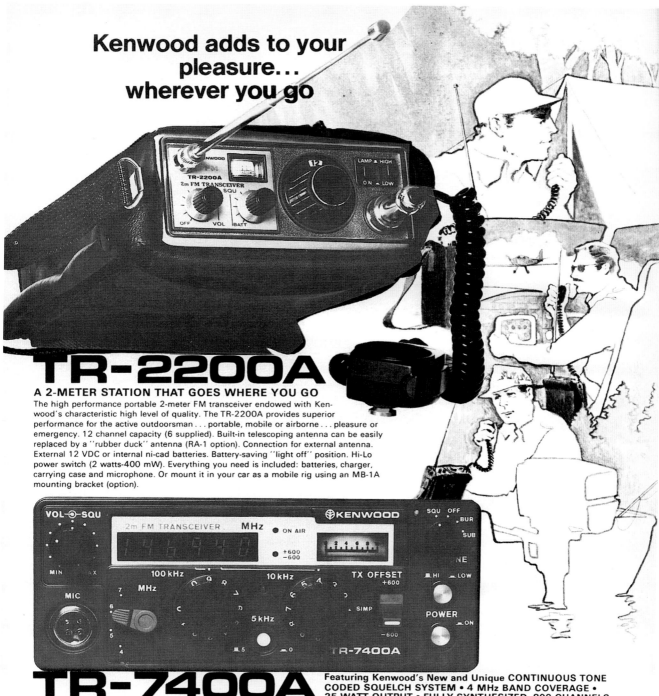

Kenwood adds to your pleasure... wherever you go

TR-2200A

A 2-METER STATION THAT GOES WHERE YOU GO

The high performance portable 2-meter FM transceiver endowed with Kenwood's characteristic high level of quality. The TR-2200A provides superior performance for the active outdoorsman . . . portable, mobile or airborne . . . pleasure or emergency. 12 channel capacity (6 supplied). Built-in telescoping antenna can be easily replaced by a "rubber duck" antenna (RA-1 option). Connection for external antenna. External 12 VDC or internal ni-cad batteries. Battery-saving "light off" position. Hi-Lo power switch (2 watts-400 mW). Everything you need is included: batteries, charger, carrying case and microphone. Or mount it in your car as a mobile rig using an MB-1A mounting bracket (option).

TR-7400A

Featuring Kenwood's New and Unique CONTINUOUS TONE CODED SQUELCH SYSTEM • 4 MHz BAND COVERAGE • 25 WATT OUTPUT • FULLY SYNTHESIZED, 800 CHANNELS

Outstanding sensitivity, large-sized helical resonators with High Q to minimize undesirable out-of-band interference, and a 2-pole 10.7 MHz monolithic crystal filter combine to give your TR-7400A outstanding receiver performance. This compact 6.2 pound package measures only 7-3/16" wide, 10-5/8" deep, and 2-7/8" high and is designed to give you the kind of performance specifications you've always wanted to see in a 2-meter amateur rig. High performance specifications of: Intermodulation characteristics (Better than 66dB), spurious (Better than −60dB), image rejection (Better than −70dB), and a versatile squelch system make the TR-7400A tops in its class.

TRIO-KENWOOD COMMUNICATIONS INC.   116 EAST ALONDRA/GARDENA, CA 90248

KENWOOD *...pacesetter in amateur radio*

Figure 7.14 — The Kenwood TR-2200A bore a striking resemblance to Drake's TR-22. Trio, Kenwood's parent company, manufactured both in Japan. The more elaborate TR-7400A was fully synthesized, with most of the features hams looked for in 1977. (Apr 1977)

Figure 7.15 — The SB-104 differed from its predecessors in Heath's SB line. The solid state, 80 through 10 meter transceiver had a no-tune output stage and digital readout. The complex kit — it had more than 2800 parts — also exhibited numerous performance problems, things Heath never entirely remedied, even with the 1977 SB-104A version. (Nov 1974)

2 Meter FM
THE BIG THREE FOR '73!

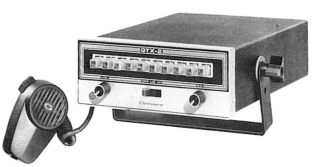

GTX-10
10 watts output power nom.; accomodates 10 channels; rotatable frequency selector; adaptable for portable operation (with HamPak, below).

$199.95
(Includes 146.94 MHz)

GTX-2
30 watts output power nom.; accomodates 10 channels; pushbutton frequency selection; backlighted for night operation.

$249.95
(Includes 146.94 MHz)

GTX-200
30 watts output power nom.; accomodates 100 channel combinations; features independent selection of transmit and receive frequencies, and switch for preselected pairing.

$259.95
(Includes 146.94 MHz)

HamPak
Battery pack for GTX-10 portable operation. Uses 10 D cells (not included).

$39.95
(Includes portable antenna, carrying handle & mike clip)

$6.50
per crystal

Additional Crystals for Xmit or receive

Made in U.S.A. In Facilities Inspected by U. S. Gov't.

VISIT YOUR LOCAL AMATEUR DEALER
AND MEET THE "BIG THREE" IN PERSON!

General Aviation Electronics, Inc., 4141 Kingman Drive, Indianapolis, Indiana 46226 — Area 317 - 546-1111

Figure 7.16 — General Aviation Electronics of Indianapolis, Indiana, manufactured the Genave amateur VHF FM transceivers and accessories alongside the general aviation communications gear implied by the company name. (Jun 1973)

Wilson Electronics Presents The Finest 2 Meter Handie Talkie
With the Hottest Rx Front End on The Market.

2 METER FM TRANSCEIVER MODEL 1402SM

FREQUENCY ....140 - 150 MHZ
(2 MHZ SPREAD)

NUMBER OF CHANNELS 6
Supplied with 146.94 Simplex
146.34/94 - 146.16/76

R.F. Output .... 2 Watts minimum

Sensitivity ....better than 0.3
MV/20 DB Q.S.

Audio Output ....500 mv

Meter ....Monitors battery voltage
on Tx, S meter on Rx

Weight ....1 lb. 4 ounces
without
battieres

Current drain .... 15 MA Rx
410 MA Tx

Size 8 7/8'' x 1 7/8'' x 2 7/8''

Includes Adjustable Whip Ant

$239 00
Amateur
Net Price

MODEL # ACCESSORIES

1410A   12 Watt Power Amplifier
Also Includes Steel Case
For 1402SM - Charges 1402 SM
When Pluged into Cigarette
Lighter   **99.00**

LCL LEATHER CASE **12.00**
14BC BATTERY CHARGER ...**29.95**
SM1 SPEAKER MIKE **24.00**

WRITE FOR COMPLETE SPEC SHEETS.
SEE YOUR NEAREST DEALER FOR
THE FINEST AMATEUR HANDIE
TALKIE ON THE MARKET

DEALER INQUIRIES INVITED
COMMERCIAL VERSION AVAILABLE   **1410A**

SM1

Wilson Electronics

P.O. Box 794   **Henderson, Nevada 89015**
Telephone (702) 451-5791 451-6650

Figure 7.17 — Wilson Electronics, well-known for its antennas, added its name to the list of companies selling handheld VHF transceivers in the 1970s. (Mar 1974)

Figure 7.18 — The FPM-300 appeared near the end of Hallicrafters' long run as a ham equipment manufacturer and *QST* advertiser. A Mark II version followed the original transceiver in 1974 with production ceasing altogether three years later. (Jun 1972)

Figure 7.19 — Dovetron made regenerative RTTY terminal units for both commercial and amateur applications. The regenerator and speed conversion functions required installation of an additional PC board assembly. (May 1976)

The world's first digitally tuned 80M-10M SSB transceiver
with over 40,000 frequency synthesized channels.

- **Ultra-stable frequency synthesizer** •
Large LED readout • **200 Watts PEP
input** • *All* **solid state including
electronic tuning** • **Front end filtering**
• **Built-in TVI filtering** • **Modular
construction** • **WWV Receiver,
Squelch, Noise blanker, VOX, Speech
processing are standard** • **Full
metering.**

Discover a whole new world of
communications with the CIR ASTRO 200
. . . the Ham SSB Transceiver that has
established a new plateau of sophistication
for the serious enthusiast.

The built-in digital synthesizer with LED
readout gives you over 40,000 crystal
controlled channels in the 80 through 10
meter bands with 100Hz resolution. Just
press a momentary switch and tune your
frequency with no moving parts.

Calibrate it with WWV at the turn of a
switch for absolute accuracy. No more
crystal calibration.

And, as for frequency drift, the

ASTRO 200 is ten times better than VFO
types. Total filtering sets the ASTRO 200
above all others for TVI and harmonic
suppression. Selectable USB or LSB allows
you complete flexibility, and extended band
coverage covers many MARS frequencies.
CW operation features include semi
break-in CW with adjustable delay and side
tone . . . no key click or CW chirp.

CIR offers a complete range of
accessories including fixed station console
and external frequency synthesizer for
crossband DX work.

This extremely compact transceiver is
only 2.8″ high by 9.5″ wide by 12.3″ deep
including heat sink. With all of these features
incorporating rugged militarized type
construction, it has no equal for SSB and
CW operation.

Be the first to learn more about the
exciting new CIR ASTRO 200 . . . ham
radio's next generation transceiver.
Available in March. Write or phone for
complete details.

CIR Industries, Inc., 1648 N. Magnolia Avenue, El Cajon, California 92020 U.S.A., Phone (714) 449-7633, Telex 69-7989

**Figure 7.20 — The CIR Industries Astro 200 transceiver tuned the 80 through 10 meter amateur bands
in 100 Hz steps by toggling switches up or down. Power output on SSB and CW was 100 W. (Feb 1977)**

Rugged...compact (10"x17.5"x4.5")...lightweight (17.5 lbs.)

For the first time...
An <u>all solid state</u> mobile kilowatt

No tuning or adjustment whatever over 80, 40, 20, 15 and 10 meters

- Mobile 12V — no separate power supply required
- Base station with optional 13.6V power supply
- Fully remote controlled
- Suitable for use with any transceiver in the 100W class
- Heatsink convector-cooled and thermostatically controlled
- 8 power transistors of latest stripline RF linear devices; rated for operation at infinite VSWR

For further details, send for free informative brochure and name of your nearest dealer.

Dealer inquiries invited.

Power input . . . . 13.6V DC 1000W
Power output . . . . 13.6V DC 600W PEP typical
Frequency range . . . . 2-30MHz continuous coverage, no tuning
Filter selection . . . . Front panel rotary switch or
by remote control
Intermodulation distortion . . . . −24dB 1kw input 3rd order
−32dB 500W PEP output 2-18MHz
Harmonics . . . . −50dB all amateur bands
Drive level . . . . 60W PEP 50 ohms
Power source . . . . 11-13.6V DC 70A peak; avg. voice 40A
Size . . . . 10" wide; 17.5" deep; 4.5" high
Weight . . . . 17.5 lbs.

30-day money back (less shipping) guarantee.
Send check or money order. Illinois residents add 5% sales tax.

MA1000 $795   **PS75 $395**
F.O.B. Escondido, CA or Chicago, IL   (Plug-in power supply)

MAGNUS ELECTRONICS CORPORATION

5715 N. Lincoln Avenue, Chicago, Illinois 60659 • 312 334-1502 • Telex 25-3503

Figure 7.21 — Magnus Electronics' MA1000 solid state amp provided mobile operators with a kilowatt input on 80 through 10 meters. A cautionary note: the amp placed a 70 A burden on the vehicle's electrical system in addition to whatever the exciter required. (May 1977)

FM SYSTEM SCHOOL

144
220
+440
UV-3

thoughts to consider about the new

DRAKE UV-3

Optional
Drake 1525EM
Encoding Mike

UHF-VHF FM SYSTEM

only $995 for 3-band UV-3

*How does the cost of the Drake system **really** compare to alternative methods of getting on 144-220-440 MHz fm?*

A First of all, there is *no* direct comparison possible, because the Drake UV-3 is the only rig in the world offering 144-220-440 MHz fm in a single box — and it is fully synthesized on each band.

B The nearest comparison would be to add the suggested list prices of 3 separate units of the most popular fm rigs presently available. It would work out approximately as follows:

2 Meters (Synthesized to 5 kHz) . . . . . .$	400.00
220 MHz (12 channels, crystal)	230.00
440 MHz (12 channels, crystal)	300.00
Crystals (Assuming 20 per radio)	200.00
TOTAL	**$1130.00**

But wait— even at that price you'd be missing features included in the UV-3:

1. Full synthesis on all three bands
2. Extra diode-programmable fixed channels on each band
3. Priority scan feature on each band
4. Remote, trunk mount operation (optional)
5. Everything in a *single* box!

For your homework, then, ponder the following — at a suggested amateur net of $995.00, the Drake UV-3 (144-220-440) is, to say the least, an incredible value.

R. L. DRAKE COMPANY

 **DRAKE** ®

540 Richard St., Miamisburg, Ohio 45342
Phone: (513) 866-2421 • Telex: 288-017

Western Sales and Service Center, 2020 Western Street, Las Vegas, Nevada 89102 • 702/382-9470

Figure 7.22 — R.L. Drake set off on a new path with its UV-3 UHF/VHF system. Essentially a 2 meter FM transceiver, it also operated on 220 and 440 MHz with the addition of circuit boards for those bands. The UV-3 was the first FM transceiver manufactured by Drake in house. (Dec 1977)

KLM presents
FORCE 5

the technology-time-warp 5-band transceiver!

Techniques expected only at 1980 . . . and beyond . . . have been skillfully advanced to make this sensational transceiver available in **1977** . . . today . . . **NOW**!

★ **No tuning dials.**

★ **PLL frequency synthesis** of highest stability

★ **6 figure, high intensity digital readout to 100Hz.**

★ **Built-in WWV receiver** for high accuracy correlation.

★ **Entirely solid state.**

★ **No tuning controls. Broad band amplifier output.**

★ **Frequency change simple, positive** with Up/Down/Fast/Slow panel switches. Also, fast or "inching" Hi/Lo push buttons on the hand microphone. Simple to "scan" band or to "track" with any station.

★ **Single sideband operation** with USB/LSB selection. (CW operation when Base Console is used).

★ **Front-end automatic gain control.** Copes with very strong signals without overload. PIN diode control.

★ **8 pole crystal filter** offers very high adjacent channel rejection.

At your KLM dealer. Write for brochure.

★ **Speech processor** for high, breakthrough speech power.

★ **Attractive, with grained wood end pieces on cabinet**

★ **13.6VDC mobile operation** (110/220VAC-13.6VDC power supply optionally available for base station use).

5 band transceiver for 13.6VDC operation (less speaker) with dynamic frequency control hand microphone. . . .

Suggested list **1095.00**

Matching Base Station Console with Phone Patch/VU meter/VOX/CW/24 hour digital clock/audio-visual 10 minute timer.

Suggested list **379.00**

Power Supply/Speaker unit. Input 110/220VAC, output 13.6VDC @ 20A.

Suggested price **249.95**

Freq. coverage: 3.5000 to 3.999MHz
7.0000 to 7.4999MHz
14.0000 to 14.4999MHz
21.0000 to 21.4999MHz
28.0000 to 29.9999MHz

Modes: SSB w/USB/LSB (CW with base console accessory.

Sensitivity: 0.5μV for 10db S+N/N.

Selectivity: Crystal lattice 8 pole filter. Shape factor 1.8.
2.7kHz @ 6db
4.9kHz @ 60db

Image rejection: >50db, 80-15 M
>40db, 10M.

AGC: 6db change in audio level, 1μV to more than 0.1V (100db).

Audio output: 2W @ 10% distortion, 300-3000Hz.

Power inp.: 200W p.e.p. inp. @ 13.6VDC.

Power out.: 80W p.e.p. @ 13.6VDC (10M)
100W p.e.p. @ 13.5VDC (80-15M)

Two tone mod.: 30db below peak power level.

Harmonic output: Meets or exceeds FCC 20777 requirements.

Transmit control: PTT (also VOX with Base accessory).

Microphone: Hi Z dynamic w/cord/plug (mic also has Up/Down frequency changing buttons).

Operating voltage: 13.6VDC nom. (no damage 10-15V). Neg. ground.

Dimensions: 3"H, 12.1"D, 10.5"W. (depth includes heat sink).

Weight: 8 pounds.

KLM electronics, inc.
17025 Laurel Road, Morgan Hill, CA 95037 (408) 779-7363

Figure 7.23 — An accessory console gave KLM's synthesized, solid state SSB transceiver CW capability as well. A pair of front panel switches or buttons on the handheld microphone did the tuning. (Dec 1977)

there's a world of difference
in TEN-TEC's *all-new*
hf transceiver—

Figure 7.24 — TEN-TEC's product line continued to evolve as the Omni HF transceiver replaced the older Triton series. The Omni-A's analog dial gave way to a digital readout when the D model arrived a year later. (Oct 1978)

MOTOROLA
METRUM II 2M FM Transceiver

MOTOROLA — Big name, but now priced for the Ham. The Metrum II features high Quality and High Performance in the Motorola Tradition. The Metrum II has 12 Channel capability (146.94 MHz supplied) And requires only one crystal per channel. Repeater operation is accomplished by installing an optional Repeater Offset crystal. In Repeat mode, the transmitter frequency is shifted.

Receiver specs are on par with their commercial models; Typical: .35uv-20db quieting (.25uv sinad), Intermod −50db, Spurious and Image rejection −65db. Very sensitive! — But provides "Garbage-free" reception in metro areas where some rigs are "Wiped out" by adjacent channel interference and intermod.

Available in two models — 10 or 25 watts output. Both have hi/lo power switch to reduce output to one watt. Other features include back-lighted control panel, polarity and antenna mismatch protection and 5 watts of audio power. Microphone and mobile mount included. Ready to go on 12vdc. 2¾" h, 9¼" d, 11" w.

Amateur Electronic Supply has been selected to distribute this fine new product. Write or phone today for more info — Trades — Financing — etc.

INTRODUCTORY OFFER: If you purchase a new Motorola Metrum II FM rig at the Regular price and without a trade-in, you may take a $50.00 "Bonus Credit" toward the purchase of other merchandise (such as xtals, antennas, supplies, etc.)

Branch Stores in:
ORLANDO, FLORIDA
&
CLEVELAND, OHIO

MOTOROLA METRUM II PRICES
10 watt Model $399.95
25 watt Model 499.95
Crystals (one per channel) 9.00
600 KHz Repeater Offset Crystal 13.50

Figure 7.25 — Much of the early amateur VHF FM activity used Motorola equipment converted from commercial use. Motorola entered the ham market directly with the Metrum II transceiver. Modar Electronics, Motorola's marine radio division, manufactured the 2 meter FM rig. (Nov 1973)

the super-compact
alda 103

only 3¼" high x 9" wide x 12½" deep • less than 8¼ pounds

ALDA 103, the trim little powerhouse with incredible performance for the price! ALDA 103 provides a full 250 watts PEP input for SSB operation, and 250 watts DC input for CW. And when it comes to performance, ALDA 103 is the hottest little transceiver going — all solid state, totally broadbanded and super-stable VFO.

Ideal first transceiver for brand new novices! You'll want a full-capability CW/USB/LSB unit with all the power and performance you can use. ALDA 103 gives you 250 watts DC input for CW, the maximum allowable power for your novice license. When you upgrade to technician, you've got 2 bands for CW operation. And with your general license, just plug in your mic and use the ALDA 103's full 250 watts PEP on SSB!

Perfect second or mobile unit for seasoned hams! If you're looking for a super-sharp, compact unit to use in your car or boat, ALDA 103 will live up to your expectations. Absolute worst case sensitivity 0.5 uV for 10 dB S+N/N — a must for mobile operation. Receiver audio output of 3 watts minimum — another must. Also, very low receiver power drain of only 5.5 watts — that's 0.4 amps at nominal 13.8 VDC including power for dial and meter lamps!

GENERAL SPECIFICATIONS

Semiconductors:	39 diodes, 23 transistors; 11 integrated circuits
Power Requirements:	Nominal 13.8 VDC input at 15 amps, negative ground only
Power Consumption:	Receive — 5.5 watts (includes dial and meter lamps); Transmit — 260 watts
Dimensions:	3-1/4" high x 9" wide x 12-1/2" deep (82.55 mm x 228.6 mm x 317.5 mm)
Weight:	8-1/4 lbs. (3.66 kg)

PERFORMANCE SPECIFICATIONS

Frequency Range:	80 meter band — 3.5 to 4.0 MHz 40 meter band — 7.0 to 7.5 MHz 20 meter band — 14.0 to 14.5 MHz
Modes:	CW; USB; LSB
RF Input Power:	SSB — 250 watts PEP nominal CW — 250 watts DC maximum (adjustable)

Transmitter:

Antenna Impedance:	50 ohm, unbalanced
Carrier Suppression:	Better than −45 dB
Side-Band Suppression:	Better than −55 dB at 1000 Hz

Distortion Products:	Better than −26 dB
AF Response:	500 to 2500 Hz
Spurious Radiation:	Harmonics better than −45 dB below 30 MHz; better than −60 dB above 30 MHz
Frequency Stability:	Less than 100 Hz drift per hour (from a cold start at room temperature)
Microphone:	High impedance 3000 ohm

Receiver:

Sensitivity:	Better than 0.5 watts audio output for 0.5 μV input
Signal-to-Noise Ratio:	Better than 10 dB S+N/N for 0.5 μV input
Image Ratio:	Better than −60 dB (typical with respect to 0.5 μV input: 80 meters — −130 dB; 40 meters − −100 dB; 20 meters − −75 dB)
IF Rejection:	Better than −70 dB (typical with respect to 0.5 μV input: 80 meters — 110 dB; 40 meters — 80 dB; 20 meters — 75 dB).
Intermodulation Intercept Point:	Better than 10 dBM
Selectivity:	2.5 kHz − 6 dB; 5.0 kHz − 60 dB
Audio Output Power:	More than 3 watts
Audio Distortion:	Less than 5% at 3 watts

$495
including microphone and mobile mount, too.

OPTIONS & ACCESSORIES

Noise Blanker —
Model No. PC 701 .... **$29.95**

100 kHz and 25 kHz
Dual Crystal Calibrator —
Model No. PC 801 .... **$14.95**

Portable Power Supply — Model No. ALDA PS 115: average duty 15 amp unregulated; input — 115/230 VAC, 50/60 Hz; output — 13.8 V nominal at 15 amps **$79.95**

Heavy Duty Power Supply — Model No. ALDA PS 130: output — regulated 30 amp at 13.8 VDC; input — 115/230 VAC, 50/60 Hz **$149.95**

alda communications, inc. 215 Via El Centro Oceanside, CA 92054 (714) 433-6123

ALDA 103 is completely manufactured in the U.S.A.

Figure 7.26 — The ALDA 103 SSB and CW transceiver covered 80, 40 and 20 meters. The fully solid state rig used tone-generated CW. An 80, 40 and 15 meter Novice band version, the 103A, and the five band model 105 filled out the ALDA product line. (Apr 1978)

Figure 7.27 — A Microlog AVR-2, AKB-1, video monitor and station transceiver gave the CW or RTTY operator capability to transmit, receive and display on both those modes. (Mar 1979)

What every Amateur
has been waiting for....
the new HF-200A Transceiver ™

Build a complete station with *DenTron*®

DenTron Radio Company, Inc. / 2100 Enterprise Parkway / Twinsburg, Ohio 44087 / (216) 425-3173

Figure 7.28 — Known for amplifiers and antenna tuners, Dentron brought out a 200 W transceiver, power supply/speaker and external VFO to round out its station in 1979. (Apr 1979)

Figure 7.29 — HAL Communications' DS3100ASR represented the company's latest achievement in its decade-long development of RTTY gear. The DS3100ASR became a mainstay of networks, such as those used by the Military Auxiliary Radio System (MARS), tasked with handling large volumes of traffic. (Apr 1979)

Figure 7.30 — Following a number of published pieces about narrow band voice modulation (NBVM) in *QST* and *The Radio Amateur's Handbook*, Henry Radio announced the VBC-3000 transmit and receive adapter for the narrow band mode. The technology failed to gain traction among amateurs. (May 1979)

Figure 7.31 —The Swan Astro 102BX reappeared as the Cubic Astro 102BXA when Cubic Communications of Oceanside, California, acquired the Swan amateur line. The all solid state transceiver numbered twin PTOs and full QSK among its features. (Oct 1979)

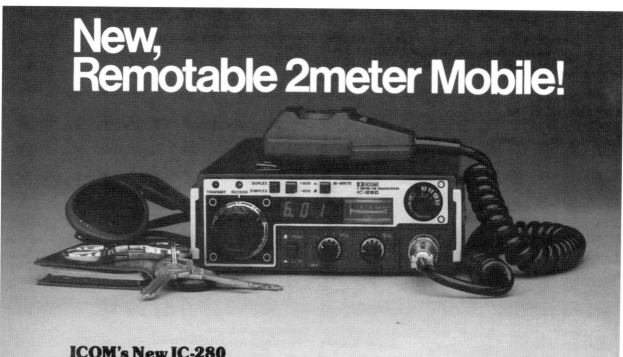

New, Remotable 2meter Mobile!

ICOM's New IC-280

ICOM introduces its new 2 meter mobile radio with the detachable microprocessor control head, the **IC-280**. Bright, easy to read LED's and a new style meter grace the brushed aluminum "new look" front panel of the detachable control head, which provides memory and frequency control for the remotely mountable main section.

The **IC-280** comes as one radio to be mounted in the normal manner; but, as an option, the entire front one third of the radio detaches and mounts by its optional bracket and the main body tucks neatly away out of sight. Now you can mount your 2 meter mobile radio in places that seemed really tight before.

With the microprocessor head the **IC-280** can store three frequencies of your choice, which are selected by a four position front panel switch. These frequencies are retained in the **IC-280's** memory for as long as power is applied to the radio. Even

when power is turned off at the front panel switch, the **IC-280** retains its programmed memories; and when power is completely removed from the radio, the ±600 KHz splits are still maintained!

Frequency coverage of the **IC-280** is in excess of the 2 meter band; and the new band plan (144.5-145.5 MHz repeaters) can easily be accommodated, since it was included in the **IC-280's** initial planning by the ICOM design team.

The main section of the **IC-280** puts you up to the minute with the latest state of the art engineering. The new **IC-280** includes the latest innovations in large signal handling FET front ends for excellent intermodulation character and good sensitivity at the same time. The IF filters are crystal monolithics in the first IF and ceramic in the second, providing narrow band capacity for today and tomorrow's crowded operating conditions. Modular PA construction with broad band tuning provides full rated power across the full 2 meter band (plus a little).

Figure 7.32 — ICOM designed the IC-280 to coexist with increasingly confined automobile interiors. The IC-280's detachable front panel could be mounted within reach of the operator, offering remote control of the main unit through a connecting cable. (Jul 1978)

Chapter 8

The 1980s

Ham Radio in Space, WARC Bands, Packet and Volunteer Examiners

Plans for the ultimate mobile operation got off the ground in May 1983 when the National Aeronautics and Space Administration (NASA) gave astronaut Dr. Owen Garriott, W5LFL, permission to carry a 2 meter transceiver on his upcoming space shuttle flight. The operation really got off the ground the following November when NASA launched space shuttle *Columbia* with Garriott and his transceiver aboard.[1,2]

Lance Collister, WA1JXN, made the first contact with W5LFL. The ham astronaut logged more than 250 contacts during operation on seven of the mission's ten days. Contacts with W5LFL aboard the space shuttle opened not only new communication possibilities but also unique educational opportunities. The ARRL, local clubs and individual hams used Columbia and missions to follow as unprecedented public relations opportunities for ham radio, staging space communications demonstrations in schools and other public venues.

A long tradition changed with the creation of the Volunteer Examiner (VE) program for amateur license tests. No longer was it necessary to appear at an FCC field office or other examination point for a nervous meeting with a stern-faced Commission examiner. With the VE program, the testing would be done by licensed amateur volunteers.[3] The FCC rules establishing the program required a Volunteer Examiner Coordinator (VEC) to oversee the operation. The League established the ARRL/VEC to become a national level coordinator. The organization administered its first exams under the VE program on September 1, 1984, in Santa Clara, California.[4]

Packet radio, a digital error-correcting mode that sends information in small bursts, was first used by Canadian amateurs in 1978 after their Department of Commerce authorized it. The FCC approved packet for US hams in 1980.[5] Packet activity built slowly at first but by the middle of the decade seemed to spread through the amateur community with the speed of a radio wave. Dedicated repeaters (digipeaters) added to the packet activity already taking place on the VHF bands, and HF packet became a valuable tool for routing messages over long distances. Even VHF packet operation had a long reach utilizing linked networks. Writing on QST's June 1984 editorial page, David Sumner, K1ZZ, saw the relaying aspect of packet as a logical extension of the purpose for which Hiram P. Maxim had organized the ARRL in the first place.[6]

Amateurs without any interest in the digital mode except for purposes such as DX spotting used packet too. In early 1986, the ARRL estimated that 14,000 packet stations were already on the air,

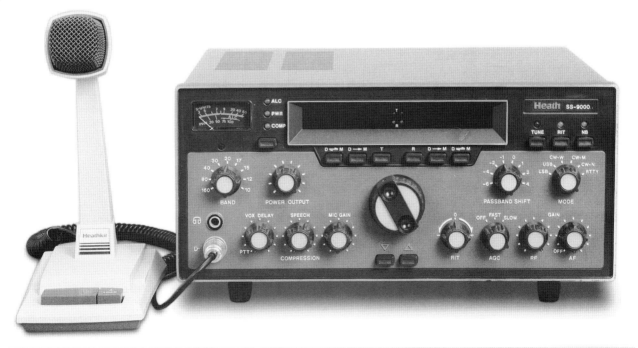

Heath decided the SS-9000 was too complicated to construct in the company's traditional kit form and sold it instead as a completely factory-built transceiver. ($2795, 1982)

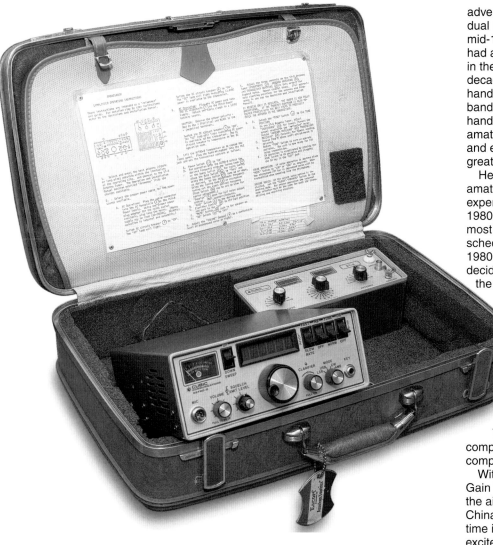

The Cubic Communications Ambassador set consisted of an Astro-D transceiver and power supply, along with an ST-5 antenna tuner, housed in an American Tourister case. Its secure voice modes could be used to communicate with another similarly-equipped radio. (1983)

advertising experienced an explosion of dual band VHF/UHF transceivers. By the mid-1980s all the major manufacturers had a full size dual band transceiver in their lineups and by the end of the decade they each had a dual band handheld unit on offer. Whether single band or multiband, the proliferation of handheld and mobile VHF gear equipped amateurs to participate in public service and emergency communications to a greater degree than ever before.

Heathkit's traditional role of supplying amateurs with the build-it-yourself experience changed somewhat in the 1980s. In 1982 the company issued its most ambitious project yet. Heath had scheduled the SS-9000 transceiver for a 1980 release but, as the time drew near, decided to step back and reconsider the project. In the end, Heath thought it best to sell the SS-9000 as a completely assembled and tested product. It reached the marketplace in 1982 and never appeared in kit form.[10] Heath followed the same route with the release of the SB-1400 transceiver at the end of the decade.[11] Heath sold the SB-1400, manufactured by Yaesu and similar to the Japanese company's own FT-747GX, as a completely assembled product.

With a Yaesu FT-107 hooked to a Hy-Gain TH6DXX beam, BY1PK took to the airwaves on March 29, 1982, putting China on the amateur bands for the first time in decades.[12] The operation created excitement among DXers and massive pileups on the bands. Few fighting the 1982 pileup battles realized how large a role China would play in the electronics world in the near future.

Yaesu's FT-980 CAT (Computer Aided Transceiver) gave 1983 amateurs a look into the future. With an optional interface and software, a personal computer's keyboard could control functions such as band, VFO, mode, split frequency operation, RIT/XIT, IF shift and width and FSK shift. Even without the computer, the FT-980 CAT presented the operator with 60 knobs, switches and buttons. In a November 1984 *QST* product review, the article's author wrote, "When there is one program that will control the rig, keep the log, and operate RTTY, the CAT system will really purr."[13] Just wait. A few years down the road, all that and more would come to pass.

Vic Clark, W4KFC, the sitting president of the ARRL, passed away suddenly on November 25, 1983 at age 66. Clark was known worldwide for his operating prowess, his selfless and tireless efforts

with more to come.[7] All this activity did not escape the notice of manufacturers. Heath, AEA, Kantronics and MFJ, among others, produced packet equipment that built on early development work by the nonprofit Tucson Amateur Packet Radio group (TAPR) to meet the growing demand. As a pleasant surprise to those purchasing the new gear, only a change in software was needed to accommodate new digital modes as they came along.

The June 1981 issue of *QST* carried an article by Peter Martinez, G3PLX, describing a mode he called AMTOR (Amateur Teleprinting Over Radio). AMTOR, a computer based, error-free version of RTTY, was not permitted in the US when the article was published, although the FCC had issued Special Temporary Authority to four amateurs

to test the mode.[8] In January 1983, the FCC approved AMTOR on frequencies above 50 MHz and made it legal on the HF bands in April.

The new digital modes tended to add to total amateur activity rather than siphon away participants from other modes. In 1980, the League's Long-Range Planning Committee commissioned the Institute for Social Research of Florida State University to conduct a survey on the current state and future prospects of Amateur Radio.[9] The comprehensive and complex survey report cannot be characterized in a few words, but it is safe to conclude that phone operation on the HF bands and repeater operation at VHF ranked among the most popular amateur pastimes.

Small wonder, then, that *QST*

on behalf of Amateur Radio, and a personality that all with whom he came in contact found welcoming. He was the first ever recipient of the Hiram Percy Maxim Memorial Award in 1936. Clark served as President of the League from March 1982 until the time of his death and had also been Vice President and President, Region 2 of the International Amateur Radio Union.[14]

An ARRL Board of Directors meeting in October 1984 introduced the ambitious goal of increasing the amateur population by 50 percent by the end of the decade.[15] The goal's secondary purpose was to produce not just more amateurs, but more *active* amateurs. A chief concern dealt with making the entry-level Novice license more attractive.[16] The League expressed support for Novice Enhancement, which became a reality in March 1987.[17] A far cry from the restrictive early 1950s Novice privileges, the mid-1980s enhanced Novice license permitted operation on the RTTY, AMTOR and packet digital modes.[18]

The FCC announced the opening of the 17 meter band on January 30, 1989, a decade after the conclusion of WARC-79.[19] With the final WARC-79 band in the fold, the regulatory battles returned to familiar territory. The League found itself again defending the 220 MHz band in the face of an FCC proposal to reallocate a part of it to the Land Mobile Service.[20] Even after the Commission finalized its ruling and shifted 2 MHz of the band to commercial users, the ARRL carried the battle into the following decade.[21]

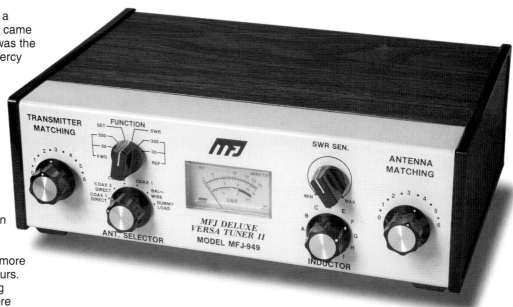

The MFJ Model 949 became the world's largest-selling antenna tuner, remaining in production through a series of variants and upgrades well into the 21st Century. ($129.95, 1980)

Notes

[1] R. Neal, K6DUE, "W5LFL: First Ham in Space," *QST*, Jul 1983, p 46.
[2] "Well Done, W5LFL!," *QST*, Feb 1984, pp 11-14.
[3] C. Holsopple, K9CH, "Another Step Toward Volunteer Examining," *QST*, Dec 1983, pp 51-55.
[4] "Up Front in *QST*," Nov 1984, p 11.
[5] W. Silver, Ed., *The ARRL Handbook,* 90th Edition (Newington: 2013) p 16.22.
[6] D. Sumner, K1ZZ, "It Seems To Us — Our Next Great Challenge," *QST*, Jun 1984, p 9.
[7] D. Sumner, K1ZZ, "It Seems to US — Packet Fever," *QST*, Apr 1986, p 9.
[8] P. Martinez, G3PLX, "Amtor, An Improved Error-Free RTTY System," *QST*, Jun 1981, pp 25-27.
[9] D. Sumner, K1ZZ, "Long-Range Planning — Phase II Report Accepted by Board," *QST*, Dec 1981, pp 56-60.
[10] C. Penson, WA7ZZE, *Heathkit: A Guide to the Amateur Radio Products* (Hicksville, New York: 2003) pp 261-262.
[11] *Ibid.* p 258.
[12] R. Baldwin, W1RU, "China: Active Once Again," *QST*, Jul 1982, pp 48-49.

[13] J. Ward, K8KA, "Product Review: Yaesu FT-980 HF Transceiver," *QST*, Nov 1984, pp 50-53.
[14] D. Sumner, K1ZZ, "It Seems To Us — Victor C. Clark, W4KFC – 1917-1983," *QST*, Jan 1984, pp 9-11.
[15] Minutes of the 1984 Second Meeting of the Board of Directors The American Radio Relay League, Inc. October 25-26, 1984, Item 44.
[16] D. Sumner, K1ZZ, "It Seems To Us — Novice Enhancement," *QST*, Jul 1985, pp 9, 48.
[17] P. Sager, WB4FDT, "Novice Enhancement is a Reality!," *QST*, Apr 1987, pp 64-67.
[18] D. Newkirk, AK7M, "Novice Enhancement Goes Digital," *QST*, Jul 1987, pp 46-49.
[19] J. Hennessee, KJ4KB, "Happenings — 17 Meter Band Open!," *QST*, Apr 1989, p 58.
[20] J. Hennessee, KJ4KB, "Happenings — FCC Declines to Reconsider 220-MHz Decision; ARRL to File in Federal Court," *QST*, Aug 1989, p 56.
[21] J. Hennessee, KJ4KB, "Happenings — FCC Proposes Service Rules for Land Mobile Service Operation on 220-222 MHz: ARRL Court Battle Continues," *QST*, Feb 1990, p 53.

Figure 8.1 — Dentron's DTR components were made to be either rack mounted or stacked together on a desktop. (Apr 1980)

Figure 8.2 — The Cubic Astro 103 built on its predecessors, the Swan Astro 102BX and Cubic Astro 102BXA, by adding 30/17/12 meter coverage, a separate receiver input and an RTTY mode. (Nov 1980)

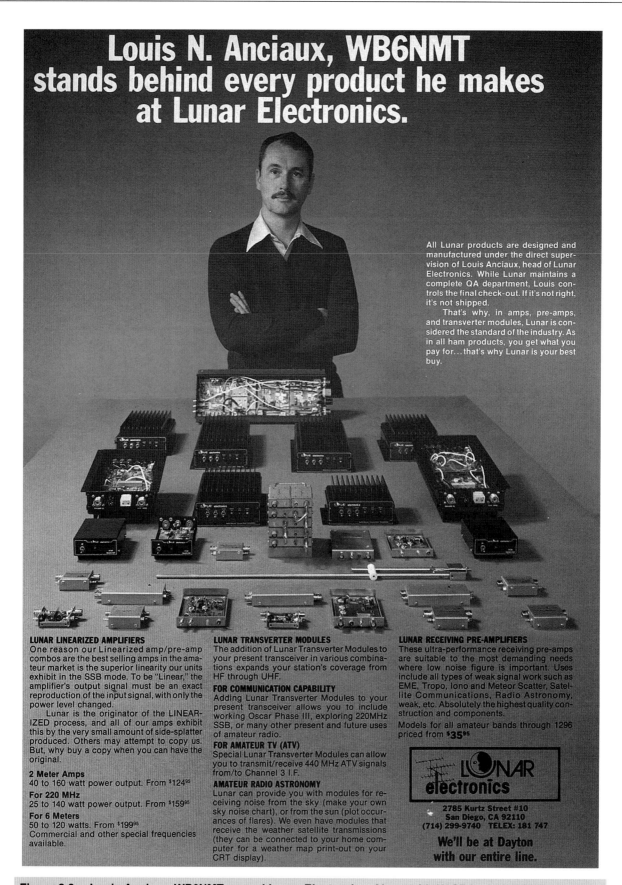

Figure 8.3 —Louis Anciaux, WB6NMT, owned Lunar Electronics. Along with K2CBA and W7CNK, he won the ARRL Technical Merit Award for 1971 in recognition of their 220 MHz moonbounce work. Mr. Anciaux is currently active from Panama as HP3TA. (Apr 1980)

Figure 8.4 — Macrotronics made a CW and RTTY terminal for the popular Radio Shack TRS-80 computer. The company also made terminals to work with computers from Commodore, Exidy and Apple. (Apr 1980)

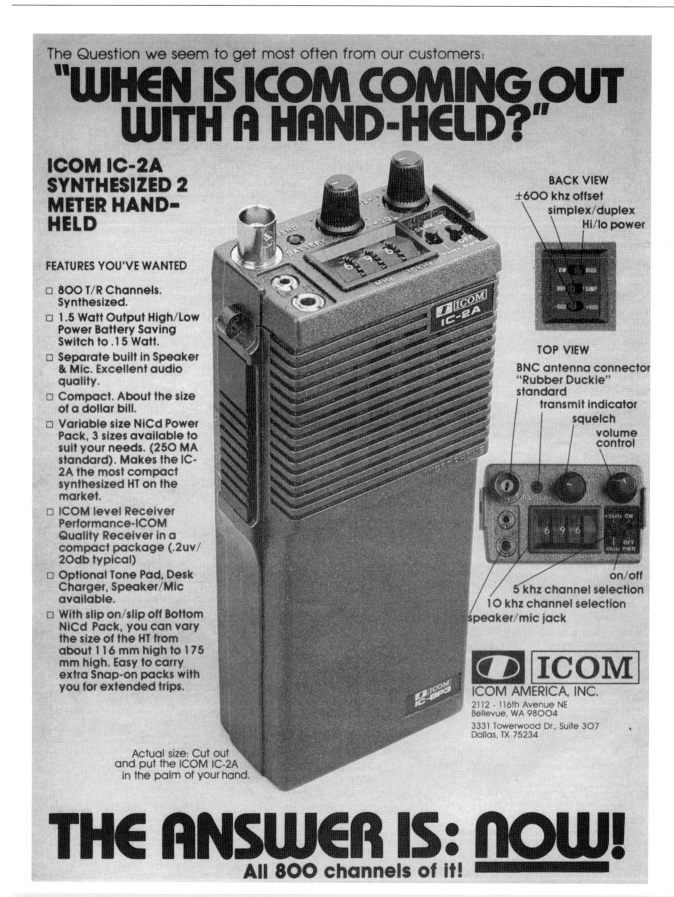

The Question we seem to get most often from our customers:

"WHEN IS ICOM COMING OUT WITH A HAND-HELD?"

ICOM IC-2A SYNTHESIZED 2 METER HAND-HELD

FEATURES YOU'VE WANTED

☐ 800 T/R Channels. Synthesized.

☐ 1.5 Watt Output High/Low Power Battery Saving Switch to .15 Watt.

☐ Separate built in Speaker & Mic. Excellent audio quality.

☐ Compact. About the size of a dollar bill.

☐ Variable size NiCd Power Pack, 3 sizes available to suit your needs. (250 MA standard). Makes the IC-2A the most compact synthesized HT on the market.

☐ ICOM level Receiver Performance-ICOM Quality Receiver in a compact package (.2uv/20db typical)

☐ Optional Tone Pad, Desk Charger, Speaker/Mic available.

☐ With slip on/slip off Bottom NiCd Pack, you can vary the size of the HT from about 116 mm high to 175 mm high. Easy to carry extra Snap-on packs with you for extended trips.

BACK VIEW
±600 khz offset
simplex/duplex
Hi/lo power

TOP VIEW
BNC antenna connector "Rubber Duckie" standard
transmit indicator
squelch
volume control

on/off
5 khz channel selection
10 khz channel selection
speaker/mic jack

ICOM
ICOM AMERICA, INC.
2112 - 116th Avenue NE
Bellevue, WA 98004

3331 Towerwood Dr., Suite 307
Dallas, TX 75234

Actual size: Cut out and put the ICOM IC-2A in the palm of your hand.

THE ANSWER IS: NOW!
All 800 channels of it!

Figure 8.5 — ICOM answered the question, "When is ICOM coming out with a hand-held?" with its IC-2. That first ICOM handheld radio enjoyed a long production life, with a number of additions to the basic 1980 design. (May 1980)

THE GIANT AZDEN® COMPANY

REVOLUTIONIZES THE STATE OF THE ART

AWE AND AZDEN. INTRODUCE THE BRILLIANT NEW PCS-2000

MICROCOMPUTER CONTROLLED

SUPERIOR COMMERCIAL GRADE 2 METER FM TRANSCEIVER

NOT $550.00
SPRING SALE
$299⁰⁰
REG. $369.00

NOT $550.00
SPRING SALE
$299⁰⁰
REG. $369.00

COMPARE THESE FEATURES WITH ANY UNIT AT ANY PRICE

- **FREQUENCY RANGE:** Receive and transmit: 144.00 to 147.995 MHz, 5Khz steps + MARS-CAP and MULTIPLE OFFSET BUILT IN.
- **ALL SOLID STATE-CMOS PL DIGITAL SYNTHESIZED.**
- **SIZE:** UNBELIEVABLE! ONLY 6 3/4" x 2 3/8" x 9 3/4". COMPARE!
- **MICROCOMPUTER CONTROLLED:** All scanning and frequency-control functions are performed by microcomputer.
- **DETACHABLE HEAD:** The control head may be separated from the radio for use in limited spaces and for security purposes.
- **SIX-CHANNEL MEMORY:** Each memory is re-programmable. Memory is retained even when the unit is turned off.
- **MEMORY SCAN:** The six channels may be scanned in either the "busy" or "vacant" modes for quick, easy location of an occupied or unoccupied frequency. AUTO RESUME. COMPARE!
- **FULL-BAND SCAN:** All channels may be scanned in either "busy" or "vacant" mode. This is especially useful for locating repeater frequencies in an unfamiliar area. AUTO RESUME. COMPARE!
- **INSTANT MEMORY-1 RECALL:** By pressing a button on the microphone or front panel, memory channel 1 may be recalled for immediate use.
- **MIC-CONTROLLED VOLUME AND SQUELCH:** Volume and squelch can be adjusted from the microphone for convenience in mobile operation.
- **ACCESSORY OFFSET:** Provides three additional offset values: +0.4 MHz, +1 MHz and +1.6 MHz. Other offsets may also be obtained.
- **25 WATTS OUTPUT:** Also 5 watts low power for short-distance communication.
- **DIGITAL S/RF METER:** LEDS indicate signal strength and power output. No more mechanical meter movements to fall apart!
- **LARGE ½-INCH LED DISPLAY:** Easy-to-read frequency display minimizes "eyes-off-the-road" time.
- **PUSHBUTTON FREQUENCY CONTROL FROM MIC OR FRONT PANEL:** Any frequency may be selected by pressing a microphone or front-panel switch.
- **SUPERIOR RECEIVER SENSITIVITY:** 0.28 uV for 20-dB quieting. The squelch sensitivity is superb requiring less than 0.1 uV to open. The receiver radio circuits are designed and built to exacting specifications, resulting in unsurpassed received-signal intelligibility.
- **TRUE FM, NOT PHASE MODULATION:** Transmitted audio quality is optimized by the same high standard of design and construction as is found in the receiver. The microphone amplifier and compression circuits offer intelligibility second to none.
- **OTHER FEATURES:** Dynamic Microphone, built in speaker, mobile mounting bracket, external remote speaker jack (head and radio) and much, much more. All cords, plugs, fuses, microphone hanger, etc. included. Weight: 6 lbs.
- **ACCESSORIES:** 15' REMOTE CABLE.....$29.95. CS-6R A/C POWER SUPPLY.....$49.95. TOUCHTONE MIC. KIT.....$39.95. EXTERNAL SPEAKER.....$18.00.

AMATEUR-WHOLESALE ELECTRONICS ORDER NOW TOLL FREE

8817 S.W. 129th Terrace, Miami, Florida 33176
Telephone (305) 233-3631 ● Telex: 80-3356
U.S. DISTRIBUTOR
DEALER INQUIRIES INVITED

1·800·327·3102

CREDIT CARD HOLDERS MAY USE OUR TOLL FREE ORDERING NUMBER.

Figure 8.6 — Japan Piezo Company began producing Azden brand amateur FM gear for the world market in the 1970s. The company discontinued sales in the US in 1997. (Apr 1980)

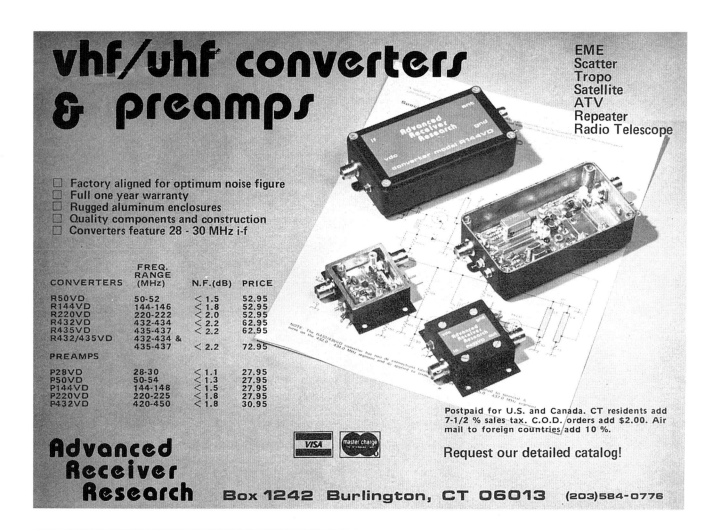
Figure 8.7 — Advanced Receiver Research makes equipment for the serious VHF/UHF/microwave enthusiast. Former ARRL staffer Jay Rusgrove, W1VD, founded the company in 1978. (Dec 1980)

Figure 8.8 — For more than 40 years, Palomar Engineers has advertised its products in *QST*. Jack Althouse, K6NY, is president of the company. Janel was known for preamplifiers and other VHF/UHF accessories. (Nov 1980)

Figure 8.9 — Collins introduced its final amateur product, the KWM-380, in 1979. The solid state transceiver married radio and computer technology in a 48 pound package. The company discontinued production of the KWM-380 in 1983, more than a half century after Art Collins placed that first *QST* ad for his amateur transmitter. (Apr 1981)

SIGNALCRAFTER INTRODUCES

The Most Advanced Automatic Computing RF Measuring Instrument in Amateur Radio!

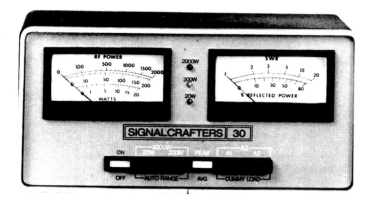

MODEL 30

This new Signalcrafters SWR/Power Meter is in a class by itself. Signalcrafters custom-designed integrated circuits compute SWR automatically, thus eliminating need for "set" or "sensitivity" controls. The built-in analog computer operates over the power range of only one watt to several kilowatts with unparalled accuracy. Our auto-ranging feature automatically selects the proper range of 0 to 20, 0 to 200, or 0 to 2,000 watts according to the RF level detected on the transmission line and indicates the proper range on one of three front panel LED's. The operator can assume manual control of this feature by selecting one of the three basic ranges on the front panel switches. Two large taut-band meters indicate forward power and SWR. Complete hands-off operation! The amateur may also choose between either average or peak RF power. Self-indicating push buttons allow selection of any of three antennas or a dummy load when used with external 12-volt coaxial relays or our Model 50 Antenna Relay/Dummy Load. The 1.5 to 30 mhz coupler is plug-in mounted on the rear apron and can be unplugged and remote-mounted for convenience. The attractive, heavy-duty, low profile metal cabinet complements the latest transceiver designs. DC output receptacles supply analog voltages that track the meter readings. These outputs can be used to control many different accessories, such as analog to digital converters, remote meters, control and alarm devices. Operates from 110 volt 60 hz AC. Width: 8½" (216 mm), Height: 4½" (108 mm), Depth: 6" (152 mm) $225.00

SIGNALCRAFTERS, INC.

5460 Buena Vista Drive
Shawnee Mission, Kansas 66205
913/236-7300; Telex: 42-4171
All Signalcrafters products are designed, engineered and produced in the U.S.A.
Prices include shipping to all U.S.A. — VISA and Master Charge accepted.
Kansas residents please add 3½ percent.

Figure 8.10 — Shortly after Signalcrafters was formed in 1979, it produced this power and computing SWR meter for the ham market. The Shawnee Mission, Kansas, company moved to East Hanover, New Jersey, in 1996 and changed its name to Signalcrafters Tech, Inc. (Dec 1980)

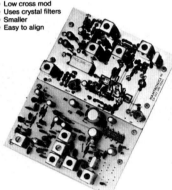

Figure 8.11 — Jerry Vogt, WA2GCF, and wife Joan Vogt, WA2YTK, co-founded Hamtronics in 1962. The company originally supplied equipment for the VHF and UHF amateur bands, including modular repeater components. Hamtronics remains active today, doing 80% of its business in the industrial, scientific, broadcast and government markets. (Dec 1980)

Figure 8.12 — ETO's ad for its Alpha 76 amplifier was both creative and convincing. (May 1981)

Figure 8.13 — Jim Long, W4ZRZ, started Long's Electronics in his hometown of Birmingham, Alabama. The business went on to become a giant in the industry, serving both the consumer electronics and amateur markets. (Jan 1981)

MORE PERFORMANCE FOR YOUR DOLLAR!
COMPETITORS KNOW ABOUT THE
ISOPOLE™
DO YOU? STUDY THE FACTS ...

The IsoPole is building a strong reputation for quality in design and superior performance. The IsoPole's acceptance has already compelled another large antenna producer to make a major design modification to his most popular VHF Base Station antenna. Innovative IsoPole conical sleeve decouplers (pat. pend.) offer many **new** design advantages.

All IsoPole antennas yield the **maximum gain attainable** for their respective lengths and a zero degree angle of radiation. Exceptional decoupling results in simple tuning and a significant reduction in TVI potential. Cones offer greater efficiency over obsolete radials which radiate in the horizontal plane and present an unsightly bird's roost with an inevitable "fallout zone" below. The IsoPoles have the broadest frequency coverage of any comparable VHF base station antenna. This means no loss of power output from one end of the band to the other, when used with SWR protected solid state transceivers. **Typical SWR is 1.4 to 1· or better across the entire band!**

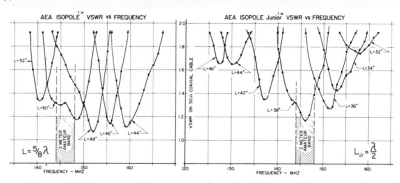

Outstanding mechanical design makes the IsoPole the only logical choice for a VHF base station antenna. A standard 50 Ohm SO-239 connector is recessed within the base sleeve (fully weather protected). With the IsoPole, you will not experience aggravating deviation in SWR with changes in weather. The impedance matching network is weather sealed and designed for maximum legal power. The insulating material offers superb strength and dielectric properties plus excellent long-term ultra-violet resistance. All mounting hardware is stainless steel. The decoupling cones and radiating elements are made of corrosion resistant aluminum alloys. The aerodynamic cones are the only appreciable wind load and are attached directly to the support (a standard TV mast which is **not supplied**)

Operating on MARS or CAP? The IsoPole and IsoPole Jr. antennas will typically operate at least ± 2 MHz outside the respective ham band without re-tuning. However, by simple length adjustment, the IsoPoles can be tuned over a wider range outside the ham bands.

Our competitors have reacted to the IsoPole, maybe you should too! Order your IsoPole or IsoPole Jr. today from your favorite Amateur Radio Distributor. For more information on other exciting AEA products, contact Advanced Electronic Applications, Inc., P.O. Box 2160, Lynnwood, WA 98036. Call 206/775-7373

ISOPOLE 144
$49.95
ISOPOLE 220
$44.95
MAST NOT SUPPLIED

ISOPOLE 144JR
ISOPOLE 220JR
$39.95
MAST NOT SUPPLIED

AEA Brings you the Breakthrough!

PRICES AND SPECIFICATIONS SUBJECT TO CHANGE WITHOUT NOTICE OR OBLIGATION.

Figure 8.14 — The Isopole, with its twin resonant decoupling sleeves, is said to do a good job of radiating in a low-angle pattern that delivers power directly toward the horizon. AEA's Isopole vertical is effectively a pair of ⅝ wavelength antennas in phase. (May 1981)

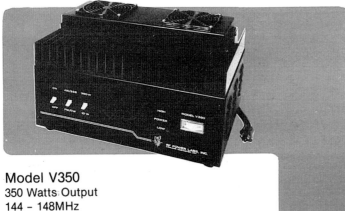
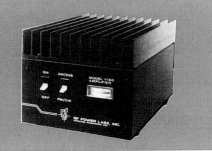
Figure 8.15 — RF Power Labs was founded by Frank Kalmus, WA7SPR. When he passed away in 1998, the company became Kalmus Engineering. (Jun 1981)

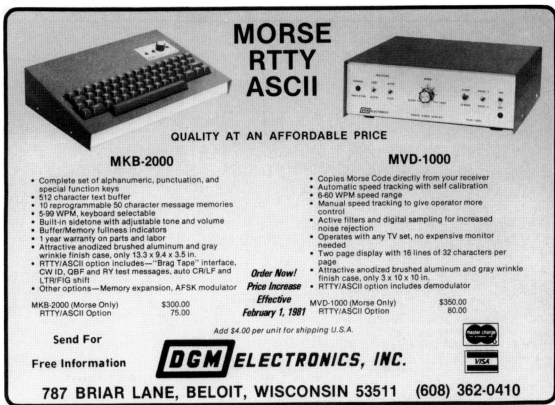

Figure 8.16 — DGM Electronics in Beloit, Wisconsin, made equipment for the generation and reception of amateur CW and RTTY. Today the company is located in Roscoe, Illinois, and manufactures timing instrumentation devices for military and government customers. Datong, an English company, made a line of station accessories that included a filter that automatically located and notched heterodynes. (Jan 1981)

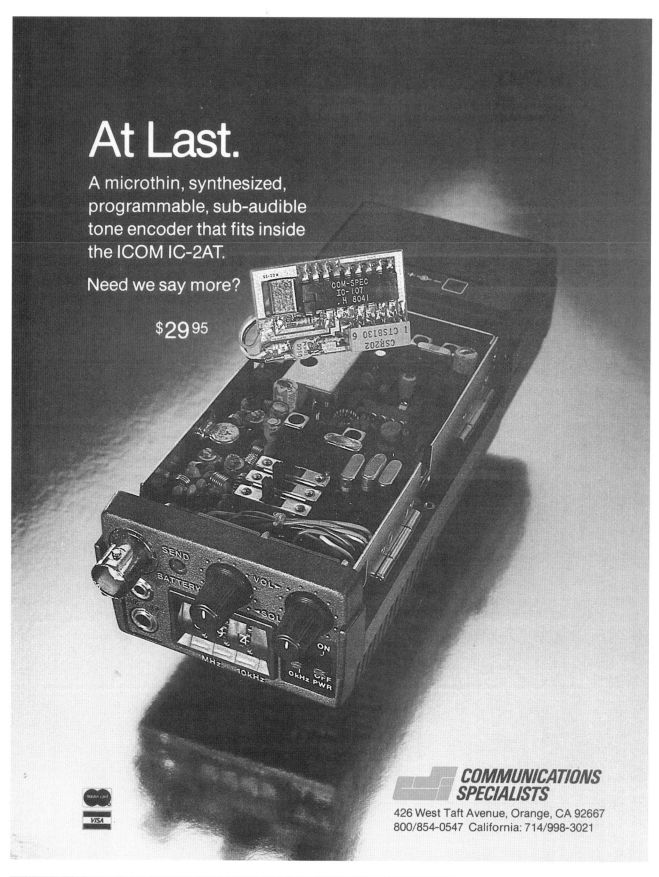

Figure 8.17 — Communications Specialists made tone encoders, necessary for operation on some repeater systems, to fit inside ham gear growing smaller with every equipment generation. (Jan 1982)

Figure 8.18 — IRL's FSK-1000 terminal unit gave RTTY operators the flexibility of a tunable TU and the selectivity of a fixed-frequency unit. The FSK-1000 was designed to deliver landline quality copy over a radio link. (Nov 1981)

Figure 8.19 — The Flesher Corporation sold its TU-300 both wired and in kit form. An optional CW demodulator card plugged into the main circuit board. (Apr 1982)

HL-32V — 10W to 80W 2 mtr power amp with 12db gain MOS-FET Rx preamp. Selectable output power levels and a precision output power meter. SSB or FM/CW operation. $159.95 Suggested Retail.

HL-160V —3W input to 12W input produces 160W of output with 12db MOS-FET preamp. SSB, CW, FM, AM modes. Coaxial relay on output side. If you want to "hawg" the frequency, this is it...the "Boss Hawg" amp. $349.95 Suggested Retail.

HC-150 — Our most popular antenna coupler. Handles 150W output transceivers from 3.5 to 30 MHz WARC bands, 10 ohms, to 250 ohms & accurate SWR & power meter (±10%). Coupler or direct function. Ceramic coils. Quality throughout. $99.95 Suggested Retail.

HC-2000 — The ultimate in quality transmatch design and construction. Takes a full 2 kW output at peak on most bands. Accurate VSWR and separate FWD metering. 3 coax & 2 wire antennas and dummy port, plus bypass. One box, coax switch, power meter, antenna tuner: what could be more convenient! $349.95 Suggested Retail.

TOKYO HY-POWER LABS., INC.

Long the quality leader among fine Japanese communications equipment manufacturers, TOKYO HY-POWER LABS now makes these outstanding units available to you through American dealers. Now you can get our advanced features and quality at your kind of prices.

NEW
from
TOKYO HY-POWER LABS

HL-32V

This is it! The compact HL-32V VHF handy-amplifier from THL. This low profile unit produces 10W to 30W of output with drive from your 0.5W to 3W handheld.

Turn it on with the convenient front panel controls including PWR LED and TX LED or slip the package under the seat out of sight and out of mind. Low insertion loss on receive and selectable power level design provides low VSWR to the transceiver. Use with any talkie from 0.5W to 3W for 10W to 30W output. Linear mode for SSB or FM (switch selected). And the best news of all: the price is only $89.95! Suggested Retail. At your favorite dealer now!

TOKYO HY-POWER LABS.. INC.
SAITAMA, JAPAN

Distributed by
Encomm, Inc.
2000 Avenue G, Suite 800, Plano, Texas 75074
Phone (214) 423-0024   TLX 79-4783 ENCOMM DAL

Figure 8.20 —Nobuki Wakabayashi, JA1DJW, founded Tokyo Hy-Power Labs in 1975. The company developed into a leading manufacturer of solid-state amplifiers. It also made low-power, single band SSB/CW transceivers sold by Kantronics in the US. (Feb 1982)

THE FIRST...
FULLY SYNTHESIZED* HF TRANSCEIVER.

milspec 1030

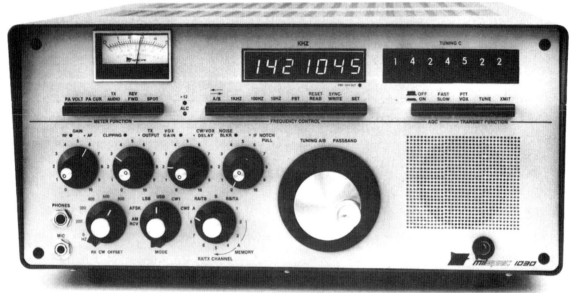

The Signal One Corporation continues its leadership with the introduction of the Milspec 1030, a **NEW** concept in synthesizer technology. *Combining the entire digital frequency control system, including **PASSBAND TUNING** and **BFO FREQUENCIES**, with the main tuning, frequency preset and remote computer control . . we have achieved an ultra fast, real time frequency controlled, high performance, military grade, fully synthesized communications system that will out perform any HF transceiver ever offered in the amateur and commercial market.

Featuring:
● **Fully Synthesized General Frequency Coverage:** 10 kHz — 30 MHz in 1kHz,100 Hz or 10 Hz steps. tunable with encoder or thumbwheel preset. stability of 1 Hz/C°
● **Lever Switch Frequency Pre-Set:** Provides instantaneous band change,sets to within 10 Hz,automatically returns to Tuning A/B. The fastest and most convenient method of frequency entry and recall with additional digital display and memory. **TUNING C.** make this superior to keyboard systems.
● **New Synthesizer Technique:** 120 dB/Hz phase noise close to carrier, extensive CMOS circuitry used for improved spectral purity and great reduction of digital noise—a problem that plagues other HF transceivers causing unwanted mixing products—that insures weak signals will not be covered by internally generated noise due to adjacent strong signals.
● **Real Time Frequency Acquisition:** Not multiplexed, unique synthesizer design allows frequency jumps of 30 MHz in 10 milliseconds, useful in military surveillance applications that demand ultrafast synthesizer switching.
● **Remote Control and Programability:** Permits transceiver use in computer based communication systems. (Optional interface req)
● **Unequaled Receiver Dynamic Range and Front End Selectivity:** + 20 dBm. 3rd. order intercept point and .25 uV sensitivity offer the best immunity to strong signal overload currently available to the commercial and amateur market. Specially developed high level monolithic. double quad balanced mixers combined with low synthesizer phase noise and up-conversion to 40.455 MHz 1st I-F thru 8 pole crystal filter. Better with a ± 4 kHz bandwidth, designed for low intermodulation distortion products. makes this performance possible.
● **Synthesized Passband Tuning:** 1st. and 2nd. I-F tune in 10 Hz steps over ± 5 kHz range with respect to 1st. and 2nd. I-F filter passbands, a unique dual passband feature for maximum interference rejection Controlled by tuning A/B
● **Collins/Rockwell* Mechanical Filters:** For maximum selectivity and ultimate rejection performance. Demanded in most military/commercial applications. 2.1 kHz (USB/LSB), each selected for optimum performance on SSB, cascaded with front end VHF 8 pole crystal filter, active I-F notch filter, passband tuning and noise blanker deliver 16 pole, 1.4:1 performance (6/60 dB) and add up to the most powerful anti-QRM system available.
● **Noise Blanker:** Pre I-F blanker with adjustable threshold and 80 dB dynamic range, gating effectively placed in receiver RF path and triggered by pulsed noise such as over-the-horizon radar.
● **I-F Notch Filter:** Active 300 Hz notch in 2nd. I-F. Adjustable ± 1.5 kHz with 40 db rejection. Receiver AGC not affected by notched signal.

YOU EXPECT THE BEST. WE GUARANTEE IT!

● **High Power Transmit System:** Motorola* high power final amplifiers with 150 watt CW/SSB output or 200 watt option.
● **RF Speech Processing:** Clipped transmit RF signal is passed through mechanical and crystal filters for unequaled SSB talk power and elimination of unwanted intermodulation distortion products. This is a preferred process and considered superior to audio type processors.
● **QSK CW Full Break-In:** Vacuum relays and 200 Hz filter offer a superb full break in CW System.
● **Construction:** All circuit boards. including synthesizer modules. plug-in. ribbon cable interconnection and Miniserit* sockets for transistor and IC replacement insure ease in self servicing. military and computer grade components used exclusively.

RECEIVER PERFORMANCE
Sensitivity: .25 uV (−118 dBm or better) for 10 dB S N ratio at antenna input 1.6-30 MHz (2.1 kHz width in SSB).
Selectivity: 1st. I-F: 40.455 MHz ± 4kHz @ -6 dB. 1 dB ripple. 8 pole crystal filter.
2nd. I-F .455 kHz mechanical filters. @ 3 dB
Standard	Optional	
USB 2.1 kHz	CW2 375 Hz	AM 5.8 kHz
LSB 2.1 kHz	CW2 200 Hz	AFSK/LSB 300 Hz
CW1 1.9 kHz	(extra steep skirts)	(CF high tone pair)

Mixers: Specially developed, high-level, monolithic double balanced mixers with hot carrier diodes used in first and second mixer stages.
Intermodulation Distortion: (typical) 3rd. order input intercept point + 20 dBm for separated signals of 20 kHz.
2nd. order IMD is −80 dB.
Cross Modulation: Unmodulated wanted signal of 100 uV together with a modulated (30% at 1 kHz) unwanted signal of 100 mV spaced 30 kHz apart produces 10% Cross Mod.
Blocking: Attenuation of a wanted AF signal of 50 uV and caused by an unmodulated unwanted signal of 1V spaced 30 kHz apart then produces 3 dB blocking.
IF and Rejection: 80 dB
Synthesizer Phase Noise: Mean S/N ratio of 1st. L.O. (typical, reference to 1 Hz bandwidth). 90 dB measurement 1 kHz from carrier, 135 dB measurement 20 kHz from carrier

TRANSMIT PERFORMANCE
Power Amplifier: Solid state, broadband 1.6 — 30 MHz 150 W or 200 W (high power option) CW/PEP output keydown all bands and modes Automatic power cutback under excessive VSWR conditions. Heavy duty Hypersil* transformer for exceptional regulation and power. For continuous full power ''key down'' operation, blower option required
Third Order Intermodulation Distortion: 25 dB below each of two tones at full PEP output
Unwanted Signal Suppression: Carrier −50 dB min. undesired sidebands, 1 kHz −55 dB min. harmonic (all: −40 dB 10 log of mean power output. mixer products −50 min.

GENERAL
Frequency Coverage: 10 kHz to 29.9999 MHz receive, 10 kHz to 1.6 MHz at reduced sensitivity, 1.6 to 29.9999 MHz transmit.
Frequency Control: Memory provides split tuning A/B — using opto-electrical shaft encoder tuning in increments of 1 kHz 100 Hz and 10 Hz (180 kHz, 18 kHz, and 1800 Hz/360° respectively). selectable with front panel push buttons. **Tuning C** — preset frequency settable to 10 Hz with front panel lever switch. frequency entered by set button,display and BCD registers updated.
Memory: — frequencies stored in any of 9 memories, recalled for Tuning A/B frequencies with read push buttons. frequencies from Tuning A/B or C entered into memories with Auto Write or Write push button.
Stability: 1 ppm/month, 1 Hz/C°, 1 ppm after 15 min. warm-up at 25°C typical. For more demanding requirements, high stability reference oscillator option available — will meet military and commercial standards for specialized data transmissions.
Modes: USB, LSB, CW, AFSK, AM — receive. USB, LSB, CW AFSK/LSB — transmit.
Remote Computer Control: via rear panel 60 pin connector
1. BCD (1-2-4-8) 12 V CMOS parallel command for:
A Frequency / handshake   2 Pulse input to drive shaft
B Mode detection   encoder counters
C Bandpass tuning   3 AGC output
D. BFO tuning   4 Receiver mute command
Power Supply: Built-in heavy duty AC/DC supply. 115/230V ± 5%, 50 to 400 Hz. 12 to 15 VDC at 40 AMPS max., negative ground. 120 W max. in receive, 600W peak at full transmit input. Thermal and current overload protection
Size: 16.2'' wide. 7.8'' high; 17.8'' deep. **Weight:** 50 lbs.
Specifications are subject to change without notice or obligation.
*Introductory price — $4995.00.

Black Canyon Industrial Park/8146 N. 23rd Ave. Phoenix, Arizona 85021 (602) 995-0608

signal/one

Figure 8.21 — Signal/One introduced the Milspec 1030 as "The first fully synthesized HF transceiver." It sold for $5740 and went head-to-head with the Collins KWM-380 in the high-end transceiver category. Borrowing a bit from the competition, the Milspec 1030 used Collins mechanical filters in its 2nd IF. (Apr 1982)

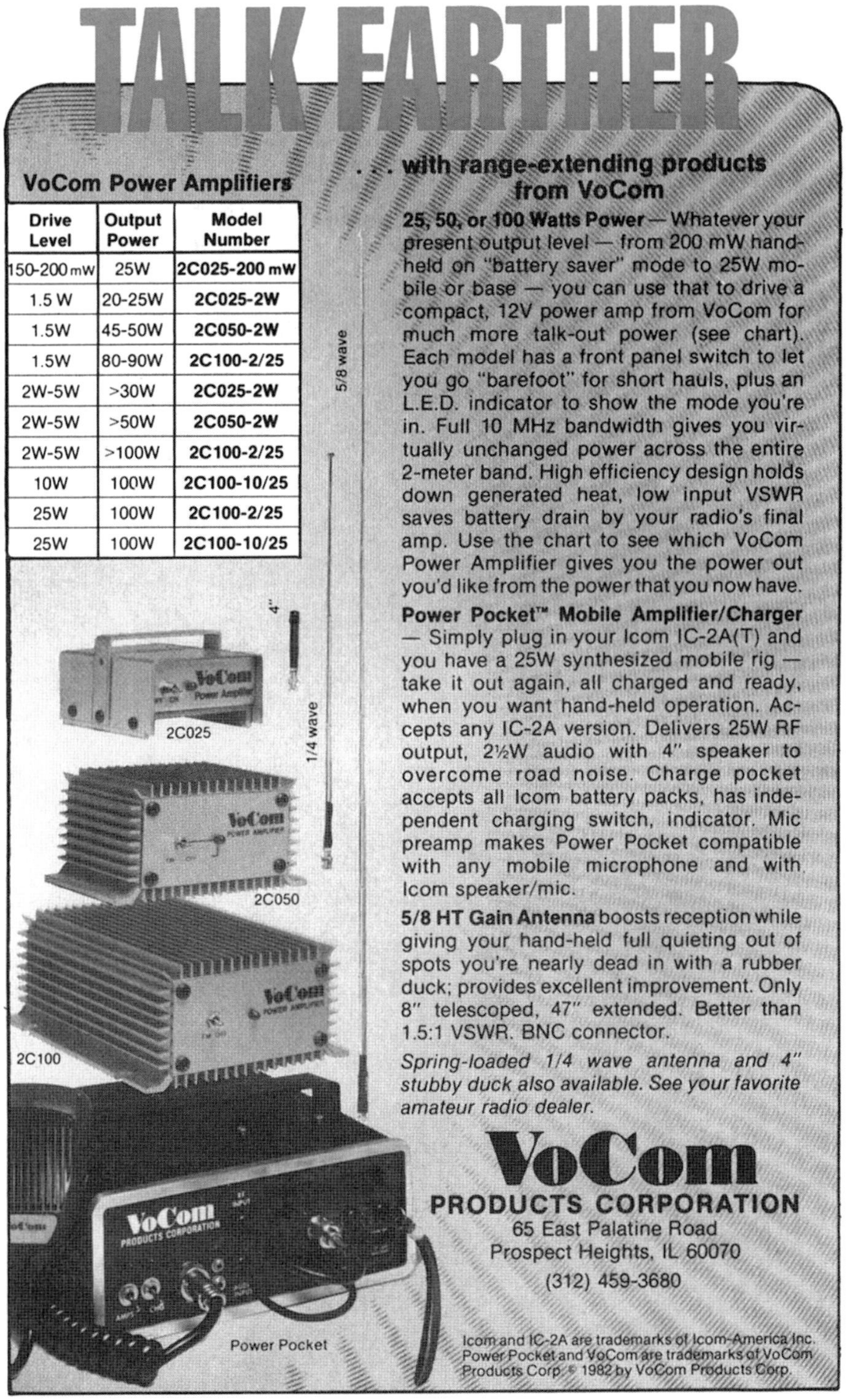

Figure 8.22 — VoCom manufactured power amplifiers and accessories for the VHF/UHF amateur bands in Prospect Heights, Illinois. The company changed its name to Crescend Technology in 2001, later relocating to nearby Schaumburg. It now serves military, medical, broadcast and avionics clients. (May 1982)

Figure 8.23 — Ameritron manufactured amplifiers, along with antenna tuners and switches, in Ohio before the company was sold to MFJ and moved to Mississippi. (Sep 1982)

Now you can chirp back!

Figure 8.24 — The FCC approved AMTOR (AMateur Teleprinting Over Radio) operation in January 1983 and equipment ads for the new ham mode appeared soon afterward. (Feb 1983)

Figure 8.25 — Heathkit called the SS-9000 "The Transceiver of the Decade." The company deemed the microprocessor-controlled transceiver too complicated for the average kit builder and sold it already assembled. The nearly $2800 rig failed to attract sufficient buyers. Heathkit discontinued the SS-9000 two years after its introduction. (Nov 1982)

Figure 8.26 — Yaesu's early entry in the Computer Aided Transceiver race used the company's proprietary CAT system and required an optional interface. (Mar 1983)

Figure 8.27 — Rock and roll sound innovator Bob Heil, K9EID, brought his audio expertise to ham radio as well. His first product line — an audio equalizer, a mic element and a speaker — grew into a catalog full of gear designed to improve communications audio. (Mar 1984)

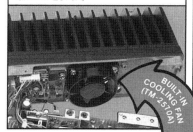

Figure 8.28 — As mobile FM transceivers acquired sophisticated feature sets, they also became more powerful. Kenwood's TM-2570A pushed the wattmeter reading to 70 W. (Jan 1986)

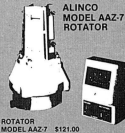
Figure 8.29 — Japanese manufacturer Alinco Electronics expanded its US product line to include amplifiers,
power supplies and antenna accessories in addition to its transceivers. (Apr 1986)

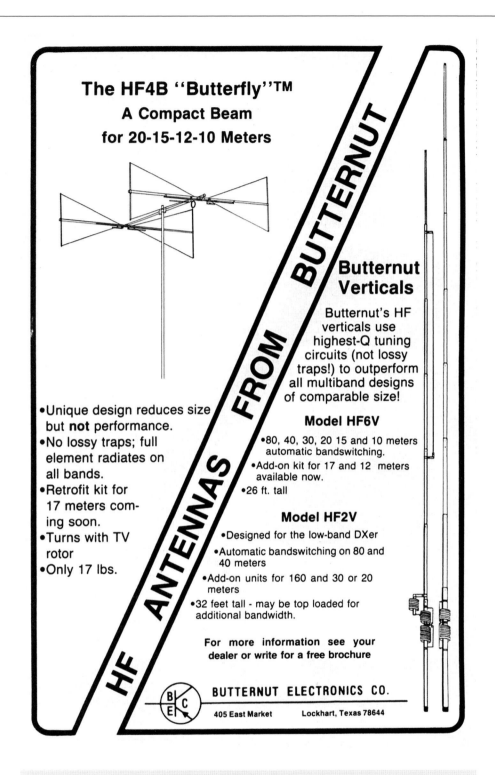
Figure 8.30 — Butternut's HF4B "Butterfly" beam appears to be a refinement of the single element "Wonderbar" antenna described in November 1956 *QST*. The Butternut verticals are now part of the Bencher, Inc. product line. (May 1986)

MFJ TUNERS

Figure 8.31 — By 1986, MFJ's product line had grown from that single CW filter advertised in 1973 to one with enough antenna tuners alone to fill an entire page. (Jun 1986)

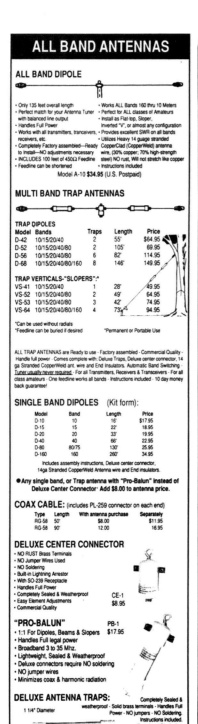

Figure 8.32 — The Bencher company entered the Amateur Radio market in 1977 with its revival and refinement of the W8FYO keyer paddle design. Spi-Ro Manufacturing offered a wide range of dipole antennas, baluns, traps and accessories. (Dec 1987)

Harness the Titan Power!

The TITAN has it all! Maximum legal power with ease, all bands 160 through 15 meters (through 10 meters after authorized modification), lightning fast QSK for full break-in CW and the digital modes, plus a two speed blower for quiet operation on phone. This awesome performance from a desk top amplifier is made possible by a pair of Eimac® 3CX800A7 ceramic triodes and an absolute "horse" of a power supply.

The heart of the power supply is our own tape wound, four core, Hypersil® transformer which weighs in at an impressive 41 pounds. This transformer is conservatively rated at 2.5KVA CCS (continuous commercial service) or 9KVA IVS (intermittent voice service). The power supply is housed in a separate utility enclosure for remote operation and is nearly noiseless even at full power.

Front panel features include an instantaneous 10 element LED peak output power indicator, a dedicated plate current meter, a multi-meter to read grid current, forward power, reflected power or plate voltage, HI/LO plate voltage select, STBY/OPR switch and power ON/OFF switch. A red LED warns you if grid current becomes excessive and three other LEDs indicate status: WAIT, STBY and OPERATE. Vernier TUNE and LOAD controls, in combination with an outstanding RF deck design, make the Titan a real "pussy cat" to load and operate.

The low drive requirement of the Titan (65 watts in for 1500 watts output typical) makes life much nicer for your exciter too. Operating temperatures are significantly lower and component life extended accordingly. This is especially comforting using "keydown" modes such as RTTY. Adjustable ALC is provided for controlling exciter RF output levels.

The Titan has been the subject of two "product review" magazine articles. See QST, April 1986; CQ February 1986.

The Titan is designed to match our 100 watt exciters but it pairs up nicely, no matter what exciter you operate. If you are ready to choose your dream amplifier the Titan has everything but the highest price. Check it out!

Write for our new full-line catalog.

Figure 8.33 — TEN-TEC's Titan legal limit amplifier, with its pair of Eimac 3CX800A7 tubes, is a sharp contrast to the company's Power-Mite QRP transceiver from 1969. (Apr 1988)

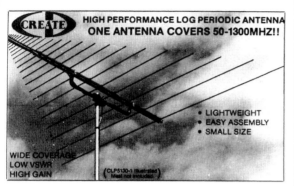
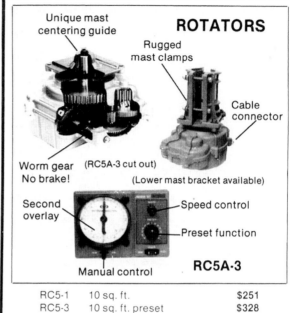
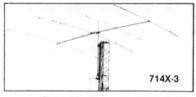

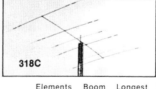
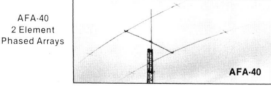

Figure 8.34 — Creative Design Company, a Japanese antenna manufacturer, sells antennas and accessory products worldwide under the Create name. (Feb 1988)

THE FUTURE OF
AMATEUR COMMUNICATIONS

Once in a lifetime, a transceiver is introduced that's so extraordinary and innovative that it opens a totally new era in HF communications. ICOM's pacesetting IC-781 proudly exhibits that hallmark achievement with futuristic designs and features of true legendary proportions. Whether DX'ing, contesting, pioneering new interests or enjoying unquestionable top-of-the-line performance, the IC-781 is indeed today's standard of excellence!

Multi-Function Five Inch CRT. Displays frequencies, modes, memory contents, operating notes, RIT, two menu screens, plus a panoramic view of all signals in a selected range. A portion of the screen also serves as a display for data modes like RTTY, AMTOR, and PACKET.

Unique Spectrum Scope. Continuously indicates all signal activities and DX pileups with your operating frequency in the center. Selectable horizontal frequency spans of 50,

100, and 200KHz for each side of the frequency you're listening to. Vertical range indicates relative signal strengths. A contester's dream!

Dual Width Noise Blanker includes MCF filter plus **level and width controls** to eliminate pulse and woodpecker noise with minimum adjacent-signal interference.

Incomparable Filter Flexibility. Independent selection of wide and narrow SSB filters plus CW filters. Second and third CW IF filters are independently selectable!

Dual Watch. Simultaneously **receives two frequencies in the same band!** Balance control adjusts VFO A/B receive strength levels. You can check additional band activity, even tune in your next contact, while in QSO without missing a single word!

DX Rated! 150 watts of exceptionally clean RF output. Easily drives big amplifiers to maximum power.

Twin Passband Tuning with **separate controls for second and third IF stages!** Increases selectivity and narrows bandwidth, independently varies low and high frequency response, or functions as IF shift. **It's DX'ing Dynamite!**

A Total Communications System! Includes built-in 100% duty AC supply, high speed automatic antenna tuner, iambic keyer, semi-automatic or full QSK CW break-in to 60 wpm, Audio Peaking Filter (APF), RF speech processor, multiscanning, 105dB dynamic range, all-band/all-mode receiver with general coverage, and much more!

ICOM Dependability. The phenomenal IC-781 is built for action and backed with the most extensive warranty in the industry.

See the IC-781 at your local ICOM dealer.

ICOM
First in Communications

ICOM America, Inc., 2380 116th Avenue N.E., Bellevue, WA 98004
Customer Service Hotline (206) 454-7619
3150 Premier Drive, Suite 126, Irving, TX 75063
1777 Phoenix Parkway, Suite 201, Atlanta, GA 30349
ICOM CANADA, A Division of ICOM America, Inc.,
3071 - #5 Road, Unit 9, Richmond, B.C. V6X 2T4
All stated specifications subject to change without notice or obligation.
All ICOM radios significantly exceed FCC regulations limiting spurious emissions. 781188.

Figure 8.35 — With a 5-inch CRT as the centerpiece of its front panel, the IC-781 looked every bit the "Future of Amateur Communications" that ICOM's ad proclaimed. The high-performance transceiver weighed in at 51 pounds and carried a $6000 price tag. (Jul 1988)

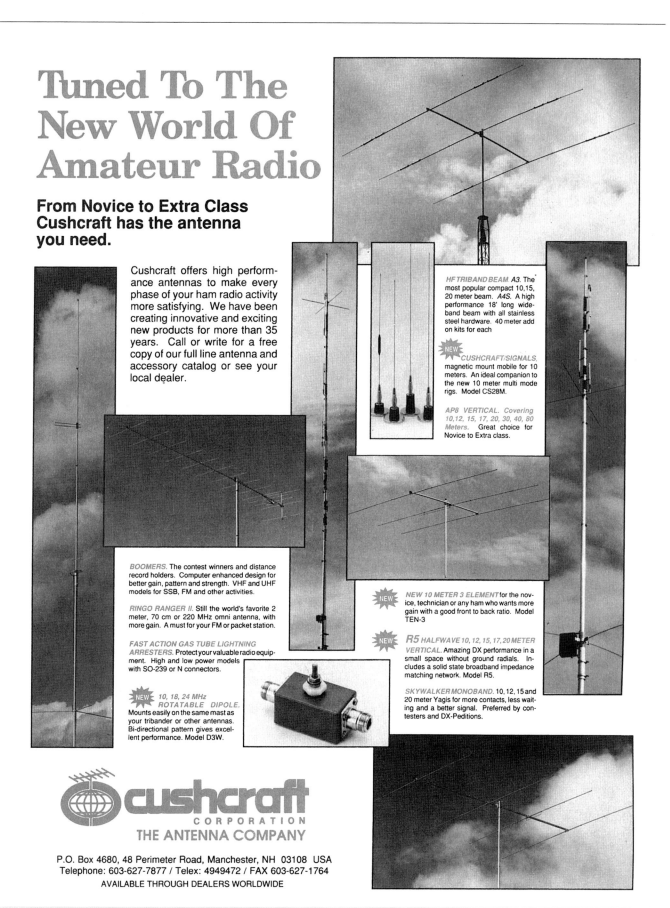

Tuned To The New World Of Amateur Radio

From Novice to Extra Class Cushcraft has the antenna you need.

Cushcraft offers high performance antennas to make every phase of your ham radio activity more satisfying. We have been creating innovative and exciting new products for more than 35 years. Call or write for a free copy of our full line antenna and accessory catalog or see your local dealer.

HF TRIBAND BEAM. A3. The most popular compact 10,15, 20 meter beam. *A4S.* A high performance 18' long wideband beam with all stainless steel hardware. 40 meter add on kits for each

NEW *CUSHCRAFT/SIGNALS,* magnetic mount mobile for 10 meters. An ideal companion to the new 10 meter multi mode rigs. Model CS28M.

AP8 VERTICAL. Covering 10,12, 15, 17, 20, 30, 40, 80 Meters. Great choice for Novice to Extra class.

BOOMERS. The contest winners and distance record holders. Computer enhanced design for better gain, pattern and strength. VHF and UHF models for SSB, FM and other activities.

RINGO RANGER II. Still the world's favorite 2 meter, 70 cm or 220 MHz omni antenna, with more gain. A must for your FM or packet station.

FAST ACTION GAS TUBE LIGHTNING ARRESTERS. Protect your valuable radio equipment. High and low power models with SO-239 or N connectors.

NEW *10, 18, 24 MHz ROTATABLE DIPOLE.* Mounts easily on the same mast as your tribander or other antennas. Bi-directional pattern gives excellent performance. Model D3W.

NEW *NEW 10 METER 3 ELEMENT* for the novice, technician or any ham who wants more gain with a good front to back ratio. Model TEN-3

NEW *R5 HALFWAVE 10, 12, 15, 17, 20 METER VERTICAL.* Amazing DX performance in a small space without ground radials. Includes a solid state broadband impedance matching network. Model R5.

SKYWALKER MONOBAND. 10, 12, 15 and 20 meter Yagis for more contacts, less waiting and a better signal. Preferred by contesters and DX-Peditions.

cushcraft
CORPORATION
THE ANTENNA COMPANY

P.O. Box 4680, 48 Perimeter Road, Manchester, NH 03108 USA
Telephone: 603-627-7877 / Telex: 4949472 / FAX 603-627-1764
AVAILABLE THROUGH DEALERS WORLDWIDE

Figure 8.36 — Cushcraft's product line expanded by two antennas after the FCC authorized US amateurs to use the 18 MHz band. The R4 vertical became the R5 when the new band opened, and the D3W dipole covered 10, 18 and 24 MHz. (Aug 1989)

Figure 8.37 — Vibroplex is the oldest name in ham radio. It was incorporated the same year *QST* published its first issue. In the mid-1980s, Vibroplex added new paddle designs, including a model with a keyer built into the base, to the company's traditional bugs. (Oct 1989)

Chapter 9

The 1990s

DSP, Vanity Calls, Mini Handhelds and PC-Based Radios

When Harold Price, NK6K, heard what he thought might be an amateur packet radio signal while watching the movie *Star Trek IV — The Voyage Home*, he challenged Bob McGwier, N4HY, to demodulate the signal.[1,2] McGwier had access to a Cray-2 supercomputer at work and he set about writing software for a demodulator to run on the speedy machine. Phil Karn, KA9Q, helped decode the resulting data. When their work was done, the mysterious signals proved to be an HF packet transmission from Bill Harrigill, WA8ZCN. Using digital signal processing (DSP), 20th century hams had successfully decoded signals from a fictional twenty-third century starship.

Digital signal processing technology appeared first in outboard accessories and later became part of internal radio architecture. The initial DSP project articles in *QST* were for things such as a spectrum display and an audio processing filter for receivers.[3,4] Commercial manufacturers likewise concentrated on DSP-based accessories to begin with. Packet radio benefitted from DSP early on. Because of the wide variety of data rates and modulation schemes, a technology that could handle it all with just a software change was a welcome development.[5]

Late in 1995 ICOM announced its IC-775DSP transceiver.[6] The full-featured HF rig used digital processing at both IF and audio frequencies. Kenwood stayed right on ICOM's heels with the TS-870S DSP transceiver.[7] Kenwood's rig held its own in the selectivity department without additional analog filters. Yaesu entered the DSP game with the FT-1000MP. The transceiver's double-barreled approach to filtering used a combination of analog crystal and mechanical filters along with DSP filtering.[8]

As amateurs adopted new technologies, some kept one foot in older technology as well. The mid-1990s saw a groundswell of interest in collecting and restoring vacuum tube equipment from years gone by. Recreating one's first Novice station inspired some. Others purchased equipment that had been beyond their means at an earlier time. Gear from Collins, Hallicrafters, National, Hammarlund and others — all the great names from old *QSTs* — joined modern equipment in ham shacks. Interest in a special area such as heavy-iron AM or early SSB provided a theme for some collectors. Equipment from a particular manufacturer motivated others. After its restoration, the vintage gear was often returned to the air rather than just sitting on display. Groups devoted to one brand of equipment, or a particular mode of operation, formed clubs, created nets and held conventions.[9]

The interest in vintage gear made vacuum tubes a hot hamfest commodity and several suppliers popped up online as well. With US manufacturers all but shut down, hams turned to suppliers in Russia, Eastern Europe and China for new tubes. Svetlana Electron Devices from St Petersburg, Russia, became a major source of power amplifier tubes and opened offices and distribution centers in the US.[10]

In 1996 the FCC revived its Vanity Call Sign program which let amateurs choose their own calls.[11] Only Extra Class licensees had been eligible under a 1976-77 version of the program. All amateurs could participate in the 1996 program as it moved through a series of four qualifying gates. The first gate opened on May 31, 1996. The program proved wildly popular as tens of thousands of amateurs lined up to change their calls from those dealt to them by chance and the FCC computer.

Another activity took off mid-decade, gaining popularity and participants as it soared. Bob Bruninga, WB4APR, developed the Automatic Packet Reporting System (APRS), a digital communications and tracking medium.[12] The March 1999 "Digital Dimension" column in *QST* reported APRS to be the fastest growing amateur activity of the decade.[13] New APRS software and

The Drake R-8 tuned from 100 kHz to 30 MHz. Introduced in 1991, it remained in production (in A and B models) until 1998. ($1090)

ICOM offered an attractive feature set for a mid-priced transceiver with the introduction of the IC-746 in 1998. The 100 W SSB, CW, AM, FSK, AFSK and FM rig covered 160 to 10, plus 6 and 2 meters. It carried a manufacturer's suggested list price of $2280.

Radio Shack's shirt pocket-size 2 meter FM hand held put out 200 mW of RF using its internal AA batteries but could manage 2 W when connected to an external 9 V source. ($179.99, 1999)

hardware surfaced in the wake of the mode's growth. Kenwood's TH-D7A handheld transceiver put a complete APRS station in the palm of its owner's hand.

A pair of general purpose handhelds shrank to almost science-fiction size. The DJ-C1T (144 MHz) and DJ-C1T (440 MHz) from Alinco were the length and width of a credit card and not much thicker. They were introduced at the 1997 Hamvention. Alinco one-upped itself the following year with a dualbander the same size.[14]

Commercial gear, and not just the micro-dimensioned handheld, was becoming increasingly difficult for most amateurs to service. Component size and construction techniques often meant a trip back to the manufacturer for repairs. With Heathkits and Knight-Kits long since vanished from the scene, TEN-TEC and Vectronics rode to the rescue of the amateur who wanted to build something. In turn, a home builder might have a better shot at fixing it if something went wrong later.[15,16] Elecraft produced kits with performance rivaling that of factory built equipment.[17]

Amateur Radio mobile operation benefited from 1990s innovations. The smaller size of both HF and VHF transceivers brought installation convenience at a time when it was becoming difficult to find room for a mobile rig in the contemporary automobile. Radios with detachable control heads made it possible to mount the head in an easily accessible spot while stashing the bulk of the radio under the seat or in the trunk. This feature added a measure of anti-theft security as well because the control head was easily removed or hidden when the operator left the vehicle. Multiband, remote-tuned HF mobile antennas proliferated as the trend of taking ham radio on the road grew.

Low power (QRP) HF communication continued to attract a following in the 1990s. *QST* published nearly 100 items or articles on QRP equipment and operating during the decade. The most basic QRP rigs operated only on CW and generally used a direct conversion receiver. TEN-TEC's Argonaut transceiver with a superhet receiver included SSB as well as CW. The 5 W rig celebrated its 20th birthday in 1992 but the Argonaut 505 and its successor models still enjoyed popularity among the QRP crowd. The Argonaut had become a classic as had Heathkit's HW series of QRP transceivers. The last of that line, the HW-9, remained on the market until 1991.[18]

New QRP gear appeared in the '90s as well. Companies such as Index Laboratories, MFJ, Small Wonder Labs, Gary Breed, Oak Hills Research, Wilderness Radio, G QRP Club, and S&S Engineering sold transceiver kits.[19] In addition to the commercial gear, *QST* presented QRP enthusiasts with construction projects by designers such as Wes Hayward, W7ZOI, and Roy Lewallen, W7EL.[20,21]

Kachina introduced the first computer-controlled amateur HF transceiver at the 1997 Dayton Hamvention. The 505DSP lacked a conventional rig's front panel and knobs but included things such as on-screen logging software, a spectrum analyzer with point-and-click tuning, and a Smith Chart for the station's antenna. A separate box contained the bulk of the transceiver's hardware and a control head fit into one of the accompanying computer's drive bay slots.[22] The 80-10 meter, 100 W rig depended upon IF DSP for selectivity, much as Kenwood's more conventional TS-870S had.

Competition for the Kachina arrived in 1999 in the form of TEN-TEC's Pegasus, a 100 W, computer-based HF transceiver.[23] When introduced, the Pegasus did not interface with existing logging programs. For those not accustomed to tuning a radio with a mouse or keyboard arrows, TEN-TEC made an accessory tuning knob and number entry keypad.

By the end of the 1990s, most of the basic technology of 21st century radio was already falling into place. It awaited only the turn of the millennium for further development and implementation. The view through the looking glass included computer-based radios such as the Kachina and Pegasus, but not necessarily as separate units. The computer would take up residence inside the radio box rather than the other way around. Conventional knobs and switches would control the interior computer's functions with a familiar looking physical front panel as an interface.

Two days before the end of 1999

the FCC issued a Report and Order changing the face and structure of the Amateur Radio Service. The action reduced the number of license classes to three — Technician, General and Amateur Extra — and instituted a single 5 WPM code speed requirement for all license classes.[24]

Notes

[1] *Star Trek IV — The Voyage Home* (Paramount Pictures: 1986.)

[2] B. Hale, KB1MW/7, "An Introduction to Digital Signal Processing," *QST*, Jul 1991, pp 35-37.

[3] B. de Carle, VE2IQ, "A Receiver Spectral Display Using DSP," *QST*, Jan 1992, pp 23-29.

[4] D. Hershberger, W9GR, "Low-Cost Digital Signal Processing for the Radio Amateur," *QST*, Sep 1992, pp 43-51.

[5] S. Horzepa, WA1LOU, "Packet Perspective — The Digital Signal Processing of Packet Radio," *QST*, Jul 1990, p 66.

[6] ICOM ad, *QST*, Dec 1995, p 17.

[7] Kenwood ad, *QST*, Jan 1996, Cover 6.

[8] R. Lindquist, KX4V and G. Swanson, KB1GW, "Product Review — Yaesu FT-1000MP MF/HF Transceiver," *QST*, Apr 1996, pp 68-73.

[9] G. Maier, K1GXT, "The Collins Collectors Association," *QST*, Mar 1999, pp 31-33.

[10] "New Products — Russian Power (Tubes!)", *QST*, Nov 1994, p 104.

[11] R. Lindquist, KX4V, "Happenings — Vanity Call Sign filing Gate 1 Opens!," *QST*, Jul 1996, p 70.

[12] S. Cubbedge, NØUEI, "Automatic Packer Reporting System," *QST*, Sep 1996, p 58.

[13] S. Horzepa, WA1LOU, "Digital Dimension — Getting on the Bus with APRS," *QST*. Mar 1999, p 88.

[14] R. Lindquist, N1RL, "Alinco's Amazing Credit Card H-Ts," *QST*, Oct 1998, pp 74-77.

[15] "New Products — New Radio Kits from Vectronics," *QST*, Feb 1999, p 70.

[16] "New Products — Ten-Tec Kits," *QST*, Aug 1994, p 35.

[17] Elecraft ad, *QST*, Jun 1999, p 122.

[18] C. Penson, WA7ZZE, *Heathkit: A Guide to the Amateur Radio Products* (Hicksville, New York: 2003), p 151.

[19] R. Lindquist, KX4V, "Low-Power Transceiver Kits You Can Build," *QST*, Jun 1996, pp 45-50.

[20] W. Hayward, W7ZOI, "A QRP SSB/CW Transceiver for 14 MHz — Part 2," *QST*, Jan 1990, pp 28-31.

[21] R. Lewallen, W7EL, "A Simple and Accurate QRP Directional Wattmeter," *QST*, Feb 1990, pp 19-23.

[22] R. Lindquist, N1RL, "Kachina 505DSP HF Transceiver," *QST*, May 1998, pp 63-69.

[23] P. Danzer, N1II, "Ten-Tec Pegasus HF Transceiver," *QST*, Feb 2000, pp 63-67.

[24] R. Lindquist, N1RL, "Restructuring is Here: Three License Classes, One Code Speed," *QST*, Feb 2000, pp 68-69.

Figure 9.1 — PolyPhaser provided amateurs with broadcast station quality lightning protection not only for towers and antenna feed lines but for rotator and other control cables as well. (Apr 1990)

Figure 9.2 — Burghardt Amateur Radio Center in Watertown, South Dakota — founded by Stan Burghardt, WØIT, in 1937 — sold ham gear for more than 70 years. In 2009, the company left the retail business to concentrate instead on equipment repair as Burghardt Radio Repair, Inc. (Feb 1994)

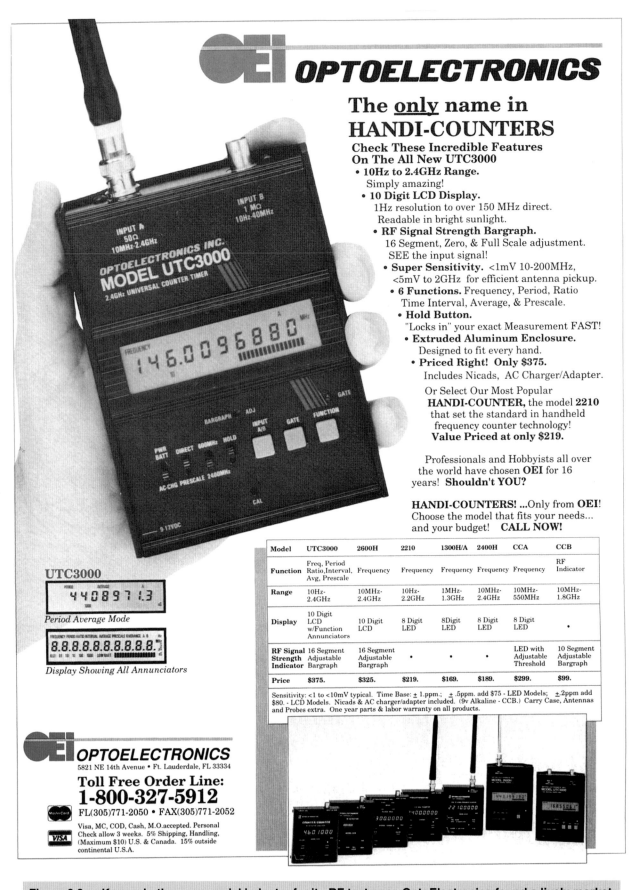

Figure 9.3 — Known in the commercial industry for its RF test gear, OptoElectronics found a lively market among amateurs for instruments such as frequency counters. (May 1990)

Commander™ HF-2500
Linear Amplifier

The **NEW** TOP GUN

Chassis Top View

R.F. Deck
Top View

R.F. Deck
Bottom View

- Two Eimac 3CX800A7 Triodes
- Built for High Duty Cycle Emissions
- 1500 watts output continuous carrier
- 1600 watts plate dissipation capability

- 3 year limited warranty
- Factory direct sales and service
- Band Coverage: 160, 80, 40, 20, and 15 meters (10 meters export)

MADE IN U.S.A. BY HAMS FOR HAMS   UPS Shipable!

COMMAND TECHNOLOGIES, INC.
1117 W. High St., P.O. Box 939, Bryan, Ohio 43506
Toll Free 1-800-736-0443

Figure 9.4 — The Command Technologies amplifier business changed owners several times before winding up in the hands of Daniel Simonds, KK3AN. (Apr 1990)

Figure 9.5 — The Japanese Marantz company manufactured the Standard brand of VHF/UHF transceivers. The product line included handheld, mobile, single band and multiband units. Yaesu Musen acquired Standard from Marantz in 1998. (Mar 1991)

Figure 9.6 — As the Bird Electronics Corporation's ad claims, its power measuring instruments have long been the industry standard. Using a variety of easily-changed elements, the Model 43 meter reads power from milliwatt levels all the way up to 10 kW. For years, Cubex offered a line of quad antennas.(Apr 1990)

See the world through Kenwood's HamWindows™

Amateur Radio enthusiasts Joe Rudi and his son Shaun use their PC to discover the new visual world of Kenwood's HamWindows.

HamWindows™ is an all new concept in the world of Amateur Radio. This program pulls together  eight full color "windows" including transceiver control, station log, world almanac, awards tracking, SWL data base, greyline maps, regional world maps, and packet TNC control.

Using a mouse to "point and click" HamWindows™ lets you see the world your transceiver hears. Use the almanac to learn more about the countries you contact, and then add the QSO to the logging program. You'll automatically track contacts for the DXCC award. The SWL data base lists thousands of frequencies and schedules from over 9,000 broadcast stations. And the  greyline and regional maps put the world at your fingertips. With the proper interface you can even control  your Kenwood HF transceiver.

HamWindows™ is the one program every amateur or shortwave listener needs. See your Kenwood dealer for system requirements and more information.

KENWOOD

...pacesetter in Amateur Radio

KENWOOD U.S.A. CORPORATION COMMUNICATIONS & TEST EQUIPMENT GROUP
P.O. BOX 22745, 2201 E. Dominguez Street, Long Beach, CA 90801-5745
© Copyright 1991 Kenwood U.S.A. Corporation All rights reserved.
HamWindows is a trademark of California Software, Inc.

Figure 9.7 — Personal computers gained a strong foothold in 1990s ham shacks. Kenwood's *HamWindows* program enabled computer control of Kenwood transceivers and packet TNC in addition to managing a host of station paperwork tasks. (Feb 1992)

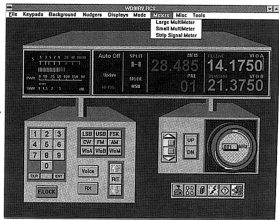

Figure 9.8 — The Microsoft *Windows* based program from California Software integrated rig control of Yaesu, ICOM, Kenwood and SGC transceivers with other functions such as DX cluster operation and band-scanning. (Jun 1993)

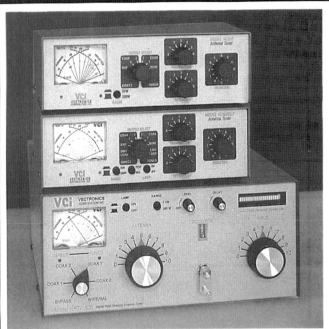

Figure 9.9 — Vectronics manufactured antenna tuners in Canada in the early 1990s. The brand was later acquired by MFJ. (Jan 1992)

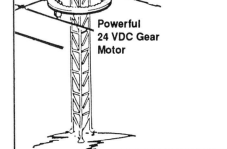
Figure 9.10 — The TIC Ring system rotated multiple antennas on a single tower, either individually or in arrays. (Feb 1993)

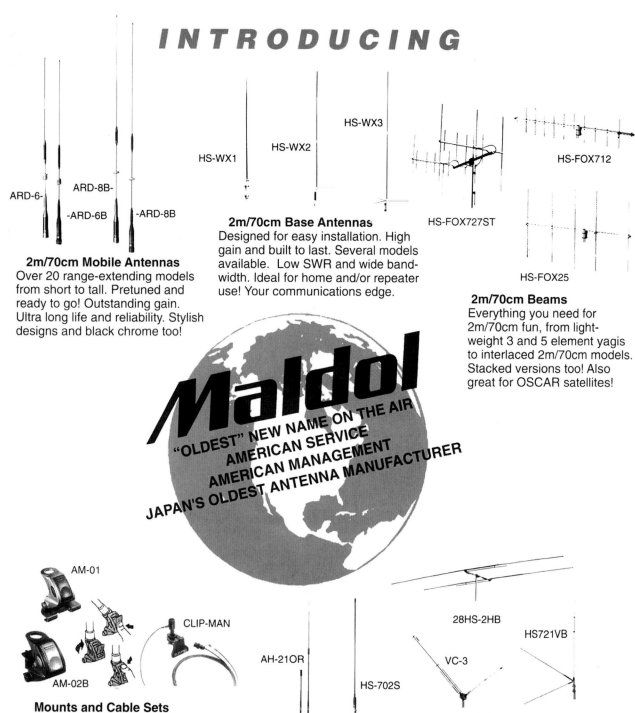
Figure 9.11 — Maldol, Japan's oldest antenna manufacturer, opened a US office in 1994 headed up by Jim Smith, KA7APJ. Maldol is now part of the NCG Company along with Comet and Daiwa. (May 1994)

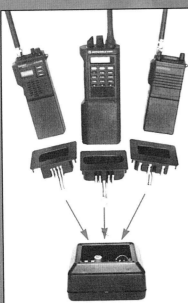

Figure 9.12 — W & W Associates in Hicksville, New York, manufactures and sells replacement batteries and chargers for ham radio gear. (Mar 1995)

Figure 9.13 — AEA's Antenna Analyst equipped the amateur with a variety of tools for diagnosing antenna performance and curing problems. The SWR-121 was made in models for both the HF and VHF/UHF ranges. (Jul 1995)

Figure 9.14 — In 1971, Pierre Goral and Don Stoner, W6TNS, formed a partnership called SGC with the goal of applying "…leading edge technology to the production of high frequency communication equipment." A number of interesting — and leading edge — products for the amateur market resulted. (Oct 1995)

QRO AMPLIFIERS™ DELIVER HIGH PERFORMANCE, EXCEPTIONAL DURABILITY, AND SUPERIOR QUALITY FOR A REASONABLE COST.

The HF-1000 one kilowatt and the HF-2000 1.5 kilowatt plus desktop linear amplifiers can put you in control. Our unique blend of high quality, durability, and performance will make your operating time both exciting and enjoyable. It can all be yours for an affordable price. Some manufacturers may offer linears with similar specifications for a cheaper price, but they fall short when you consider the overall picture of cost, performance, durability, and quality. QRO amplifiers delivers them all....

ALL HF BANDS & NO COMPROMISES

RUGGED & DURABLE CERAMIC BANDSWITCH

USER ADJUSTABLE STATE OF ART TUNED INPUT CIRCUITS

DUAL FRONT PANEL METERS

FRONT PANEL USER ADJUSTABLE (ALC) AUTOMATIC LIMITING CONTROL

FRONT PANEL OPERATE / STANDBY SWITCH

FRONT PANEL MULTIMETER SWITCH

6 to 1 RATIO VERNIER TUNE AND LOAD CONTROLS WITH LOGGING SCALES

ATTRACTIVE ALL ALUMINUM CABINET WITH LEXAN® FRONT & REAR PANEL SURFACE

A TOUGH POWER SUPPLY CAN DELIVER UP TO 2,500 WATTS OF INPUT POWER EFFORTLESSLY

A WHISPER QUIET FAN PROVIDES FULL CABINET PRESSURIZED COOLING

SAFE, DEPENDABLE, AND COST EFFECTIVE 3-500 TRIODES

ELECTRONIC CATHODE BIAS SWITCH (ECBS)

FAST SEQUENCED TRANSMIT / RECEIVE (T/R) SWITCHING

+15VDC T/R SWITCHING ACTIVATION

PI-BROAD BAND L OUTPUT NETWORK USING A 4:1 TRANSFORMER

PETER DAHL BLACK EPOXY COATED HYPERSIL® POWER TRANSFORMERS

STEP-START CIRCUIT PROTECTS AGAINST DAMAGING INRUSH CURRENTS

TWO YEAR WARRANTY

UPS SHIPPABLE

FACTORY DIRECT SALES & SERVICE

MADE IN THE USA BY HAMS FOR HAMS™

EXPORT ORDERS WELCOME

We welcome export orders. We will ship direct with no importer or dealer involvement. This allows you buy our amplifiers at US prices without those expensive importer or dealer profit margins added to the final retail price. We can ship to most major airports worldwide using several carriers and forwarding agents.

VISA, MASTERCARD, OR WIRE TRANSFER PAYMENT ACCEPTED

We accept payment using Visa, Mastercard, or wire transfer of funds in US Dollars.

LICENSED AMATEURS CALL TOLL FREE
1-800-956-2721

To request free brochures, request further details, or place your order... Call Our Toll Free Customer Service Number 1-800-956-2721 Monday thru Friday from 8:00 AM to 5:00 PM Eastern Time.

PRICES (US DOLLARS)
F.O.B. Bryan, Ohio USA

HF-1000	$1,495.00
HF-2000	$1,795.00
QSK OPTION	$100.00 Additional

SPECIFICATIONS

Band Coverage:

160,80,40,20,15,15 (12 & 10 export; also usable in USA with license)

Output Power:

HF-1000 1000w SSB, 800w CW, 400w RTTY, SSTV, FM

HF-2000 1500w SSB, 1250w CW, 800w RTTY, SSTV, FM

Drive Power Requirement:

HF-1000 80 w input 800 w output
HF-2000 110 w input 1200w output

Line Voltage Requirement:

100/110/200/220 V, 50/60 Hz, 20 amp @ 120 V, 10 amp @ 240 V

Cabinet Size: 16w x 15d x8.5h (in) 48w x 38d x 22h (cm)

Shipping Wt. 76 lbs or 34.5 kgs. Three Cartons

WE BUILD THEM LIKE THEY OUGHT TO BE!™

QRO TECHNOLOGIES, INC.
1117 West High Street
P.O. Box 939
Bryan, Ohio 43506
Tel: (419) 636-2721 / Fax: (419) 636-6039

Figure 9.15 — QRO Technologies of Bryan, Ohio, manufactures high power amplifiers. Ray Connin, KB8VU, co-owned Command Technologies from 1988 to 1994, when he left to start QRO. (Nov 1995)

Figure 9.16 — The MP part of the FT-1000MP's model number pays homage to Sakou Hasegowa, JA1MP (SK), Yaesu's founder. He named his company after its location in the Yaesu suburb of Tokyo. (Feb 1996)

Figure 9.17 — Timewave Technologies, established in St. Paul, Minnesota, in 1984, makes outboard DSP filters for use with amateur transceivers. Timewave later acquired the AEA company's data products. (Mar 1996)

Figure 9.18 — Bruce Franklin, K7DYY, designed the Index Laboratories QRP Plus CW/SSB transceiver. The 160-10 meter transceiver's output power was adjustable from 200 mW to 5 W. (Aug 1996)

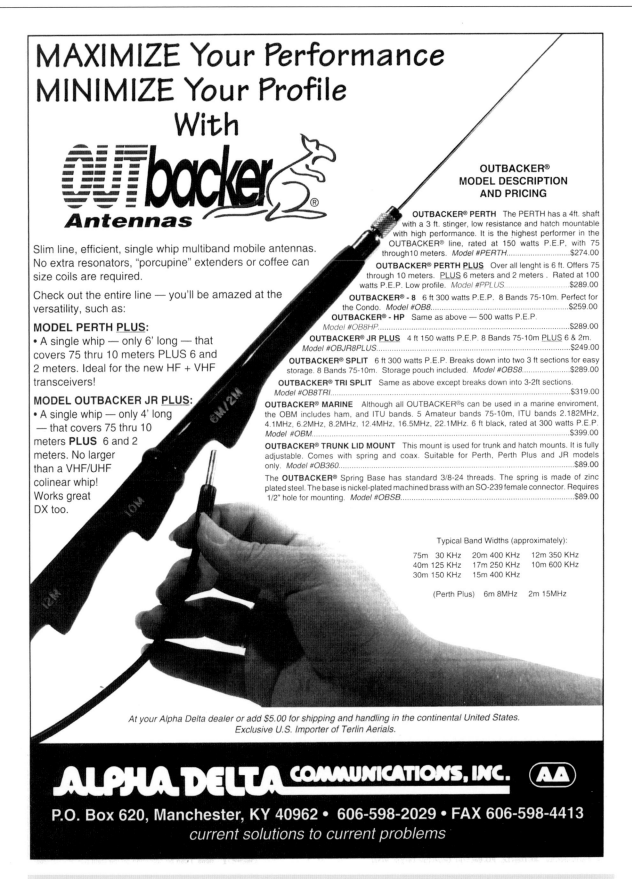
Figure 9.19 — Terlin Outbacker Antennas and Communications manufactures the Outbacker series of mobile/portable antennas in Canning Vale, Western Australia. Distribution in the US has been handled at various times by Alpha Delta, Outbacker Antenna Sales, and Outbacker North America, Inc. (Oct 1996)

Figure 9.20 — Svetlana Electron Devices, based in St. Petersburg, Russia, serves the US audio and RF markets for Svetlana-branded vacuum tubes. (Nov 1996)

Figure 9.21 — Frank Delfine, WB2UJS, president of Patcomm, introduced the company's new transceiver in late 1996. Patcomm manufactured the PC-16000, a combination of conventional transceiver and DSP filtering, in St. James, New York. (Dec 1996)

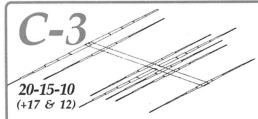

Figure 9.22 — Tom Schiller, N6BT, founded Force 12 antennas and designed its product line. The C-3 trapless tribander in the ad has at its heart the Open Cell driver element assembly for 10, 15, and 20 meters. The 20 meter driver parasitically excites the 15 and 10 meter driver elements, which have no direct connection to the feed line. (Dec 1996)

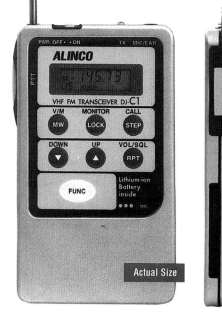
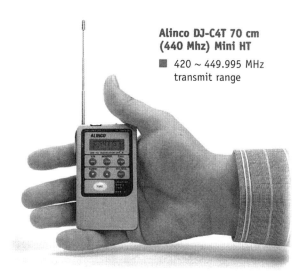

Figure 9.23 — Handheld FM transceivers kept getting smaller, perhaps nearing the irreducible minimum in the Alinco DJ-C1T and DJ-C4T. The credit card-size handhelds debuted at the 1997 Dayton Hamvention. (Oct 1997)

Figure 9.24 — The TR270 represented Drake's first new transceiver in more than 12 years. The American-made 2 meter rig included features such as both voice and data communication, 70 cm band reception, and automatic Doppler compensation when using satellites — but at a price. The TR270 sold for just under $1000. (Aug 1997)

Figure 9.25 —Bencher, Inc., well-known for its keyer paddles, also makes antennas. Their Skyhawk 3X10, a trap-free triband Yagi design, uses four elements on 10 meters and three each on 15 and 20. (Jan 1999)

Figure 9.26 — The K2 HF transceiver came in modular kit form, with performance rivaling that of top-end HF transceivers. Elecraft offered a number of options for the basic 10 W CW rig, including 100 W PA and SSB generator modules. (Aug 1999)

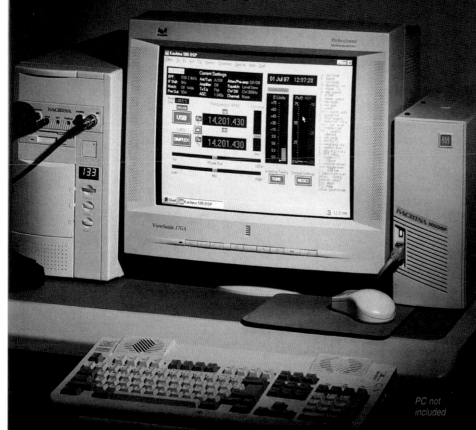
Figure 9.27 — Kachina Communications' innovative 505DSP transceiver, introduced in 1997, glimpsed at the future with its DSP-based IF filtering. The 100 W transceiver covered the 160-10 meter bands (general coverage receive from 30 kHz to 30 MHz) and worked in conjunction with a Microsoft *Windows* computer. Kachina discontinued production of all amateur gear in 2001. (Oct 1997)

Figure 9.28 — With the growing interest in restoration and operation of vintage gear, companies such as Surplus Sales of Nebraska saw a market for hard to find components. Surplus Sales specialized in parts for Collins Radio equipment. (Nov 1998)

Figure 9.29 — TEN-TEC joined the PC radio movement with the Pegasus transceiver. At the time of its introduction the Pegasus had only the Kachina 505DSP for competition. (Sep 1999)

Chapter 10

2000-2009

Morse Code Testing Ends, 60 Meters, Broadband over Power Lines and PSK31

Few things generate more excitement in the Amateur Radio community than the opening of a new HF band. However, the unusual structure and operating restrictions for the 60 meter band tempered enthusiasm for the new allocation when the FCC opened it July 3, 2003.[1] In the conventional sense, it was not really a band at all.

Rather than grant the 150 kHz wide band requested in the ARRL's petition, the FCC instead allocated five discrete 2.8 kHz wide channels between 5332 and 5405 kHz.[2] The regulations restricted amateurs to upper sideband operation with an effective radiated power (ERP) limit of 50 watts. A chief reason for the League's request for spectrum near 5 MHz was for improving the prospects for communication between the US and the Caribbean region during times of emergency. A 60 meter allocation would bridge the propagation gap that existed when using 40 and 80 meters.

The Commission granted the League temporary authority for experimental 5 MHz communications using the call sign WA2XSY. The resulting tests showed 60 meters to be more reliable than either 40 or 80 for US to Caribbean paths. The tests concluded in 2001 and when the allocation was made in 2003, it was on a shared basis. The other users were primarily federal agencies with security responsibilities.[3]

The FCC loosened the restrictions somewhat in 2012, increasing ERP to 100 W and adding CW and digital modes to the permitted modes list.[4] Despite the restrictions and channelized operation, activity on the 60 meter band grew, especially as additional nations joined those already on the band.

Opening a new band isn't the only way to create excitement in Amateur Radio. Another proven method is to change something — *anything* — that has been part of the hobby long enough to achieve institution status. The FCC did just that when it eliminated the Morse

ICOM introduced the IC-7800 in 2004 and released an upgraded version of the 160 to 6 meter, high performance transceiver in late 2006. Additions to the newer model included a 3 kHz roofing filter. ($10,600)

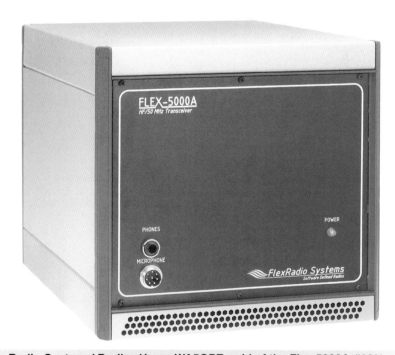

Flex Radio Systems' Dudley Hurry, WA5QPZ, said of the Flex 5000A, "80% of the radio is in the computer." Indeed, the software defined radio (SDR) used the computer's keyboard, mouse and monitor to perform functions previously done with knobs, switches and displays. ($2799, 2008)

The Kenwood TM-D710A boasted a lengthy list of features including a dual band receiver, 1000 memory channels and scanning, as well as both squelch encode and decode. An internal TNC supported APRS and AX.25 packet operation. The Italian-made AvMap G5 Personal Navigator ($650) interfaced directly with an APRS capable transceiver such as Kenwood's TM-D710A ($600). (2007)

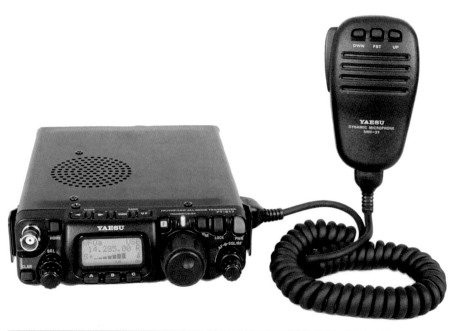

Yaesu's tiny FT-817 covered the HF bands as well as 6 meters, 2 meters and 70 cm. Available modes included CW, SSB, FM and AM. It used internal batteries and generated 5 W output (1.5 W AM carrier). ($750, 2000)

code requirement for the General and Amateur Extra Class licenses.[5] The Commission announced its long-awaited decision on December 15, 2006, and put it into practice on February 23, 2007. The League had urged retaining the 5 WPM code test for the Amateur Extra Class but the FCC decided to extend its action across all license classes. The Technician Class Morse requirement had been dropped in 1991.[6]

Amateur Radio fought its next battle against closed industry and regulatory minds. The conflict centered around Broadband over Power Line technology (BPL), an internet delivery system that polluted the RF spectrum up into the VHF range. Logic and preliminary test results should have reduced the matter to a quick skirmish but instead, the battle seemed to go on forever.[7]

Much as it had done 50 years earlier when TVI and its resolution were crucial to Amateur Radio, the League adopted a proactive stance in the BPL matter. ARRL Lab Manager Ed Hare,

W1RFI, delivered a presentation on BPL and its interference potential to both amateurs and industry professional groups.[8] Individual amateurs and ham clubs participated in tests conducted in areas where BPL field trials were taking place. The interference, not only to amateurs but also to government and commercial users, was documented and presented to the FCC.[9] Some commissioners expressed concern about the interference to amateurs while others seemed to have different priorities. At its October 24, 2004, meeting, Commission Chairman Michael K. Powell stated, "BPL's potential for the US economy is too great, too enormous, too potentially groundbreaking to sit idly by and allow any claim or any possible speculative fear" to keep the Commission from promoting adoption of BPL technology.[10]

In the late 1990s, the developer of AMTOR, Peter Martinez, G3PLX, introduced a new digital mode.[11] By the turn of the century, his PSK31 (Phase Shift Keying, 31 Baud) mode had attracted a strong following on this side of the Atlantic. PSK31 enabled real time keyboard-to-keyboard contacts and required little more equipment than a transceiver and a computer with a sound card. Early adopters of the mode discovered that signals barely audible with the transceiver's speaker produced solid copy on the computer screen. This PSK31 attribute made it attractive to those using low power or indoor antennas.

Research by the Japan Amateur Radio League into the use of digital technologies in Amateur Radio produced the D-STAR standard (Digital Smart

Technologies for Amateur Radio) in 2001.[12] While D-STAR is an open protocol available to anyone, ICOM was the only company initially producing transceivers and repeater equipment. D-STAR joined digital voice and data communication, repeaters, and RF or internet linking to produce networks with a global reach.

As the Amateur Radio and digital technology worlds continued to meld, things the readers of QST's first issue would have considered pure magic became commonplace. Writing in the July/August 2002 issue of QEX, Gerald Youngblood, AC5OG, put it perfectly. In an article on software defined radio (SDR), he observed, "A certain convergence occurs when multiple technologies align in time to make possible those things that once were only dreamed."[13] Youngblood turned his dreams to reality, founding FlexRadio Systems in 2003. He serves as President and CEO of the Austin, Texas, company that has been at the forefront of SDR development in Amateur Radio. FlexRadio's initial product, the SDR-1000, was the realization of the software defined transceiver described in Youngblood's four-part QEX article "A Software Defined Radio for the Masses." The first QST ad for the SDR-1000 ran in October 2004.[14]

Radio hardware wasn't the only thing changing as the hobby entered the 21st century. The 1997 edition of the Radio Amateur Callbook with its familiar "Flying Horse" cover marked the end of an era. The publisher issued both print and CD-ROM versions of its 75th anniversary edition but the print version disappeared the following year.[15] Online lookup services and the continued availability of the CD-ROM Callbook helped make the print version a thing of the past.

After watching one after another of the small companies making up the backbone of its distributor network disappear, TEN-TEC switched to factory direct sales in 1992. Collins Radio had briefly flirted with the same concept in the late 1940s.[16] A November 2001 ad announced the opening of TEN-TEC's retail store located at the company's Sevierville, Tennessee, headquarters.[17] The store carried a full line of accessories from other companies in addition to TEN-TEC's own gear.

"This is not a test!" With those words radio amateurs in the New York City area learned of the terrorist attacks on the World Trade Center the morning

In 2003, the Model 565 Orion replaced the Omni VI Plus as TEN-TEC's flagship transceiver. The Orion's large number of high-performance features could be individually customized to accommodate the operator's needs. TEN-TEC followed up with the Orion II. ($3300, 2003)

of September 11, 2001.[18] Even before reality could sink in, organizations such as the ARRL Amateur Radio Emergency Service (ARES) and Radio Amateur Civil Emergency Service (RACES) found themselves responding as they had been trained to do. The New York City ARES net was activated within five minutes of the first plane hitting the North Tower. Tom Carrubba, KA2D, ARRL New York City-Long Island Section Emergency Coordinator reported, "We found ourselves faced with a disaster that no one in their wildest dreams could have imagined."

Radio and television broadcasters, two-way radio communications, and both landline and cellular telephone service all suffered damage in the attacks. Heavy traffic volumes quickly overwhelmed still functioning services. The ARES/RACES emergency net conducted on Manhattan's 147.0 MHz WB2ZSE repeater served as the first link in the disaster communications chain. From there ham communications spread to other repeaters undamaged in the attack. Amateurs just across the Hudson River in New Jersey served as communications liaison for the hospitals and shelters set up there.

More than 500 amateurs in the New York/New Jersey area answered the call to service in the days following the attack. Others served at the Pentagon and Somerset County, Pennsylvania disaster sites. Jayson McFerron, N4GAA, of the American Red Cross characterized the amateur contribution saying, "Hams do whatever it takes to do the job — and they're doing it."

Notes

[1] R. Lindquist, N1RL, "Happenings — FCC Declines to Grant LF Allocation, Gives Channelized Access to 5 MHz," QST, Jul 2003, p 68.

[2] R. Lindquist, N1RL, "Happenings — ARRL Petitions for New 60 Meter Amateur Band," QST, Oct 2001, p 80.

[3] D. Sumner, K1ZZ, "It Seems To Us — 60 Meters," QST, Jul 2003 p 9.

[4] S. Keane, K1SFA, "FCC Releases New Rules for 60 Meters," QST, Feb 2012, p 86.

[5] R. Lindquist, N1RL, "End of An Era," QST, Feb 2007, p 81.

[6] D. Sumner, K1ZZ, "It Seems To Us — 60 Meters," QST, Feb 1991, p 9.

[7] D. Sumner, K1ZZ, "It Seems To Us — BPL's 15 Minutes of Fame," QST, Oct 2003, p 9.

[8] D. Hassler, K7CCC, "ARRL in Action — Hare Takes BPL Presentation on the Road," QST, Jan 2004, p 12.

[9] R. Lindquist, N1RL, "Utility Cuts Short BPL Trial That Attracted Amateur Complaints," QST, Sep 2004, p 68.

[10] R. Lindquist, N1RL, "FCC Adopts New Rules To Govern BPL, Acknowledges Its Interference Potential" QST, Dec 2004, pp 68-69.

[11] S. Ford, WB8IMY, "PSK31 2000," QST, May 2000, pp 42-45.

[12] W. Silver, N0AX, Ed., The ARRL Handbook, 90th Edition, (Newington: 2013) p 16.26.

[13] G. Youngblood, AC5OG, "A Software Defined Radio for the Masses, Part 1," QEX, Jul/Aug 2002, pp 1-9.

[14] FlexRadio Systems ad, QST, Oct 2004, p 124.

[15] Radio Amateur Callbook ad, QST, Dec 1996, p 160.

[16] Collins Radio Company ad, QST, Nov 1947, p 160.

[17] TEN-TEC ad, QST, Nov 2001, p 144.

[18] R. Lindquist, N1RL and D. Ortiz, N2DO, "9/11/01: This is Not a Test," QST, Nov 2001, pp 28-34, 59.

Final Edition
ASTATIC
D-104 Silver Eagle

THE END OF AN ERA!

Few products in American history have achieved the renowned status of the Astatic D-104 Silver Eagle. From its legendary lollipop design to its time-honored break through sound, the D104 has pleased communication enthusiasts for an astonishing total of seven decades. After this long reign as a prestigious product, Astatic will discontinue the D-104 Silver Eagle.

Now for a limited time, the Final Edition series of the Silver Eagle is available to commemorate this All-American Masterpiece. The **Final Edition Silver Eagle** will fit everyone's collection as either a collector's item or as a microphone for daily use.

Each microphone comes complete with a clear collector's case, certificate of authenticity, engraved serial number and a one of a kind Final Edition Name Plate.

Order your Final Edition online at www .astatic.com or call 1-888-USA-D104 .

$199.99

Figure 10.1 — The D-104 microphone's long run in amateur communications ended with Astatic's Final Edition announcement in December 2001 *QST*. The first ad for the D-104 appeared in the magazine's November 1933 issue. (Dec 2001)

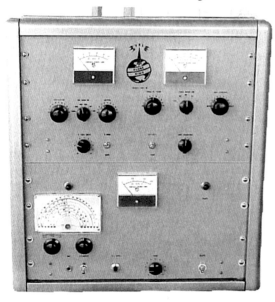
Figure 10.2 — Restoration and operation of vintage ham gear gained popularity in the early 1990s. Manufacturing *new* vintage equipment is another matter. A $3895 price tag and technical issues doomed this Globe King 500D effort. (Dec 2001)

"This is not your *ordinary, average*

microphone."

Joe Walsh, WB6ACU
• amateur radio operator
• guitarist for The Eagles
• ordinary average guy

Internal pop filter

Wide bandwidth 40 Hz.–18 kHz.

Low IMD

Balanced 600 ohm

3 pin XLR

HEIL PROLINE
Affordable Performance

Bob Heil, pioneer of live sound systems has been listening carefully to engineers, industry professionals and talented performers for many years and has now allied his vast knowledge and experience of 37 years in the sound business to his new line of microphones and audio equipment.

The introduction of this great new studio dynamic microphone marks the birth of the new "PROLINE" division at Heil Sound, Ltd. The new GOLDLINE PRO leads the way into commercial broadcast, recording studios and live sound applications for America's leading producer of microphones for the amateur radio industry.

This latest Heil technology captures every note and feeling with brilliant articulation. Clean, condensor-like sound producing an exceptionally rich, warm sound - the way you want it from the most beautiful and affordable microphone ever - The Heil GOLDLINE PRO.

For more information call 1-618-257-3000 or visit us at www.heilsound.com.

Figure 10.3 — Heil Sound owner Bob Heil, K9EID, and musician Joe Walsh, WB6ACU, both have deep roots in the rock and roll music business as well as Amateur Radio. (Feb 2003)

IC-PCR1000

TURN YOUR PC INTO A WIDE BAND RECEIVER WITH ICOM'S LITTLE BLACK BOX!

Now with Bonito Software!

Modes
Memory Channels
Functions

Volume
Squelch

Sound Card
Controls

Digital Decoder/DSP Functions
Filter Softening

100 kHz – 1.3 GHz†

AM, FM, WFM, USB, LSB, CW

Unlimited Memory Channels

Real Time Band Scope

IF Shift

Noise Blanker

Digital AFC

Voice Scan Control

Attenuator

Tunable Bandpass Filters

AGC Function

S Meter Squelch

CTCSS Tone Squelch

Computer Controlled DSP

www.icomreceivers.com

Turn your PC into a Wide Band Receiver! ICOM's IC-PCR1000 uses the power of your computer to open a new world of listening and viewing pleasure. Compatible with most PCs and laptops running Windows™ software, the 'PCR1000 connects externally – in just minutes! The new Bonito software (BON CS40) expands and enhances the 'PCR1000's versatility with the following features:

Basic Radio Control functions with spectrum scope

Computer Controlled DSP for tailoring your audio with separate bass & treble controls

Filter Smoothing for the upper and lower ends of the audio spectrum

Notch Filter reduces annoying pops, buzzes, & other interference for a crisp, clear signal. Use the power of your computer's sound card DSP to bring out the beauty of the signal for hours of enjoyable listening

Digital Decoding Package transforms your computer into a decoding machine. You no longer have to purchase an external decoder for receiving non-encrypted digital modes. Digital Decoding allows you to decode: RTTY, FAX *with Zoom, Synchronize, Slant Correction, Cut a Picture, Picture Invert and Rotate,* CW, SSTV *with Auto Sync, Slant Corrections,* Sitor-B, PSK31

Audio Record function allows you to record your favorite radio programs, local traffic, or almost anything else with your computer's sound card and hard drive. Save for friends and family to listen at a later time

See your authorized ICOM dealer for more details.

New Windows™ OS? No problem! Updated ICOM software is now available for free download! Download at www.icomamerica.com. Click Receivers>IC-PCR1000>IC-PCR1000 software (updated)

The world is waiting

www.icomamerica.com

ICOM®

Figure 10.4 — ICOM's little black box turned a *Windows* PC into a triple-conversion 10 Hz-1300 MHz receiver. The PCR-1000 connected to the computer's serial port. (Jun 2003)

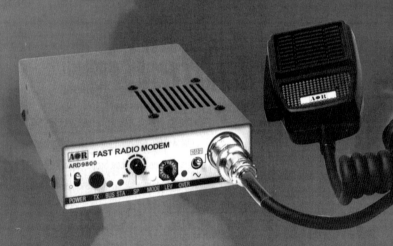

Figure 10.5 — The ARD-9800 from AOR produces digital voice transmission and reception when used with an analog transceiver. The modem connects to the radio's microphone jack. (Nov 2003)

Figure 10.6 — Bob Locher, W9KNI, founded Idiom Press in 1982. He is also part owner of Bencher, Inc. Most of the Idiom Press accessories are available either completely assembled or as kits. (Apr 2004)

Figure 10.7 — High Sierra Antennas, a division of Heath Tech, Inc is owned by Jim Heath, W6LG. The company began producing antennas in 1993. (Sep 2006)

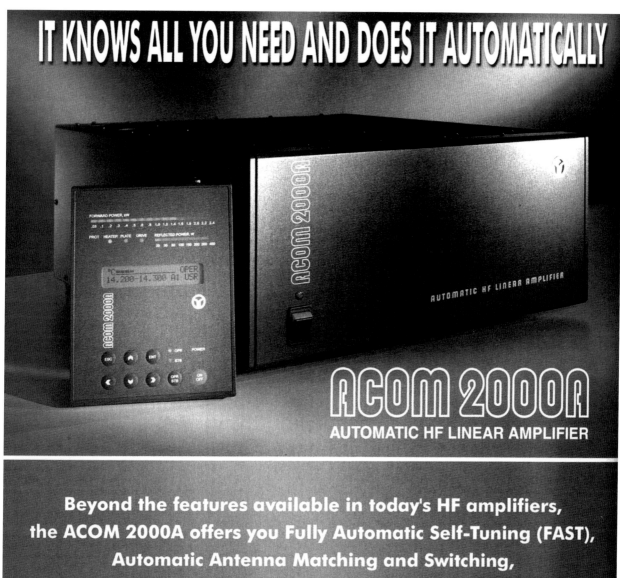

Figure 10.8 — ACOM, founded in 1988 in Sofia, Bulgaria, came to the United States as ACOM International in 1999. Operation and monitoring of the company's 2000A amplifier is done with a remote control unit. The main amplifier box has no controls except for a power switch. (May 2000)

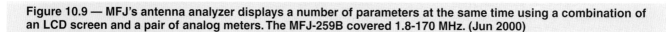

Figure 10.9 — MFJ's antenna analyzer displays a number of parameters at the same time using a combination of an LCD screen and a pair of analog meters. The MFJ-259B covered 1.8-170 MHz. (Jun 2000)

Figure 10.10 — Jake, featured in Cable X-Perts ads, served as the company's spokesdog. (Jun 2000)

Figure 10.11 — Yaesu packed a 160-6 meter, 2 meter and 70 cm band transceiver into a 2.2 × 6.3 × 8 inch case. The FT-100D put out 100 W on the HF bands and 6 meters, 50 W on 144 MHz, and 20 W on 432 MHz. (Jul 2000)

Figure 10.12 — Mike Staal, K6MYC, a principal in KLM Electronics from 1971-1982, later founded M² Enterprises with his wife Myrna, K6MYM. M² not only builds and sells antennas for the amateur market, but for government and commercial customers as well. (Dec 2000)

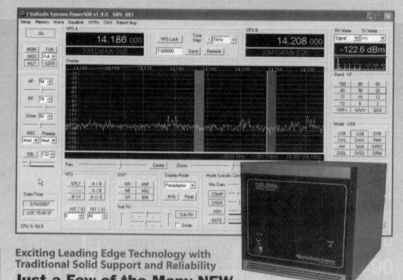

Figure 10.13 — Gerald Youngblood, K5SDR, founded FlexRadio Systems in 2003 and is now the company's president and CEO. Beginning with its introductory SDR-1000 model Flex radios have made available periodic performance and feature upgrades via software download. (Jun 2007)

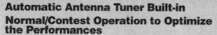

Figure 10.14 — Array Solutions, owned by Jay Terleski, WX0B, is a manufacturer of antenna switching and phasing products and other station accessories. (Nov 2007)

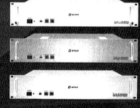
Figure 10.15 — Though not a proprietary system, ICOM's D-STAR equipment remained the only player in the game for digital voice and data transceivers and repeaters using protocols developed by the Japan Amateur Radio League. (Dec 2007)

Figure 10.16 — Jetstream power supplies, transceivers and accessories are manufactured in China and distributed in the US by Jetstream-USA in Hamilton, Ohio. (Dec 2007)

Figure 10.17 —The Prometheus DX2400L1 solid state, legal limit HF amplifier is manufactured by Mike Dishop, N8WFF, and Dishtronix in Bellefontaine, Ohio. (Dec 2007)

Searching for peak HF performance?

Introducing the Elecraft K3 transceiver

No other rig in this price class comes close to the K3's performance. Its high dynamic range, down-conversion architecture provides roofing filter bandwidths as narrow as 200 Hz, while its 32-bit I.F. DSP handles advanced filtering and noise reduction. The K3 also offers an optional fully independent, high-performance subreceiver, as well as innovative new features like variable-bandwidth, DSP-tracking roofing filters, and 8-band RX/TX EQ.

Then there's the K3's unmatched versatility. It provides state-of-the-art performance as a primary home station, yet its size and weight make it ideal for DXpeditions, RV operation, and Field Day. You *can* take it with you!

- 100-W model starts at $1749; upgradable 10 W model, $1399
- 160-6 m; SSB/CW/AM/FM/data modes
- Up to five crystal roofing filters in both main and subreceivers
- 4"H x 10"W x 10"D; only 8 pounds

- Factory-assembled or *no-soldering* kit (all PC boards pre-built, 100% tested)
- Fully isolated soundcard interface
- Built-in PSK31/RTTY for data-mode QSOs with or without a computer
- Unsurpassed customer support

ELECRAFT®

Elecraft is a registered trademark of Elecraft, Inc.

www.elecraft.com • 831-662-8345
P.O. Box 69, Aptos, California 95001-0069

Figure 10.18 — Elecraft's K3 is available fully assembled or as a no-soldering kit consisting of factory tested modules. It is, essentially, an SDR transceiver in a conventional package with knobs and buttons. (Jan 2008)

Figure 10.19 — microHam's products include keyers, radio control interface, special controllers for SO2R (single operator, two radios) operation, and antenna stacking/switching devices. The company is located near Bratislava, the capital city of Slovakia. microHAM America is the US distributor. (Jan 2008)

Figure 10.20 — West Mountain Radio developed a line of RigBlaster soundcard interfaces that worked with many transceivers and most of the popular software. West Mountain's catalog also features dc power distribution hardware and DSP-enhanced audio products. (Mar 2008)

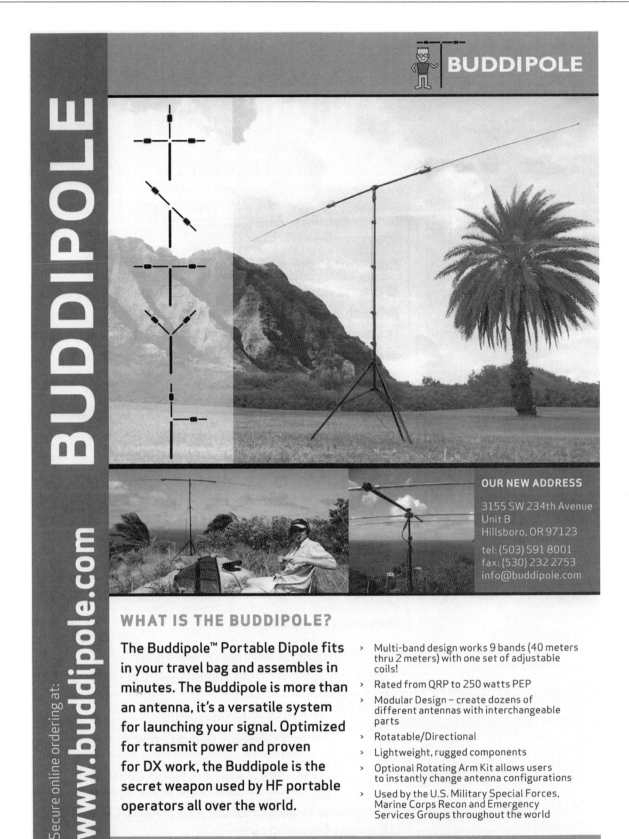

Figure 10.21 — The Buddipole is the invention of Bud Drummond, W3FF. In early 2000 he shared the plans for his homebrewed antenna with other hams interested in portable operation. Chris Drummond, W6HFP, Bud's son, turned the idea into a commercial product in 2002. (Mar 2008)

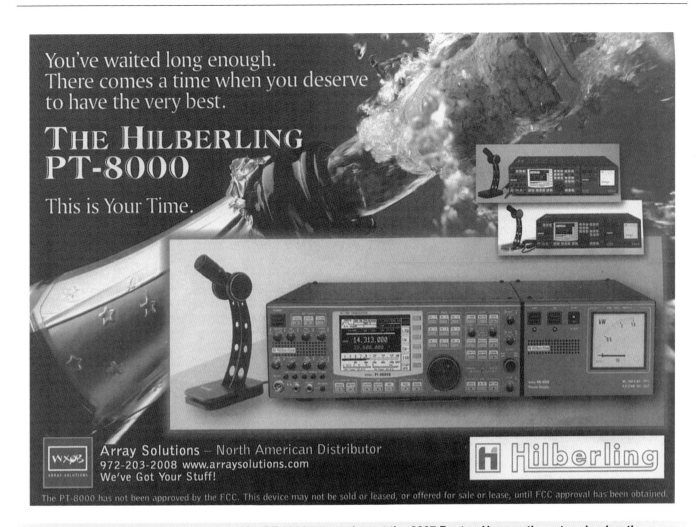

Figure 10.22 — Hilberling announced its PT-8000 transceiver at the 2007 Dayton Hamvention, stunning booth visitors with its appearance, features and $18,000 price tag. Actually, the Collins KW-1 from 1950 would cost more than $35,000 today — and that's just for an AM transmitter! (Apr 2008)

Figure 10.23— The TZ-900 AntennaSmith from Timewave performed antenna analysis from 0.2-55 MHz and was compact enough to be used on the tower. Its companion *Windows* software provided enhanced storage and display functions. (May 2008)

Figure 10.24 — Galen, WB0W, and Jean, KC0GB, Pearson are a fixture at hamfests, exhibiting at 40 to 50 shows each year. Their St. Joseph, Missouri mail order business was founded in 1985. (Jun 2006)

Figure 10.25 — Paul Hrivnak, N8PH, is president and CEO of Palstar. In addition to their antenna tuners, the Piqua, Ohio company's product catalog includes components for building your own. (Apr 2007)

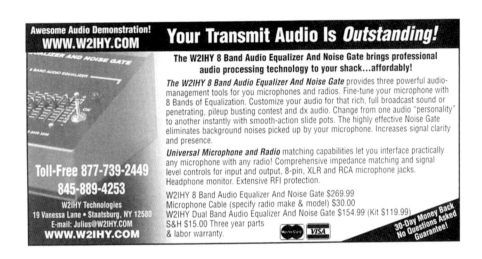

Figure 10.26 — W2IHY Technologies, the company founded by Julius Jones, W2IHY, specializes in audio equipment for the amateur station. The company also makes gear designed to provide audio and RF switching solutions. (Mar 2009)

Figure 10.27 — Texas Towers supplies amateurs with towers, rotators, antennas, feed lines, and associated hardware from its location in Plano. (Jul 2007)

Figure 10.28 — Happy Holidays from Kenwood with a couple of subtle hints for Santa. (Dec 2008)

Figure 10.29 — Bob Bruninga, WB4APR, developed the Automatic Packet Reporting System (APRS) in the early 1990s. The Yaesu VX-8R incorporates APRS as well as the Bluetooth technology often found in automobiles, computers, and consumer electronics. (Mar 2009)

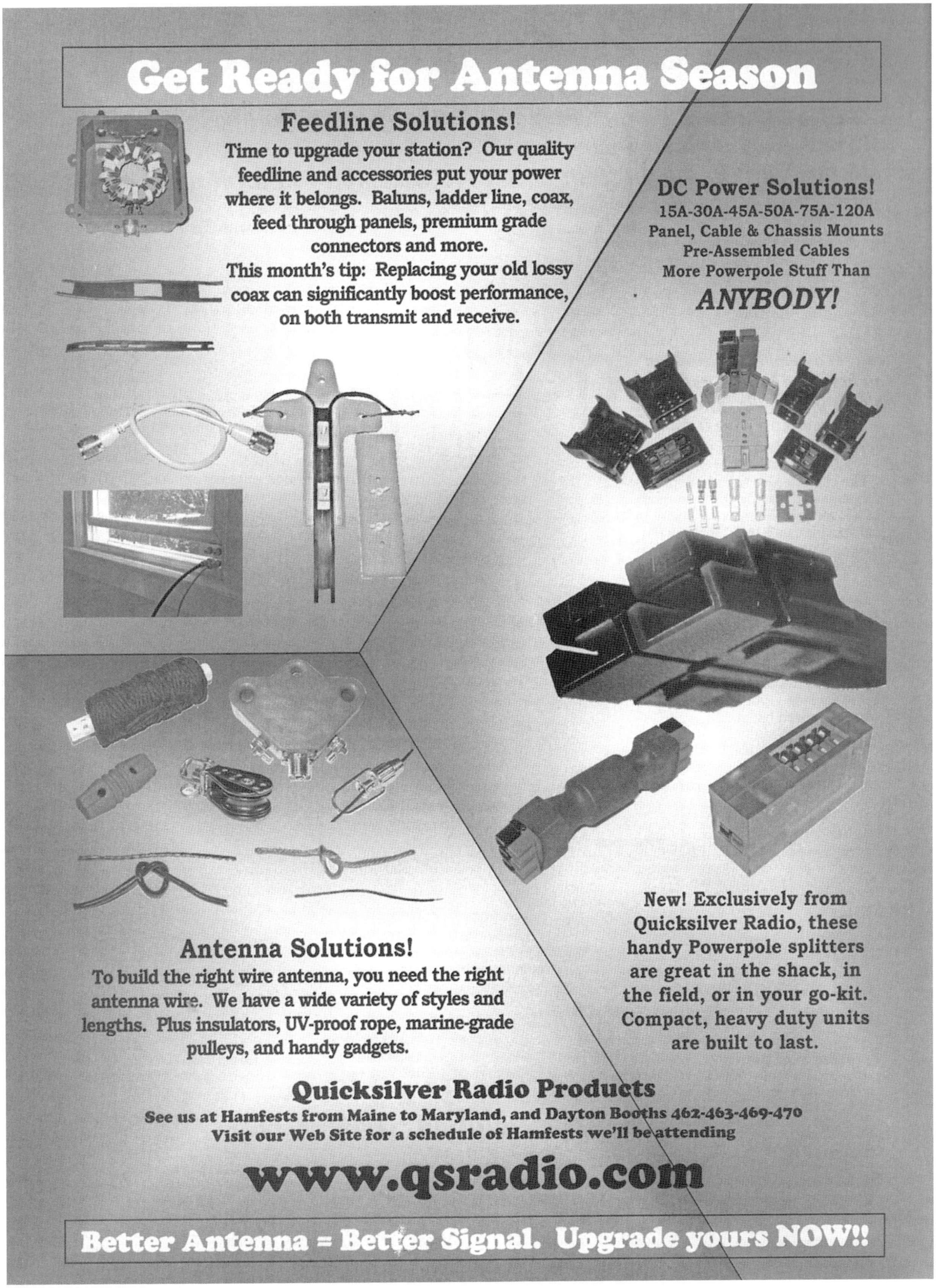

Figure 10.30 — Quicksilver Radio Products, Meriden, Connecticut is owned by John Bee, N1GNV. John worked as *QST's* advertising manager in the late 1990s and early 2000s. (Mar 2009)

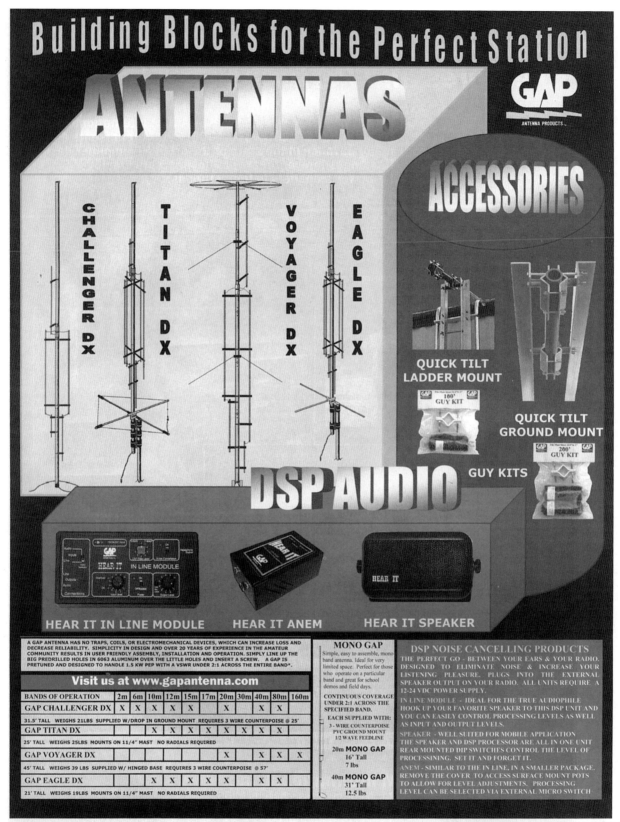

Figure 10.31 — The Gap vertical antennas function without traps or coils. (Oct 2009)

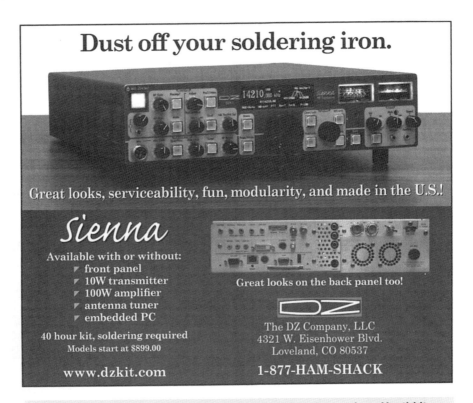
Figure 10.32 — With the disappearance of companies such as Heathkit, Brian Wood, WØDZ, formed DZKit to bring the electronic kit building experience to a new generation. The Sienna HF transceiver is the company's ultimate expression of that experience. (Dec 2009)

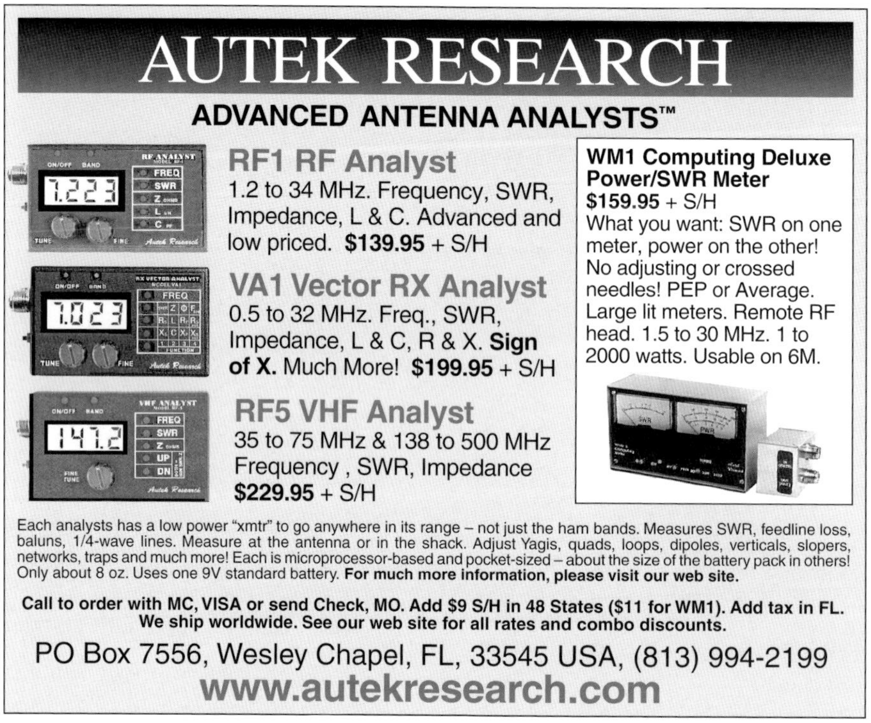

Figure 10.33 — Autek Research has been around for years, offering accessories such as keyers, audio filters, wattmeters and most recently, antenna analyzers. (Dec 2009)

Chapter 11

2010 and Beyond

100 Years of ARRL and *QST*

Amateur Radio in the US entered its second century in a growth mode. On New Year's Eve 2012, the number of licensed amateurs stood at an all-time high of 709,575.[1] The ARRL Volunteer Exam Coordinator (VEC), the largest of 14 VEC groups, coordinated approximately 70 percent of all Amateur Radio exams.[2]

Any headcount of amateur licenses raises the question, "How many are inactive but not yet expired?" Licenses issued or renewed since December 15, 1983, have been valid for 10 years, so it is possible that census figures contain a number of persons whose interest and activity in the hobby lapsed long before their licenses expired.[3]

Looking at it from the other end, nearly everyone experiences life events that interrupt hobby pursuits. Things such as school, marriage, family, career and military duty hold higher priority for anyone who subscribes to the "The Radio Amateur is Balanced" tenet of the "Amateur's Code" found near the front of every *ARRL Handbook*.[4] Re-entering Amateur Radio after a period of inactivity in which the license has lapsed requires overcoming inertia posed by having to retake the license examination. Recognizing this, in October 2012 the FCC gave notice of its proposal to grant examination credit to holders of expired licenses.[5] The Commission saw little distinction between a person (active or not) who passed an examination and kept his license current and someone who passed the exam but let the license expire. The proposal afforded the Amateur Service an opportunity to recapture former members having renewed interest in the hobby.

Amateurs who do leave the hobby and return after even a short interval are probably surprised by the new equipment, modes and activities that appeared during their absence. Even though DXing and DXCC remain among Amateur Radio's most popular pursuits, one of its age-old mechanisms has undergone a change in recent years. No matter how hard it may have been to break a massive pileup and work a "new one," that was only the first part of the story. Getting a QSL card to the DX entity and receiving his in return often proved more difficult and certainly more time consuming. In the fall of 2003, the ARRL instituted its Logbook of The World (LoTW) program.[6] The program matched logbook data from stations on each end of a contact if they had registered with LoTW and submitted logs. A confirmed contact earns award credit without the necessity of presenting a paper QSL card. In early 2013, the LoTW secure databases contained logbooks from more than 28,000 US stations and more than 31,000 from DX stations in 339 DXCC entities.

The Dayton Hamvention marked its 60th year in 2012. The Hamvention has provided a venue to see most of the products advertised between the covers of *QST* and talk with the people who make or sell them. In 2012 over 250 different commercial exhibitors and organizations occupied more than 500

The Wouxun KG-UV2D dual-band handheld FM transceiver covers either the 146/222 or 146/440 MHz bands. The user could select English or Chinese for the radio's voice announcement of the function selected by a key press. ($107, 2010)

The IC-9100 packed all-mode HF, VHF, and UHF capabilities into a compact box. The 100 W (75 W on 70 cm) transceiver could be further upgraded with options for the 23 cm band, D-STAR operation, narrow 1st IF roofing filters, and provisions for remote operation via the Internet. ($3600, 2012)

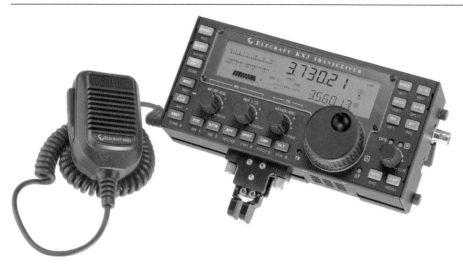

Elecraft's compact HF + 6 meter transceiver offered all the features and performance of larger competitors with the exception of output power. The KX3 put out 10 W PEP on 160 to 15 meters and 8 W on 12 to 6 meters. The price ranges from $899.95 for the basic kit to about $1550 for a factory-built unit with the most common options installed. (2012)

The FTDX3000 fills the mid-price niche in Yaesu's transceiver lineup. It employed features such as roofing filters and DSP to achieve improved performance over its predecessors in the same price range. In common with other Yaesu transceivers, it used the company's CAT (Computer Aided Transceiver) system for control by a computer. ($2700, 2012)

Small enough for HF mobile use, the TS-590S delivered top performance at a mid-range price. The 160-6 meter transceiver coverage was complemented by a receiver tuning from 30 kHz to 60 MHz. Power output was adjustable from 5-100 W (5-25 W AM). ($1800, 2011)

booths inside the Hara complex that hosts the Hamvention. The cornucopia of new gear displayed inside is complemented by the incredible variety of older gear — some of it *decades* older — in the outside flea market. To put yesterday's and today's equipment in the proper perspective requires an inflation calculator. Several new high-end HF transceivers have pushed through the $12,000 barrier. Maybe that's not such a bad deal; the classic 1955 Collins KWS-1/75A-4 station would cost well over $20,000 in today's money.

Amateur Radio is not just about equipment, but the variety of things hams do with that gear. It is much the same as owning a motor vehicle. It may be a full-size American sedan, a sporty foreign two-seater, a high performance gas guzzler, an economical hybrid, a state-of-the-art electric car, a vintage classic, pickup truck or a motorcycle. Whatever is sitting in your garage, they all have two things in common. The first is that any of them will take you someplace. The second is that only you can decide what that destination is. So it is with ham radio.

As both Amateur Radio and the ARRL embrace the century mark, it is time to ponder where do we go from here? Looking back over 100 years of *QST* ads, it is obvious that the hardware, mode and technology choices have changed greatly. By the same measure, the answers to the question, "What can I do with my station today?" have expanded exponentially.

Operating that station may no longer require the amateur's presence in the shack.[7] Remote control is possible anywhere with high-speed internet access. Some amateurs are even using cell phones to remotely operate their home stations.[8] The practice of adapting technologies and incorporating them in innovative new ways is as old as Amateur Radio itself.

Innovation in the hobby is often driven by curiosity and exploration. On other occasions the stimulus is provided by the need to solve a very real problem, such as those arising from threats to the amateur spectrum or even the freedom to operate one's own station. In the latter case, an increasing number of amateurs find themselves subject to Covenants, Conditions and Restrictions (CC&Rs) that all but put them off the air.[9] On behalf of all amateurs the League has sought relief from the CC&Rs in a decades-long battle that is not yet over.[10]

Antenna restrictions don't represent the first problem faced by Amateur Radio and will not be the last. In the course of 100 years, amateurs have been idled twice by war, been banished to radio spectrum military and commercial interests considered useless, then later had to fight to retain frequencies coveted by some of those same interests. The hobby has had to deal with interference to other services and from other services. In the midst of 21st century life, with dozens of other things competing for one's time, it has managed to grow. Amateur Radio remains strong because of both struggles and accomplishments.

A century ago, Mr. Maxim picked up *QSTs* from the printer and delivered them to the postal service in his air-cooled Franklin automobile. Today, although *QST* continues to arrive in ARRL members' mailboxes, it is also available in a digital version, downloaded instantly from the internet. Hiram Percy Maxim might not recognize where the organization and magazine he set in motion have ended up in their hundred year journey — on the other hand he might puff on his pipe, and smile. The one hundred year anniversary is not a destination. It is, rather, a mark on a timeline that continues toward the horizon of the future.

TEN-TEC's classic QRP rig the Argonaut debuted in 1971. More than 40 years later, the company produced the original Argonaut's latest ancestor, the Model 539 Argonaut VI. The new version ran up to 10 W, with new features such as a roofing filter and built-in iambic keyer, all the while retaining its ancestor's legendary QSK CW keying. ($995, 2012)

Notes

[1] http://www.arrl.org/news/2012-marks-all-time-high-for-amateur-radio-licenses.

[2] *Ibid.* 1.

[3] C. Smith, AJ2I, "Ten Year Operator and Station License, Two Year Grace Period Okayed," *QST*, Dec 1983, p 70.

[4] W. Silver, N0AX, Ed., *The ARRL Handbook,* 90th Edition (Newington: 2013).

[5] S. Keane, K1SFA, "Happenings — FCC Seeks to Change Amateur Radio Licensing Rules, Allow Additional Emission Types," *QST*, Dec 2012, p 64.

[6] W. Mills, N7NG, "Introducing ... Logbook of the World," *QST*, Oct 2003, p 46-47.

[7] S. Ford, WB8IMY, *Remote Operating for Amateur Radio* (Newington: 2010).

[8] http://www.tomthompson.com/radio/TelephoneRemote/remote.html.

[9] D. Sumner, K1ZZ, "It Seems To Us — Antenna Restrictions," *QST*, Sep 2001, p 9.

[10] D. Sumner, K1ZZ, "It Seems To Us — Restrictive Covenants," *QST*, Aug 2012, p 9.

Figure 11.1 — Balun Designs, owned by Bob Rumsey, KZ5R, manufactures a variety of baluns, ununs, and associated feed line and antenna matching devices.

Figure 11.2 — Pietro Begali's company produces electro-mechanical components for industrial knitting machines. Licensed in 1964 as I2RTF, Begali turned his design talents to manufacturing beautiful and capable CW sending instruments.

Figure 11.3 — Amateur Radio operators are noted for being, well, thrifty. CheapHam.com is an interesting marketing ploy. The business is located in Toms River, New Jersey.

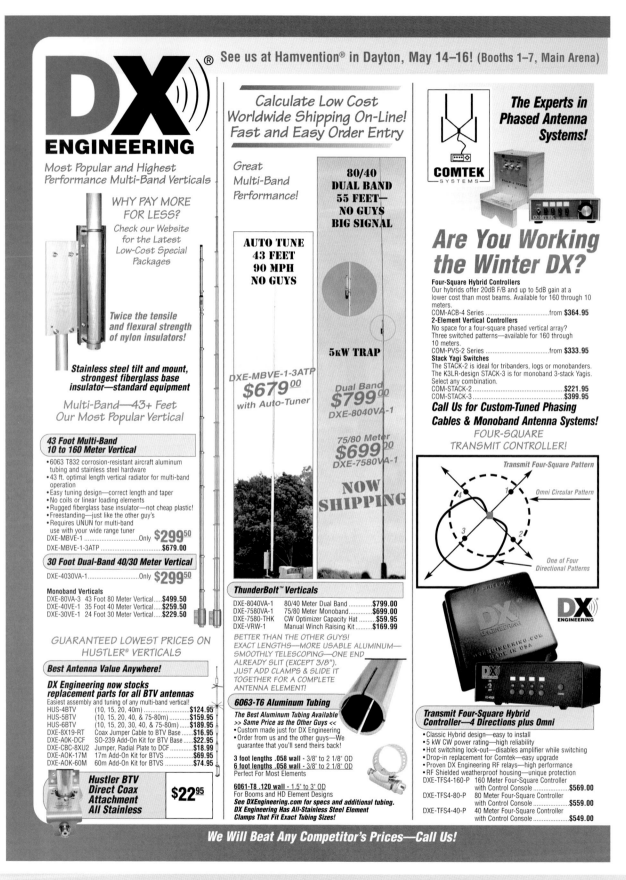

Figure 11.4 — In addition to house brand DX Engineering and Comtek products, the Akron, Ohio, company also carries gear from most other major ham manufacturers.

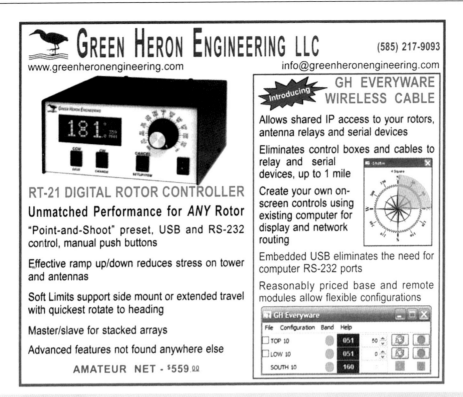

Figure 11.5 — Green Heron Engineering's RT-21 digital controller works with any brand of antenna rotator, even those made before the digital era.

Figure 11.6 — Hakko, a Japanese company, has made soldering and de-soldering equipment for more than half a century.

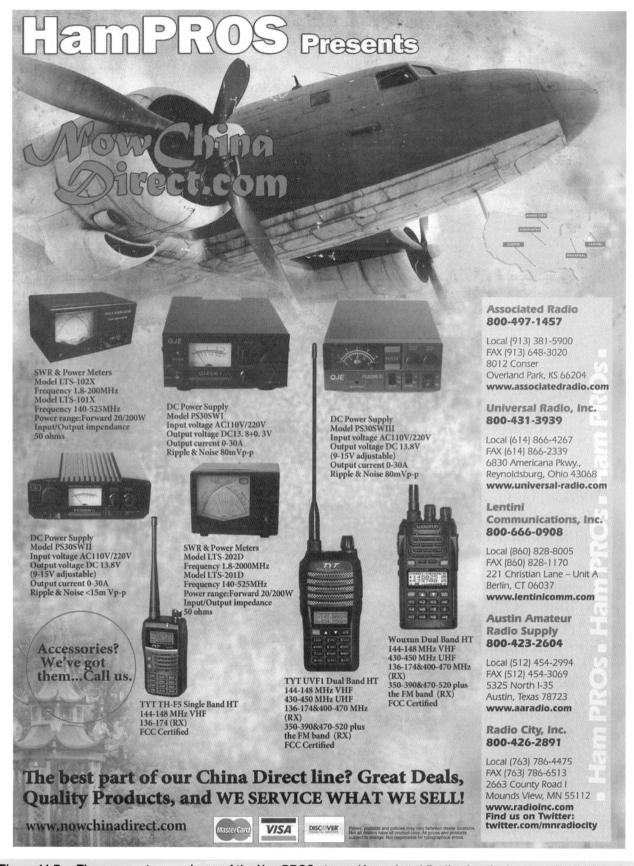

Figure 11.7 — The aggregate experience of the HamPROS stores (Associated Radio, Austin Amateur Radio Supply, Lentini Communications, Radio City and Universal Radio) totals more than a quarter millennium in the Amateur Radio business.

Figure 11.8 — Simon Brown, HB9DRV, developed the *Ham Radio Deluxe* software package, a program that integrated rig, logging, digital modes, and satellite operation. In 2011, he sold the software to a group consisting of Mike Carper, WA9PIE; Randy Gawtry, K0CBH; and Rick Ruhl, W4PC.

Figure 11.9 — John Kernkamp, WB4YJT,
and Mark Forbes, KC9C, make the stealthy
Ventennas. The patented designs are
manufactured in Huston, Idaho.

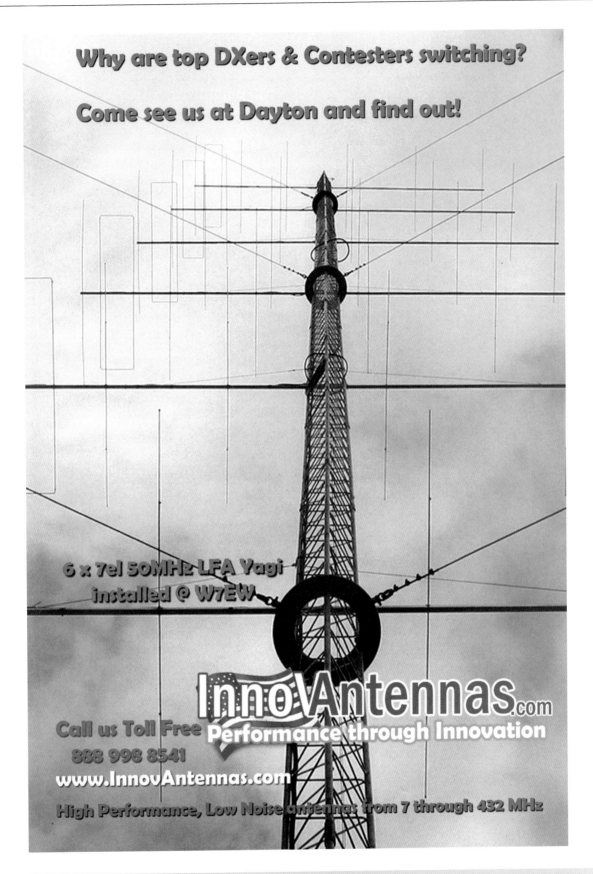

Figure 11.10 — Justin Johnson, GØKSC, turned his antenna designing hobby into a business after receiving numerous requests to make his antennas for other hams. Johnson launched InnovAntennas in 2011. The factory is located in Canvey Island, Essex, United Kingdom.

Figure 11.11 — International Radio (INRAD) is owned by well-known contesters Mark Oberman, AG9A, and Trey Garlough, N5KO. The company began life as International Radio and Computers, Inc/Fox Tango.

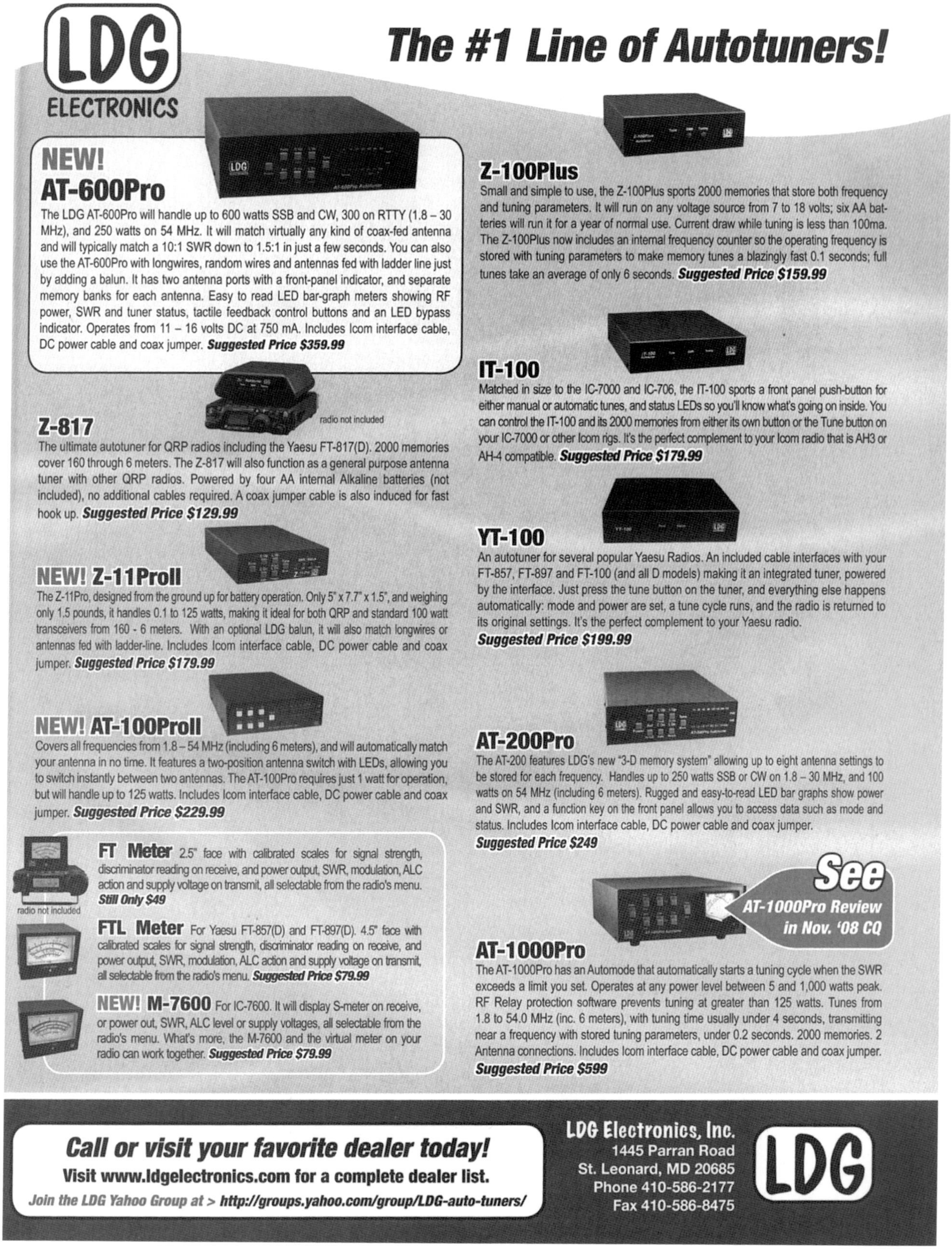

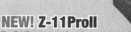
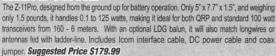

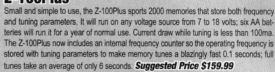

Figure 11.12 — LDG Electronics developed its first automatic switched-L antenna tuner in 1995. The St. Leonard, Maryland, company makes general application tuners as well as models intended for use with specific radios.

Figure 11.13 — MFJ's ad in September 2012 *QST* included a full-page invitation from founder Martin Jue, K5FLU, to the company's 40th anniversary celebration in Starkville, Mississippi.

Figure 11.14 — Tony Baleno, N3ZN, builds the keys bearing his call in Pittsburgh, Pennsylvania. He makes iambic and single lever paddles as well as straight keys.

Figure 11.15 — Dale Parfitt, W4OP, developed the EndFedz half wave antenna and manufactured them himself until selling the design to LNR Precision in 2010. Larry Draughn, AE4LD, owns LNR.

Figure 11.16 — Radio Wavz, a St. Louis, Missouri company, manufactures antennas and antenna accessories. Emmett Hohensee, W0QH, is Radio Wavz chief engineer.

Figure 11.17 — Power Werx sells Anderson Powerpole products along with a variety of other Amateur Radio items. Power Pole connectors and terminal blocks have become a standard among many amateurs engaged in emergency communications.

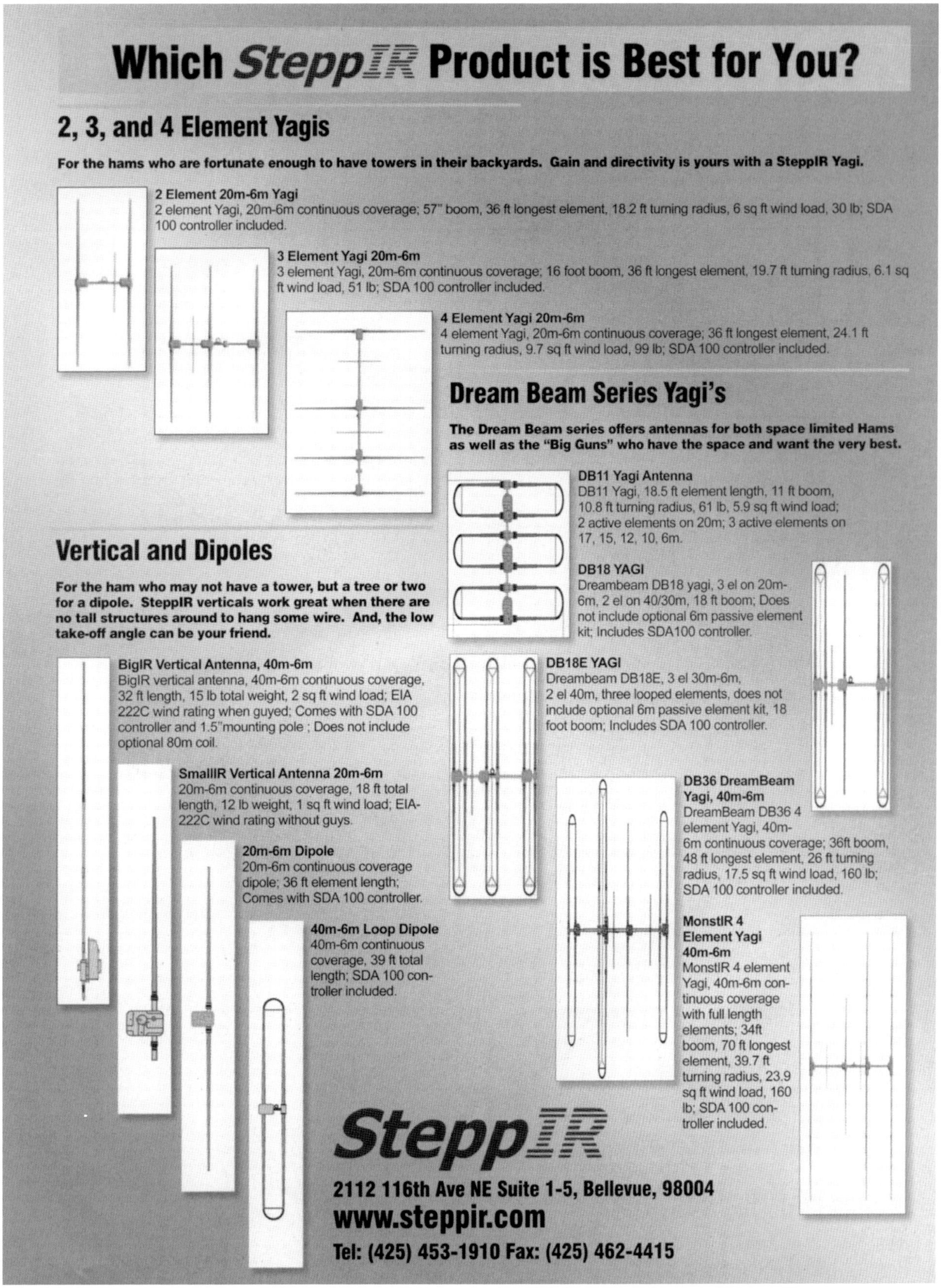

Figure 11.18 —The SteppIR antennas — Yagis, dipoles, or verticals — are always the right dimension for the operating frequency. Mike Mertel, K7IR; Jim Thomas, K7IRF; and John Mertel, WA7IR, founded SteppIR (as Fluidmotion, Inc) in May 2001.

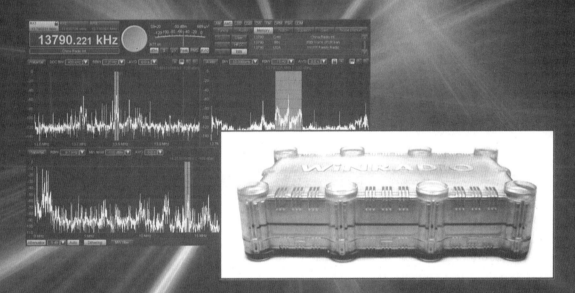

Figure 11.19 — WinRADiO Communications in Melbourne, Australia, manufactures the Excalibur SDR receiver.

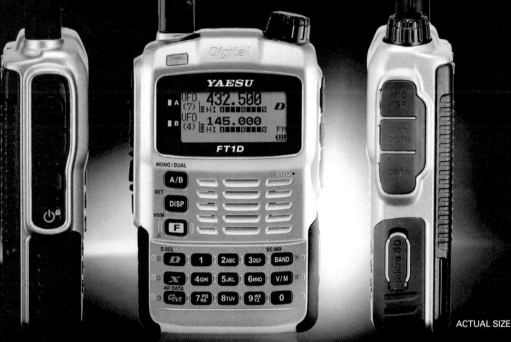

Figure 11.20 — Yaesu's FT-1D dual band handheld is also dual mode, offering both analog and digital communications on the 144 and 440 MHz bands. The FT-1D uses digital technology in competition with, but not compatible with, ICOM's D-STAR.

Figure 11.21 — Ham Radio Outlet, founded in 1971 by California Highway Patrolman Bob Ferrero, W6RJ (ex-K6AHV), grew from a single Burlingame, California store to a 12-store strong nationwide chain.